First Print Edition, April 2023

Project Director: Dale Sky Jones
Edited by: Angela Bacca
Layout by: Faith Woodward
Design Editor: Morgan Vannavilaithong

Contributors: Paul Armentano, Angela Bacca, Elizabeth Bowen, Mitchell Colbert, Natalie Darves, Goose Duarte, Maha Haq, Dale Sky Jones, Jessie Smith, Lauren Vasquez, Wensdy Von Buskirk

Published by Oaksterdam Press
Oakland, California, United States of America

Acknowledgments

First and foremost, we must thank you, dear reader, as the motivation for writing this work. We hope this educational material will empower you towards hope, harm reduction, and improved quality of life.

Many people, whether they know it or not, had an indirect influence that shaped and informed this work. So many individuals, staffers, faculty, organizations, and businesses have shared their personal stories, illustrating the substantial value of education and better-trained budtenders. In particular, thanks to Dennis Peron, Richard Lee, and Jeff Jones, who invented and popularized the art and science of budtending in the darkness of 1990s Prohibition and decided to encourage and teach others how to do it well, at significant personal risk. Oaksterdam is grateful to all advocates, patients, responsible consumers, and skeptics for sparking this social revolution, a fire that will never be put out.

— Dale Sky Jones, Chancellor of Oaksterdam University

Attention budtenders, business owners, regulators, and educators:

Oaksterdam wants to help you further your education or assist in your educational instruction. We have created a web page where you can access supplemental learning materials, including clickable endnote links. This page will continue to grow over time, and we look forward to supporting everyone as they seek to ensure more people are properly educated about cannabis. Register **www.oaksterdamuniversity.com/TBGextras** and use the password **EnsembleEffect** to learn more.

Table of Contents

Introduction

Budtenders are often the most influential connection between the consumer and the supply chain. They are the front line of the cannabis industry and do not just represent their dispensary but the plant itself. A positive interaction or a negative result from the products they recommend can directly affect the customer's experience with cannabis. That is a big responsibility for an entry-level position— and an opportunity to change someone's perception by providing them with a quick and accurate education.

The best budtenders make genuine connections with people and constantly seek more education to help customers have positive experiences. While this book is an essential training guide for professional dispensary employees, it also empowers the customer to "be their own budtender" and guides better encounters at the dispensary and better outcomes when using the products they buy.

Oaksterdam University was founded in 2007 in downtown Oakland, California, and is the cultural center of the modern cannabis industry and legalization movement. Our course content was developed and is continually updated by the activists, entrepreneurs, and front-line employees who pioneered modern retail markets. The content presented here is a result of our instructors' decades of expertise, a rigorous review process, and insights from award-winning budtenders around the world.

This book is an easy reference to essential information for consumers and a training manual for budtenders. Basics are covered in the body of the text, and we also provide recommended resources for readers who want to dive deeper. We encourage you to read this book chronologically for the first time because the information presented is designed to overview big concepts before providing more detail. Once familiar with the content, the charts and featured information in the text boxes can be used as quick references that help explain these big concepts.

Readers can find more detailed definitions of key terms that are bolded at first use throughout the text in the glossary at the end of the book, which also serves as a handy educational reference. Also found at the end of the text are appendices to guide effective political advocacy. In many parts of the world, people are still criminalized for interacting with the cannabis plant, and the policies that affect budtenders and consumers where it is legal are still actively being shaped. You can play a role in shaping these policies. The content of this book walks the reader through the history, politics, science, and customer service strategies that shape the role of the budtender:

Part I: History & Policy briefly and succinctly overviews the tens of thousands of years of human cannabis use, the origins of modern Prohibition, and the movement toward legalization. This history provides a brief foundation to understand how current laws were developed and implemented and concludes with a general overview of policies adopted in most legalized commercial markets.

Part II: Budtending Foundations provides a general overview of the job, its responsibilities, required skills and qualifications, and the basics of security and systems in a heavily regulated marketplace.

Part III: The Effects of Cannabis explains how the chemical constituents in cannabis interact with the human body to produce the effects people seek. It includes a summary of current research on these constituents and what conclusions can and cannot be made about product effects using the information on a product label.

Part IV: Cannabis Horticulture & Varieties breaks down the biology of the plant and the cultivation processes used to produce its dried resinous flowers, which make up the vast majority of dispensary sales and are the source material of all cannabis products. Crucially, Part IV demystifies the world of cannabis varieties (commonly referred to as "strains") and how to navigate this core product category.

Part V: Products, Methods of Ingestion & Dosing explains the constantly evolving landscape of cannabis-infused byproducts, how different consumption methods can alter consumer experiences, and dosage strategies that help consumers avoid negative experiences.

Part VI: Customer Service combines the basics of policy, plant, varieties, and effects to inform the most effective customer service and product recommendation strategies. This section helps budtenders identify and meet the needs of every customer through education, compassion, and connection.

At Oaksterdam University, we encourage business owners and employers to design procedures and build cultures where everyone feels informed, supported, belonging, and on a pathway toward long-term careers. Today's budtenders are tomorrow's industry leaders, and for those aspiring entrepreneurs, the information found here provides a solid foundation from which to grow.

Part I

History & Policy

Lessons in History & Policy:

The Origins of Modern Prohibition

The Origins of Legalization

Laws & Policies

Learning Outcomes:

Understand the evolution of drug policy, how medicine is regulated, and why cannabis cannot be prescribed to treat illness or disease.

Break down the risks and penalties that still exist in the space.

Become familiar with common regulatory policies employed at all levels of government.

Photo courtesy of Don E Wirtshafter and the Cannabis Museum.

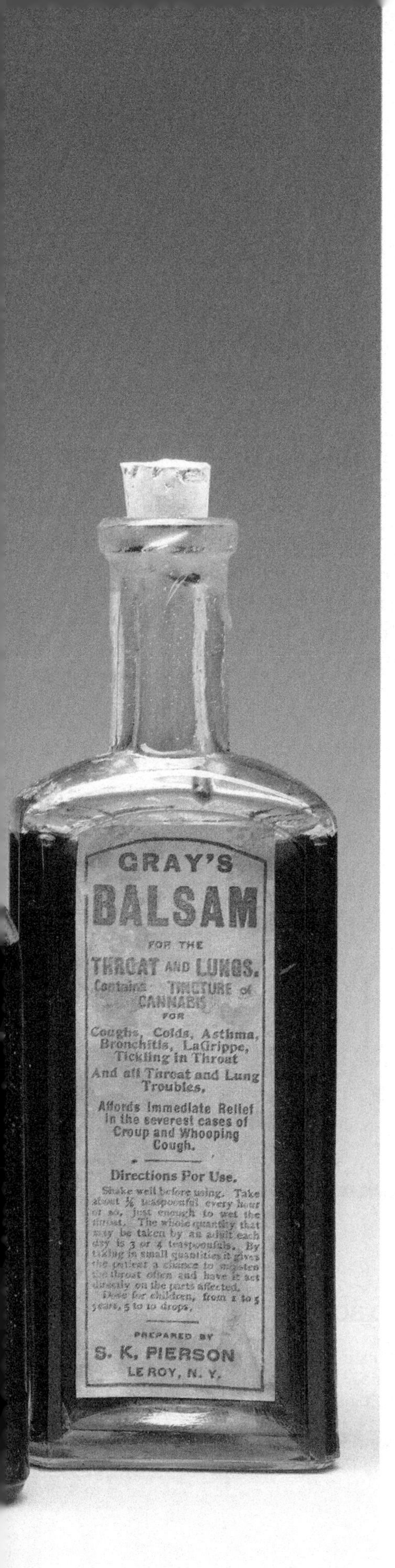

Part I Overview

Cannabis has been used for practical, medicinal, spiritual, and social purposes for millennia. This section briefly overviews the plant's social and evolutionary history, uses, and the origins of modern Prohibition and legalization. This history provides a basis for understanding current policies prohibiting or regulating commercial sales. Although legislation varies between cities, states, provinces, and countries, the final chapter in this section outlines some core universal regulatory concepts that shape the role of a budtender.

The Origins of Modern Prohibition

Budtenders are not expected to provide detailed histories of the plant, its uses, and regulatory policies. However, they will be expected to comply with current regulations and speak to therapeutic effects without crossing the line into providing unqualified medical advice. By understanding the origins of current policies, budtenders can better explain and communicate about them.

Global History of Cannabis Use

The species of plant known today as *Cannabis sativa* L.[1] first emerged in the mountains of Central Asia 28 million years ago.[2] It spread throughout the world thanks to its utility as a food, fiber, and medicinal herb and has been cultivated on every populated continent.

Although modern international Prohibition is rooted in actions taken in the 20th-century United States, cannabis prohibitions started nearly 1,000 years ago.

Cannabis Timeline: 28,000,000 BCE to Present Day

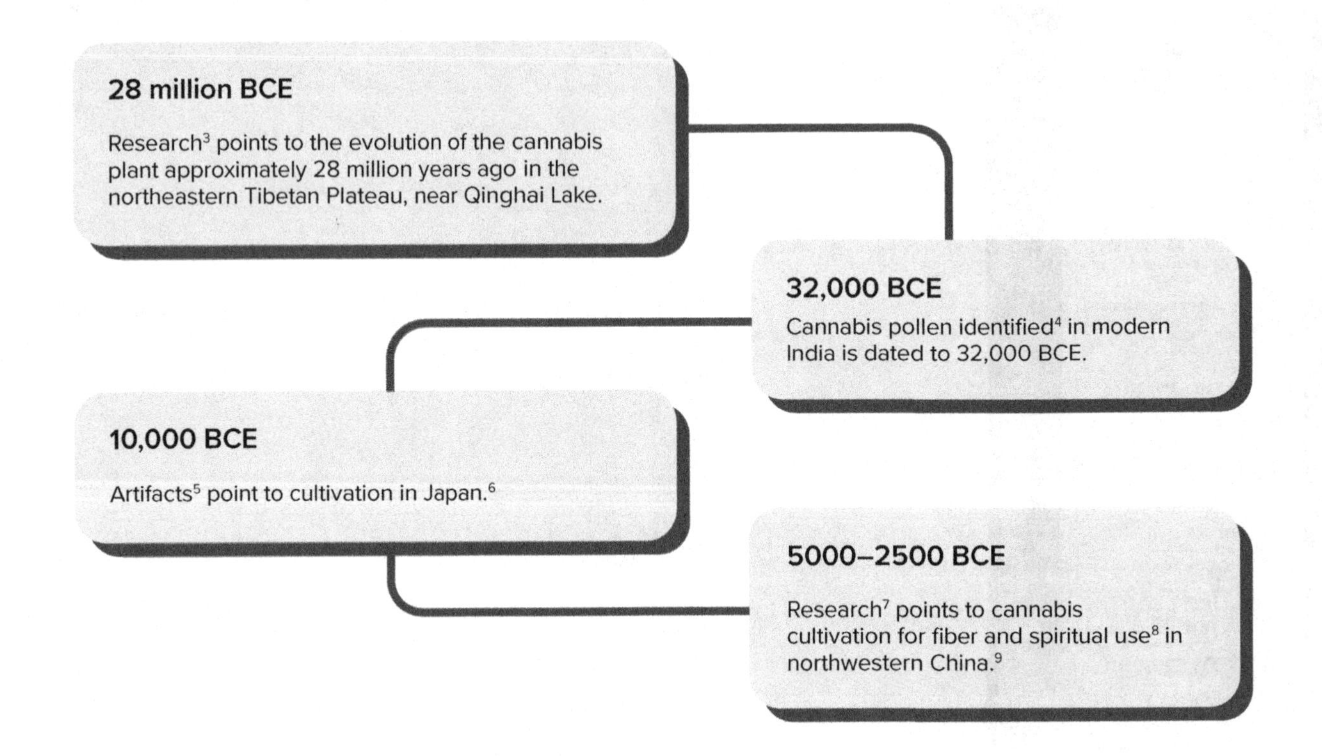

~2700 BCE

Chinese Emperor Shennong is thought to be the original author of the Pen Ts'ao Ching.[10] This early pharmacopeia includes cannabis as a treatment for many ailments, including gout, rheumatism, and malaria, and is the first known documentation of the plant's therapeutic applications.

1500–1000 BCE

Cannabis "bhang"[11] becomes popularized in ancient India and remains a popular drink in modern India.

2000–1400 BCE

Cannabis use and cultivation spreads from Asia to the Middle East.[12]

~600 BCE

Taoism gains popularity in China,[13] and cannabis and other mind-altering substances fall out of favor.

628–551 BCE

Cannabis is used in the Persian Empire[14] by followers of the Zoroastrian[15] religion.

2000 BCE–800 CE

Cannabis spreads to Europe and North Africa.[16]

1253–1368 CE

Sufi Muslims, a minority Islamic sect, use cannabis in religious practice and are targeted in Egypt[17] through the destruction of their cannabis crops.

1484 CE

Pope Innocent VIII issues a papal ban on cannabis[18] and declares it "an unholy sacrament of the satanic mass."

1500 CE

Cannabis proliferates throughout Africa,[19] where smoking (as opposed to oral ingestion) becomes popularized.

~1400–1600 CE

Hemp fibers are used in ship sails and riggings[20] during European colonialism of Africa and the Americas. Cultivation spreads[21] to the Americas.

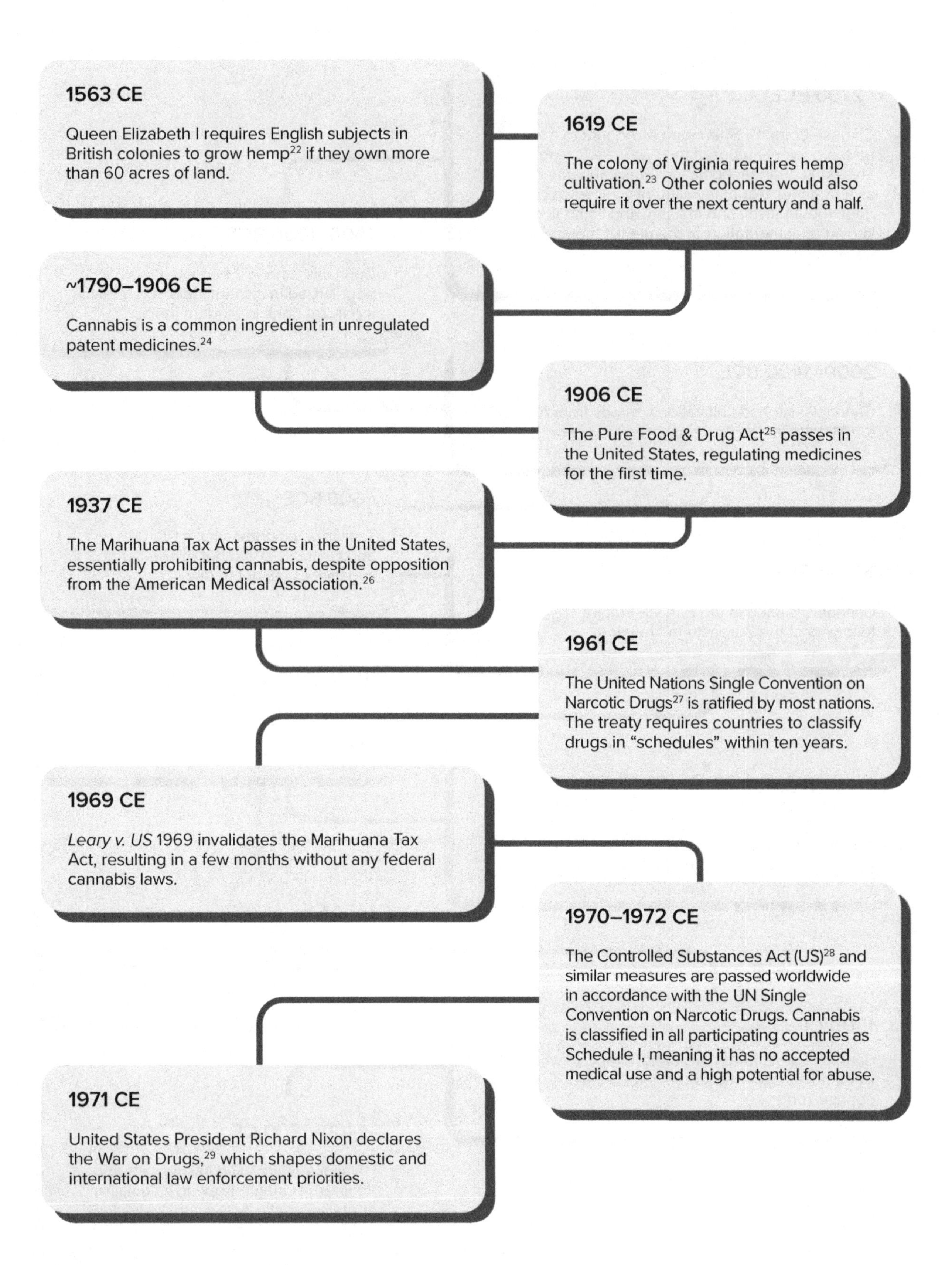
1563 CE
Queen Elizabeth I requires English subjects in British colonies to grow hemp[22] if they own more than 60 acres of land.
1619 CE
The colony of Virginia requires hemp cultivation.[23] Other colonies would also require it over the next century and a half.
~1790–1906 CE
Cannabis is a common ingredient in unregulated patent medicines.[24]
1906 CE
The Pure Food & Drug Act[25] passes in the United States, regulating medicines for the first time.
1937 CE
The Marihuana Tax Act passes in the United States, essentially prohibiting cannabis, despite opposition from the American Medical Association.[26]
1961 CE
The United Nations Single Convention on Narcotic Drugs[27] is ratified by most nations. The treaty requires countries to classify drugs in "schedules" within ten years.
1969 CE
Leary v. US 1969 invalidates the Marihuana Tax Act, resulting in a few months without any federal cannabis laws.
1970–1972 CE
The Controlled Substances Act (US)[28] and similar measures are passed worldwide in accordance with the UN Single Convention on Narcotic Drugs. Cannabis is classified in all participating countries as Schedule I, meaning it has no accepted medical use and a high potential for abuse.
1971 CE
United States President Richard Nixon declares the War on Drugs,[29] which shapes domestic and international law enforcement priorities.

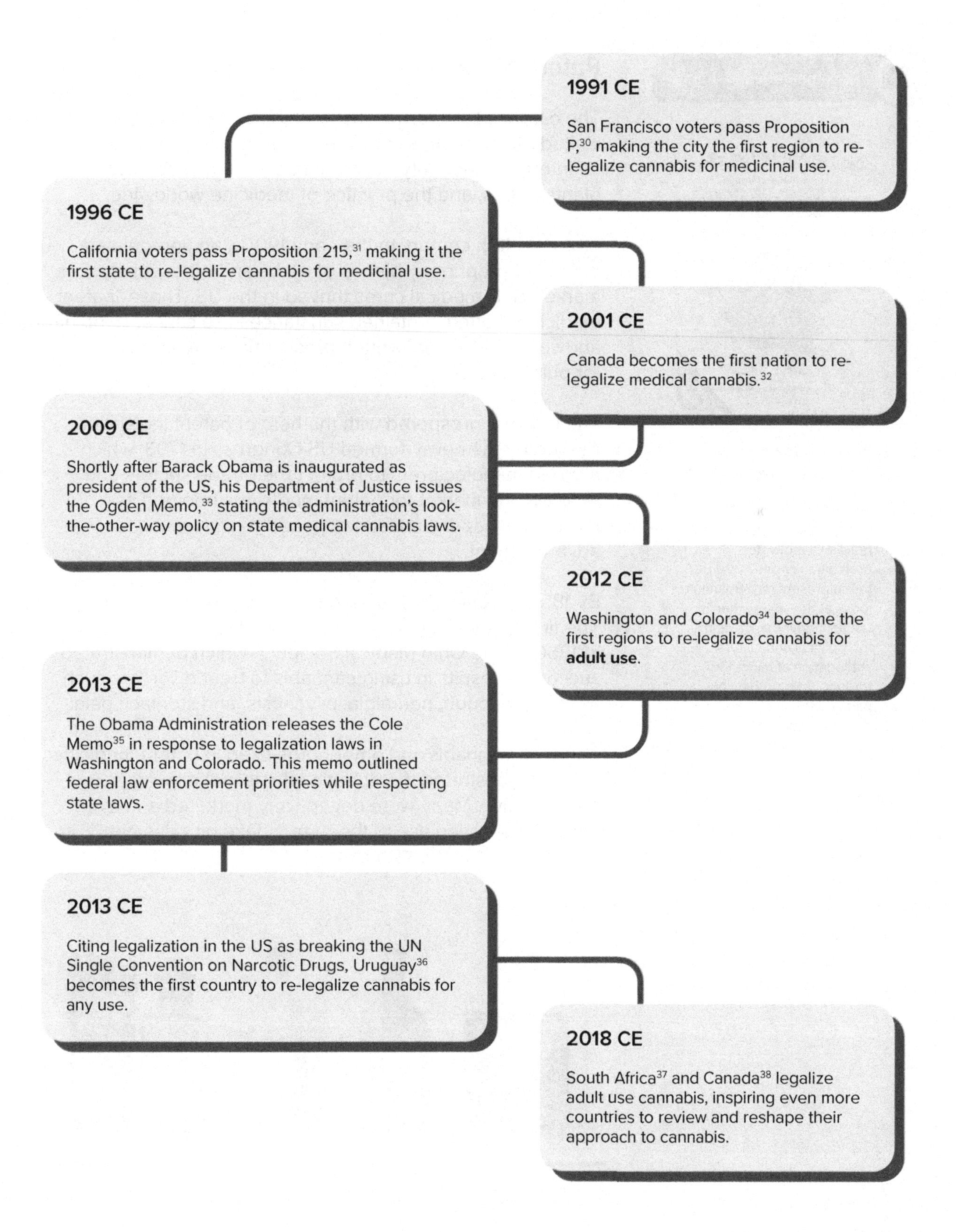
1991 CE
San Francisco voters pass Proposition P,[30] making the city the first region to re-legalize cannabis for medicinal use.
1996 CE
California voters pass Proposition 215,[31] making it the first state to re-legalize cannabis for medicinal use.
2001 CE
Canada becomes the first nation to re-legalize medical cannabis.[32]
2009 CE
Shortly after Barack Obama is inaugurated as president of the US, his Department of Justice issues the Ogden Memo,[33] stating the administration's look-the-other-way policy on state medical cannabis laws.
2012 CE
Washington and Colorado[34] become the first regions to re-legalize cannabis for **adult use**.
2013 CE
The Obama Administration releases the Cole Memo[35] in response to legalization laws in Washington and Colorado. This memo outlined federal law enforcement priorities while respecting state laws.
2013 CE
Citing legalization in the US as breaking the UN Single Convention on Narcotic Drugs, Uruguay[36] becomes the first country to re-legalize cannabis for any use.
2018 CE
South Africa[37] and Canada[38] legalize adult use cannabis, inspiring even more countries to review and reshape their approach to cannabis.

Recommended Reading

Drugs Are Not the Devil's Tools by Dr. David Bearman

This book is a complete history of drug use and politically-motivated prohibitions from 3,000 BCE to the present day. Bearman looks at the intersection of religion, governance, and the political and cultural subjugation of minorities through drug prohibitions, painting the backdrop for modern cannabis Prohibition and how to end it.

Patent Medicines

The origins of modern global prohibition developed in the United States of America, where a domestic ban led to an international treaty to categorize, control, and regulate plants, drugs, and the practice of medicine worldwide.

From the 18th century to the early 1900s, an unregulated market of proprietary blends of herbs and other substances marketed as medical cures thrived in the US. These "patent medicines" often contained substances like cannabis, opium, and coca, and formal written prescriptions were not required for purchase.

The industry prospered with the help of patent legislation passed by the newly-formed US Congress in 1793, which allowed manufacturers to protect their trade secrets and recipes. The market for patent medicines boomed as rising newspaper circulation opened new avenues for advertisement.

By 1850, cannabis was added to the US Pharmacopeia. The first medical cannabis study in the US was performed in 1860 by the Ohio Medical Society,[39] which demonstrated successful results in using cannabis to treat disorders such as chronic cough, neuralgia, psychosis, and stomach pain.

Although cannabis and other herbs used in patent medicines have demonstrated therapeutic effects, not all were safe and effective. Many were deceptively marketed and even dangerous, giving rise to the term "snake oil salesmen"[40] in the latter part of the 19th century.

To learn more about the history of the medicinal use of cannabis visit CannabisMuseum.com.

The 1906 Pure Food & Drug Act

The misuse, deceptive marketing, and collateral damage of the patent medicine industry led to the passage of the Pure Food and Drug Act of 1906. The law requires foods and medicines to include a list of ingredients on labels and regulates the use of medical claims in product marketing.

The Pure Food & Drug Act[41] established the Food & Drug Administration (FDA). The FDA[42] oversees the research and approval process for new medical drugs and regulates what claims can be made to market them. The approval process favors the standardization and consistency of pharmaceutical drugs, which has resulted in the removal of herbalism from medical care.

Most doctors and healthcare professionals do not receive training about cannabis and its interaction with the human body. As a result, budtenders are often put in the position of being asked to dispense medical advice to customers.

Herbal products can be recommended but not prescribed by doctors. A prescription includes specific information about dosage and frequency of use. Recommendations do not. Budtenders can help guide customers to products that may produce their desired effects, but they cannot make medical claims about the products they sell or prescribe their use.

Budtenders must never refer to cannabis as a "medicine" because it is not legally defined and regulated like one. Budtenders cannot treat patients, make medical claims, or prescribe dosing regimens. Research that could guide consumers and their doctors was effectively stymied by Prohibition, which began with the Marihuana Tax Act of 1937.

The Marihuana Tax Act of 1937

In the early 1900s, waves of immigration led to prohibitions on drugs and substances[43] associated with immigrant groups. This mass immigration, along with various other factors, would lead to the passage of the Marihuana Tax Act of 1937[44] (MTA), which effectively started cannabis Prohibition in the US.

The Cult of Pharmacology by Richard DeGrandpre

This book looks at America's troubled drug culture through the lens of history: the rise and fall of patent medicines, the Pure Food and Drug Act, and how herbs were supplanted with pharmaceutical analogs.

The African Roots of Marijuana by Chris S. Duvall

In *The African Roots of Marijuana*, Chris S. Duvall corrects common misconceptions while providing an authoritative history of cannabis as it flowed into, throughout, and out of Africa.

The Emperor Wears No Clothes by Jack Herer

Jack Herer's account of how and why cannabis Prohibition began and what that has meant to America has shaped cannabis activism for decades. Herer details the lost history of hemp as medicine, food, fuel, fiber, paper, and sustainable plastic alternative. This book inspired cannabis legalization efforts from the 1980s through the present day.

In 1913, California[45] became the first state to prohibit cannabis, followed by Utah in 1915. In the 1920s, an influx of immigrants came to the US from Mexico to escape the Mexican Revolution. The flow of refugees sparked racism and xenophobia, further fueled by the media. The term "marihuana" associated this "new" and "dangerous" drug with Mexicans and may have been deliberately used to obscure the fact that it was the same hemp plant being utilized for paper, fabric, and food.

Cannabis advocate Jack Herer's[46] 1985 best-selling book *The Emperor Wears No Clothes* inspired a generation of advocates. Herer assembled a detailed narrative of America's hemp history, including newspaper clippings evidencing racist media campaigns[47] that turned the American public against "marihuana." The book even unearthed a government-backed campaign pushing hemp cultivation[48] during World War II, shortly after the start of Prohibition.

Herer alleged a conspiracy between newspaper magnate William Randolph Hearst and DuPont to suppress hemp because it threatened the lumber, plastics, oil, and pharmaceutical industries, as well as law enforcement careers created to enforce alcohol Prohibition. Although this theory has proliferated through the movement and industry, it has also been debunked.[49]

In reality, a confluence of factors[50] led to the passage of the MTA, not the least of which was the anti-drug and anti-immigrant sentiment in the early 1900s and state-level bans of cannabis and opium in response.

Although the American Medical Association testified against the MTA,[51] it was passed by Congress and signed into law by President Franklin D. Roosevelt. The MTA did not "prohibit" cannabis but levied prohibitive taxes against it, effectively ending domestic cultivation. The MTA was overturned when the Supreme Court heard *Leary v. United States*[52] in 1969, but treaties were already in place to prohibit cannabis worldwide by then.

The United Nations Single Convention on Narcotic Drugs of 1961

In 1930, Harry Anslinger[53] was appointed to lead the newly formed Bureau of Narcotics and Dangerous Drugs (BNDD), the predecessor to the modern-day Drug Enforcement

Administration (DEA). He was one of the leading proponents of the Marihuana Tax Act of 1937 and an international treaty in 1961 that would extend cannabis, opium, and coca prohibitions to 186 countries.[54]

Anslinger began his career in law enforcement enforcing alcohol Prohibition, which ended with the 21st Amendment[55] in 1933. Anslinger's racism was no secret, and he used his role at the BNDD to pursue political persecutions against Hollywood celebrities and jazz musicians, notably Billie Holiday.[56]

When the United Nations was formed after World War II, Anslinger lobbied for international cooperation to enforce drug prohibitions. The United Nations Single Convention on Narcotic Drugs[57] was passed in 1961 and ratified by 186 nations. In accordance with the treaty, signees passed drug scheduling acts within ten years that effectively prohibited cannabis, coca, and opium. Cannabis was listed internationally as Schedule I, meaning it has no accepted medical use and a high potential for abuse.

In the decades following the treaty's ratification, a few countries continued to study and tolerate cannabis use. In the 1960s, Israel pioneered scientific research on cannabis and the **endocannabinoid system** and remains a leader in the field today. In the 1970s, the Netherlands established a "tolerance" policy toward cannabis. It was not technically legal, but it was sold and could be consumed in certain "coffee shops" with the tacit approval of government officials.

In 1970, US President Richard Nixon signed the Controlled Substances Act.[58] Notably, Nixon used this law to persecute minorities and political opponents.[59] Subsequent US presidents would further bolster the DEA and local law enforcement to enforce Prohibition into the 21st century. In the 1980s, President Ronald Reagan[60] expanded funding for the American Drug War worldwide.

In the 1990s, some European countries started to open up to cannabis consumption. Spain has maintained a tolerance for cannabis "clubs" while staying ambiguous about the legal status of such activities; meanwhile, Portugal decriminalized all drugs in 2001 and now has an established medical cannabis system.

In the 2010s, countries on every continent started rejecting cannabis Prohibition outright. There is increasing global support for dropping restrictions on research, cultivation, and consumption. Most American states have passed legislation allowing various forms of medicinal and adult use.

Watch This Video

While conducting the research that led him to write *The Emperor Wears No Clothes*, Jack Herer unearthed this government propaganda video, Hemp for Victory, encouraging American farmers to grow hemp to support military efforts during World War II. Search "Hemp for Victory" on Youtube.com.

In 2012, the US violated the United Nations Single Convention on Narcotic Drugs[61] when Colorado and Washington voted to legalize adult use. In 2013, Uruguay announced a plan to legalize cannabis, also breaking the treaty.[62] The UN and the World Health Organization (WHO) endorsed global decriminalization two years later. In 2018, South Africa decriminalized consumption on private property. Canada also launched the first national cannabis market in 2018, when it legalized adult use and set up a system for provincial governments to regulate cultivation and retail sales.

Since 2018 there has been a movement in and around the United Nations to repeal the treaty.[63] However, efforts continue to stall.[64] There have also been efforts to provide pathways to regulating cannabis[65] even without its repeal.

In the 21st century, a multi-billion dollar legal cannabis industry has emerged, and it is now considered one of the fastest-growing industries on earth.[66] The next chapter explores the factors, advocates, and political strategies that led to this boom, despite global prohibition.

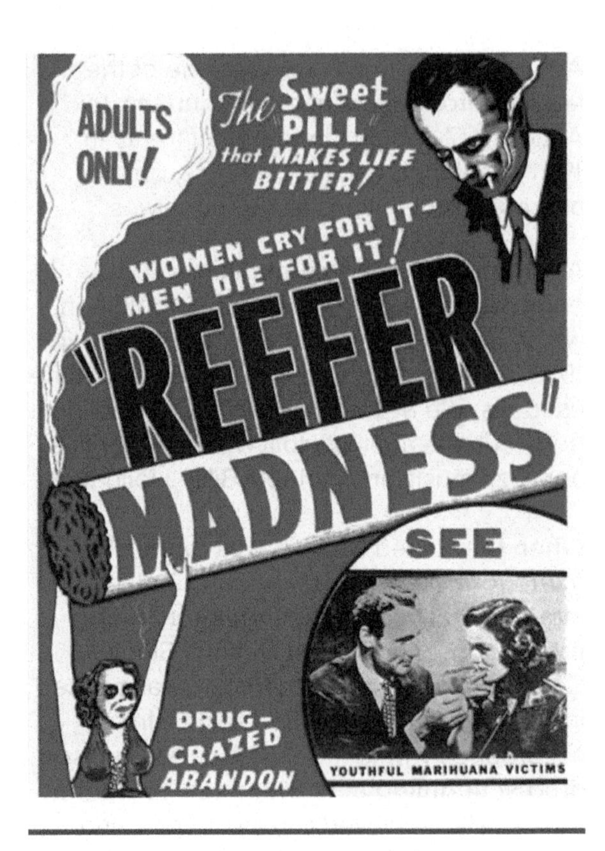

Reefer Madness

A prime example of anti-cannabis propaganda produced during the lead-up to the 1937 Marihuana Tax Act is the 1936 film "Reefer Madness." In it, two young people try the "devil weed" and slide through a series of misfortunes, from murder to an ultimate descent into madness. The film's themes are typical of the "journalism" associated with newspaper mogul William Randolph Hearst and the other low-budget filmmakers and novelists that permeated the culture of the era. Today the term "Reefer Madness" refers to any hyperbolic anti-cannabis rhetoric.

Want to learn more about international cannabis policy?

The United Nations is actively reviewing policies on cannabis, THC, CBD, and hemp and how they can contribute to sustainable development goals. Barcelona-based researcher Kenzi Riboulet-Zemouli publishes informational reports to educate international policymakers and inform global cannabis policy. Visit Kenzi.Zemou.li to download reports (available in multiple languages) and to learn more.

The Origins of Modern Legalization

The framework of cannabis Prohibition was laid with the Marihuana Tax Act of 1937 in the United States and the United Nations Single Convention on Narcotic Drugs in 1961. The declaration of the War on Drugs a decade later would prove to be its undoing. This chapter overviews the period from the 1970s through the early 2000s when the medical cannabis movement and the proliferation of domestic production in the US led to the first decriminalization and legalization laws.

The Controlled Substances Act of 1970

The classification of cannabis as Schedule I under the Controlled Substances Act is the barrier to medicinal research in the United States. Similar legislation in other countries continues to hinder the industry's maturation. As the industry's front line, budtenders are put in a precarious position of being expected to have all the answers, despite regulations preventing the research required to provide them.

In accordance with the UN Single Convention on Narcotic Drugs, the United States Congress passed the Comprehensive Drug Abuse Prevention and Control Act. Title II of the law, which is known as the Controlled Substances Act,[67] established five "schedules" used to categorize and control drugs:

President Nixon signing anti-drug legislation, 1970. AP Photo.

The New Jim Crow by Michelle Alexander

The aggressive policing tactics employed by law enforcement during the War on Drugs era, along with sweeping anti-drug and mandatory minimum sentencing legislation, caused arrest and incarceration rates to skyrocket. *The New Jim Crow* explains how Black men, in particular, were targeted under these new laws and how the US justice system has become a contemporary system of racial control. Citizens convicted of Drug War crimes have lost their right to vote and serve on juries, limiting their political influence. They also face lifelong economic barriers, such as legal discrimination in employment, housing, access to education, and public benefits eligibility.

- **Schedule I** drugs have no recognized medical use and a high potential for abuse. This includes "marihuana" (cannabis), GHB, coca, opium, and ayahuasca.

- **Schedule II** drugs have a recognized medical use but still have high abuse potential. This includes PCP, Oxycontin, methamphetamine, cocaine, and morphine.

- **Schedule III** drugs have a recognized medical use and some potential for abuse. This includes ketamine, many steroids, and Marinol, a pharmaceutical drug composed entirely of synthetic THC.

- **Schedule IV** drugs have a recognized medical use and low potential for abuse. This includes drugs that must be purchased from a pharmacist but do not require a prescription.

- **Schedule V** drugs have a recognized medical use and minimal potential for abuse. This includes aspirin and other common over-the-counter medications.

Cannabis was temporarily placed in Schedule I, which carries the strictest restrictions and penalties for distribution and possession. However, the law called for further study to explore the potential medical benefits and likelihood of abuse before the scheduling of cannabis was made permanent. The National Commission on Marijuana and Drug Abuse, also known as the Shafer Commission, after its chairman, Raymond P. Shafer, was convened to investigate. In March of 1972, the Shafer Commission presented its findings to Congress and the public in a report titled "Marihuana, A Signal of Misunderstanding."[68] The report concluded that cannabis did not pose a danger and recommended using social measures rather than criminalization to discourage consumption. The Commission's recommendations were never implemented, and cannabis remains a Schedule I drug.

In 1972, the National Organization for the Reform of Marijuana Laws (NORML) challenged the DEA's classification of cannabis as a Schedule I drug, arguing it should be included in Schedule II instead. The challenge did not receive a public hearing until 1988. At that time, DEA Administrative Law Judge Francis Young agreed that cannabis should not be included in Schedule I. In his decision, Young described[69] cannabis as "one of the safest therapeutically active substances known to man" and said its scheduling was "unreasonable, arbitrary, and capricious."

An appeals court also found that the DEA had broad discretion over the schedule and that the agency had the unilateral authority to move cannabis out of Schedule I without the approval of Congress. There have been similar challenges to the DEA's scheduling of cannabis over the years, but the agency has refused to reconsider its position.

By 1981, eleven states pushed back against the cannabis crackdown by decriminalizing possession. These laws did not make cannabis "legal," but they removed or significantly scaled back criminal penalties for possession and cultivation.

In 1982, President Reagan declared a "War on Drugs,"[70] new federal law enforcement initiatives meant to stamp out the "climate of lawlessness" surrounding the distribution and sale of illegal narcotics. First Lady Nancy Reagan launched the "Just Say No" campaign, targeted to prevent youth from using drugs by embedding its message of abstinence in the curriculum of public schools across the country.

Budtender Interview

"In my community, cannabis has always been something that has been used as a tool against us. I got into the cannabis industry and budtending because I wanted to find a way to use it as something to empower and encourage people in my community. Knowledge is power, so when you get education, you get more power."

— **William Brown,** budtender in Chicago, Illinois

First Lady Nancy Reagan's "Just Say No" campaign targeted children. Photo Wikimedia Commons.

Recommended Reading

Smoke Signals by Martin Lee

Martin Lee traces the dramatic social history of marijuana from its origins to its emergence in the 1960s as a defining force in a culture war that has never ceased. Lee describes how the illicit marijuana subculture overcame government opposition and morphed into a dynamic, multibillion-dollar industry. Lee draws attention to underreported scientific breakthroughs that are reshaping the therapeutic landscape.

The Reagan administration's efforts[71] culminated in Congress passing the Anti-Drug Abuse Act of 1986,[72] which allocated billions to waging the War on Drugs and establishing mandatory minimum sentencing for drug crimes, which would fill public and private prisons past capacity in the following decades.

While the Reagan Administration ramped up funding for the War on Drugs, a deadly new virus was sweeping the world that his administration did not want to acknowledge[73] but would begin to undo the broader War on Drugs.

Medical Cannabis Legalization

Little was understood about the AIDS virus or the resulting disease except that it caused severe pain, nausea, and wasting syndrome.[74] San Francisco's large gay community was an early epicenter[75] of the dramatic surge in cases that escalated into a crisis throughout the 1980s and early 1990s.

Patients were often prescribed a cocktail of pharmaceutical drugs meant to slow the progression of the infection and treat their symptoms. However, many found these drugs provided little relief. Nausea made it challenging to hold pills in the stomach long enough to enter the bloodstream.

Dennis Peron[76] was one of the key leaders of the cannabis reform movement in San Francisco during the AIDS epidemic. Peron was originally from the Bronx, New York, and moved to San Francisco after serving in the US Air Force during the Vietnam War. Peron operated underground dispensaries in San Francisco throughout the 1970s.

Is all cannabis use medicinal?

Dennis Peron was a leader in the medical marijuana movement of the 1990s. He played a crucial role in pioneering medical cannabis ballot initiatives in the City of San Francisco and the State of California. Dennis vehemently opposed adult use legalization laws because, as he put it, "all use is medical." He felt that bifurcating the systems and markets for medical and adult use cannabis would ultimately be harmful. Do you agree? Is all use "medical?" Why or why not?

In 1978, Peron organized the campaign for San Francisco's Proposition W, which directed the city prosecutor to halt the prosecution of cannabis possession cases. The measure was approved by voters but never enforced. In 1991, he was the driving force behind yet another initiative, San Francisco's Proposition P, a resolution that decriminalized the medical use of cannabis in the city and urged the state to adopt similar reforms. It passed with overwhelming support — 79 percent of voters approved it.

Peron was also a key provider of cannabis to patients in need. He worked with Mary Jane Rathbun, also known as "Brownie Mary," to distribute **edibles** to Bay Area patients and opened the first public dispensary, the San Francisco Buyers Club, in 1994.

In 1996, 55% of California voters approved Proposition 215,[77] making it the first state to pass a law to provide safe access to cannabis for medicinal uses. Also known as the Compassionate Use Act, this legislation did not lay out a plan for regulation. Instead, it enshrined the right to use cannabis for medicinal purposes in the state. According to the official summary, the law "exempts patients and defined caregivers who possess or cultivate marijuana for medical treatment recommended by a physician from criminal laws which otherwise prohibit possession or cultivation of marijuana." In other words, a patient with a valid recommendation from a doctor would not face criminal charges for having cannabis.

Although medical cannabis became legal in California in 1996, the first regulations did not pass until almost seven years later. In 2003, California legislators passed Senate Bill 420[78], which addressed some of the ambiguities that surrounded the state's implementation of Prop 215. According to the legislative intent statement, the new law was passed "in order to avoid unnecessary arrest and prosecution"of medical patients and "provide needed guidance to law enforcement officers."

Watch This Video

Claire Birch was a Berkeley, California-based documentarian who followed much of the early movement toward medical cannabis laws in the San Francisco Bay Area. This clip[81] includes rare footage of Brownie Mary passionately describing her work and why she does it, as well as a contextual interview about her with Dennis Peron.

Adult Use Legalization

Shortly after California legalized medical use, a steady stream of Western states passed similar citizen-led initiatives. By the end of the '90s the entire West Coast had medical cannabis laws. State regulators did little to manage the emerging industries, resulting in a booming unregulated supply chain. When President Barack Obama came into office in 2009, his administration signaled[79] that it would not use federal resources against state-legal medical cannabis, fueling a growing "Green Rush" and kickstarting state-level campaigns to legalize cannabis for all adults over 21.

Less than a month after President Obama's inauguration in January 2009, incoming Attorney General Eric Holder and DEA Administrator Michele Leonhart announced that the administration would not prosecute medical cannabis dispensaries. Later that year, Deputy Attorney General David Ogden issued a policy memo stating that the Department of Justice was committed to the "efficient and rational use" of its resources. Prosecuting those in "clear and unambiguous compliance" with state laws did not meet that standard.

Barack Obama openly admitted to smoking cannabis in his youth during his campaign for president. He said, "When I was a kid, I inhaled frequently. That was the point," drawing a direct parallel to former President Bill Clinton's comment that he had tried marijuana, but "didn't inhale."

Many advocates were optimistic about the potential for progress under President Obama. He said he supported states' right to regulate medical cannabis and pledged not to use federal money to prosecute patients. A radical shift towards cannabis policy in most states happened during his eight years in office, but Obama's justice department continued political raids and persecutions against state-legal cannabis businesses.

The Original Medical Cannabis Program

The US government has operated a medical cannabis program[82] since 1978. The program is still operating today, although participation was initially limited and no new applications have been accepted for at least 30 years.

The roots of the program date back to 1975, when Robert Randall was arrested for growing cannabis that he used to treat his glaucoma. In court, Randall argued that cannabis was a "medical necessity" for him and that he had no choice but to find some illegal way to procure it. The judge accepted his "medical necessity defense," a legal principle used numerous times to defend the production and possession of cannabis with varying degrees of success.

Randall established his right to use cannabis for medicinal purposes, however, the federal government decided they would be the providers, rather than allow him or others to grow their own.

In 1978, Randall received his first allotment of medical cannabis from the federal Investigational New Drug (IND) program. It was grown at the University of Mississippi, which became the only place in the US where cannabis could be grown legally for research and the IND program. Up to 15 people participated in the program at its height, each receiving a monthly shipment of 300 rolled cannabis cigarettes, packaged in a metal can and delivered to a local pharmacy with special permission.

In the late 1980s and early 1990s, hundreds of patients applied to the IND. The program reached a height of 30 active patients before President George H.W. Bush halted new applications in 1992. As of 2023, two existing program participants continue to receive cannabis from the government every month.

Jeff Jones and the Origins of "Budtending"

The history of the modern dispensary and much of its associated terminology can be traced to the Bay Area, where a group of advocates began to openly distribute medical marijuana in the late 1980s.

At that time, Dennis Peron and "Brownie Mary" Jane Rathbun made national headlines by openly providing cannabis to AIDS patients in San Francisco. A young Jeff Jones saw them on CNN from his home in South Dakota and was inspired to move west to be a part of it.

Jeff had lost his father to cancer when he was 13 and making marijuana available to those who needed it resonated with him.

He visited Dennis Peron's San Francisco cannabis clubs and was inspired to replicate the concept in Oakland, where he had settled. He chose a prominent location in downtown because he saw how being public provided Peron's work with legitimacy, made it more accessible by mass transit, and integrated cannabis patients into the broader community.

Jeff opened the Oakland Cannabis Buyers' Cooperative (OCBC), one of the first dispensaries in the nation. At the same time, his friend Richard Lee, founder of Oaksterdam University, launched what would become Coffeeshop Blue Sky.

In 1998, the Oakland Cannabis Buyer's Cooperative was briefly allowed to legally provide cannabis to patients by the 9th Circuit Court of Appeals before the US Supreme Court reversed the decision. In this picture, Jeff Jones is shown providing the first legal bag of cannabis to multiple sclerosis patient Yvonne Westbrook after the appeal.

"Richard really liked the idea of making it like a bar and calling it a 'bud bar,'" Jeff says. "I was always trying to describe it more in the context of a medical utility office, like a dispensary. You would go in and receive your medicine based on your doctor's recommendation."

The terms "dispensary" and "budtender" stuck and are used to this day.

With the city's blessing, and local law enforcement encouraged to look the other way, several other dispensaries cropped up in downtown Oakland.

Richard Lee opened a gift shop, a museum, and Oaksterdam University, and Jeff expanded his business as well. He started a cultivation operation on the top floor to provide flowers and distribute clones to those who wanted to grow their own. Jeff's goal was to drop the price of an eighth to $20, making it affordable to anyone in need.

In November 1996, California voters approved Proposition 215, the landmark medical marijuana initiative that exempted patients and caregivers from criminal prosecution for possessing or cultivating cannabis and kicked off more than two decades of global legislative change.

Nevertheless, cannabis remained illegal at the federal level, and Jeff was busted several times. One of these busts resulted in Jeff arguing for medicinal cannabis to the Supreme Court in *United States v. OCBC*.[83] He did not prevail, but his efforts helped pave the way for the wave of cannabis legalization. Jeff has since assisted in drafting legislation, campaigning for those that appeared on ballots, and pioneering dispensary and budtending practices still in use.

Jeff Jones preparing edibles for patients, circa 1995.

"We thought of ourselves as therapeutic counselors," he says. "When clients walked into our door, we would completely unveil what cannabis could be for them. How do they want to use it? What benefit did they get from it? We had many different products, from edibles, pills, flowers, and vaporizing, which was mostly unknown at the time and something I was trying to innovate around."

Eventually, Jeff was busted and forced to shut down. He moved to a new downtown Oakland location and converted OCBC into the Patient ID Center, which issued pre-verified identification cards to patients.

"I saw the niche of giving patients what we didn't have, which was a card that gave them some recognition and legitimacy in the field and made law enforcement take a step back," he said. "We created a sense of safety."

He operated out of that location until 2020, issuing around 150,000 ID cards. The business is now defunct "due to social change," Jeff says. "I always told people I will be here as long as we are needed. As soon as needs change, I have to change my mission."

Jeff continues to advocate for cannabis and share his wealth of knowledge as a horticulture instructor at Oaksterdam University. Jeff observes that as cannabis mainstreams, the budtender's job changes.

"Back then, it was a very exclusive, very limited, very grateful group of people you were helping on the other side of the counter," he says. "You risked going to jail for conspiracy of sale just for talking to them."

As cannabis becomes commercialized, he advises the next generation of budtenders to stay true to education.

"A budtender in the past was both an interpreter and a guidance counselor. They needed to interpret the patient's problem and then guide them into their solution," Jeff says. "Today, it is not much different, but budtenders also have the opportunity to advocate as new policies are shaped. Budtenders get to talk to the public and give feedback to public officials that could, long-term, actually push these issues in a more legitimate fashion because they are the ones on the front line."

In 2009, Oaksterdam University founder Richard Lee spent over $1 million of his own money on a campaign to legalize cannabis for adult use in California on the 2010 ballot. Oaksterdam University became the de facto headquarters for the Proposition 19 campaign, the first adult use legalization initiative of the modern era. Amid an industry and movement divided over the details of "how" to legalize, Prop 19 failed by 4%.

Oaksterdam University founder Richard Lee funded and campaigned for California's Proposition 19 (2010), the first adult use campaign of the legalization era.

Campaigns to legalize in Colorado and Washington State began immediately

Budtender Interview

"During my own cannabis journey, I became aware that the plant helped reduce my anxiety and put me at ease in social situations. I was self-medicating. I thought I was doing it for fun, but then I realized I use cannabis regularly because I need it to live a normal life. Since then, I believe anyone with a portion of their budget dedicated to purchasing cannabis is not a 'recreational user.' They are not doing it for fun. They are doing it because they need it one way or another. They are using it to reach some level of homeostasis in their lives."

— **Goose Duarte,** former budtender and current director of operations at Oaksterdam University

following the 2010 election. Both initiatives passed in 2012, making them the first regions in the world to regulate and license commercial cannabis for non-medicinal use.

In 2013, the Obama Administration released the Cole Memo.[80] This policy statement said the Department of Justice did not intend to interfere with adult use cannabis laws as long as states had "strong and effective regulatory and enforcement systems" in place to prevent the diversion of cannabis outside of the regulated market and prevent sales to minors.

The release of the Cole Memo marked a significant turning point — many entrepreneurs and investors felt that the legal and financial risks associated with federal enforcement had been greatly diminished and started to pour money into new ventures. The Cole Memo is largely credited as the impetus for the formation of the modern cannabis industry, which now features massive multi-state operators and publicly traded companies. Cannabis is still illegal at the federal level, but this has not stopped more states from launching their commercial adult use markets.

US and World Legalization Maps

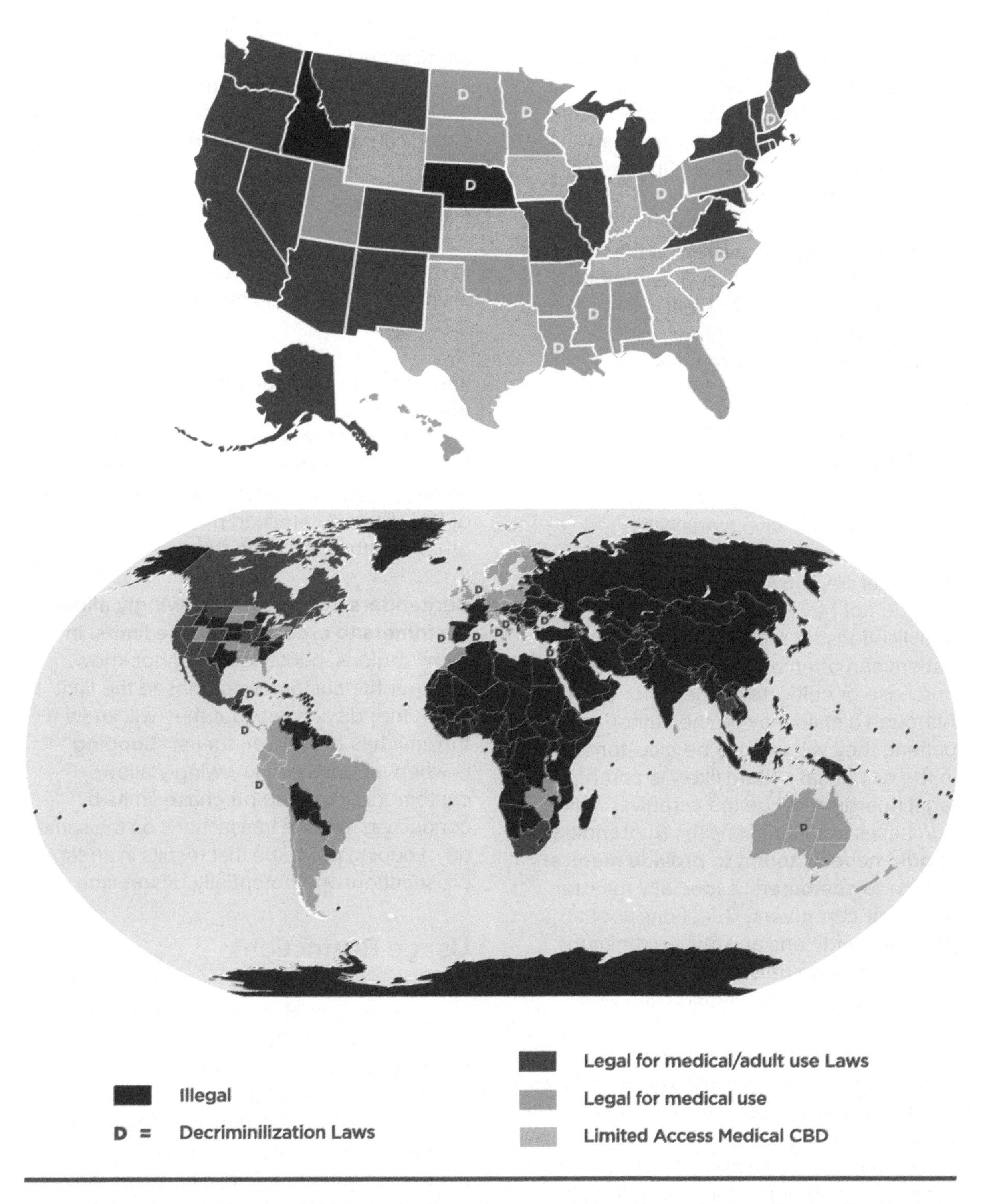

This map was prepared in December 2022. Legislative change happens quickly, and laws vary at the national and local levels. Budtenders and consumers must stay informed of their local laws and regulations.

Laws & Policies

Cannabis is a heavily-regulated industry, and budtenders are the front line of compliance. Laws regulating commercial marketplaces change rapidly and vary between nations, states, provinces, and even cities and counties.

Budtenders should be aware of all the laws that govern cannabis where they live. Although these cannabis laws are highly variable, the following standard regulatory policies have been adopted in many regions.

Age Limits & Medical Authorization

Customers must have a qualifying condition to purchase cannabis at a medical dispensary. Most medical laws do not have age limits but stricter qualifications for minors. A qualifying patient can often authorize a caregiver to purchase or cultivate cannabis for them. Although a child may be the authorized patient, they will unlikely be a customer in the dispensary. More likely, a parent or legal guardian will be the caregiver making purchases in the dispensary. **Budtenders should never attempt to provide medical advice to customers, especially minors and their caregivers.** Questions about medical conditions and dosing regimens must politely be deflected to the healthcare professional recommending cannabis.

Checking in a customer and verifying their age or medical status is usually a separate job, but in smaller dispensaries, this may be the budtender's responsibility. Government-issued photo identification, such as a driver's license or passport, is sufficient to verify that the customer is of legal age. Medical customers will be asked to show identification and their authorization, which could include the doctor's recommendation or a medical cannabis registry identification card.

Purchase & Possession Limits

In regulated cannabis markets, the amount a single customer can buy in a given period is set by the law.

In states with medical and adult use markets, medical possession limits and home garden sizes are often higher than for adult use customers. In more restricted medical marketplaces, there may be monthly or daily limits determined by the doctor or other healthcare professionals.

Budtenders must never knowingly allow customers to exceed purchase limits. In many regions, budtenders cannot know whether the customer purchased the limit in another dispensary, but they will know if the limit has been hit in theirs. **"Looping"** is when a budtender knowingly allows customers to exceed purchase limits by conducting multiple transactions on the same day. Looping is a crime that results in arrest, prosecution, and potentially prison time.

Usage Restrictions

Consuming cannabis products in private homes is usually legal, but sometimes this does not extend to renters or people living in public housing. Tourists in adult-use markets may find they can easily buy cannabis but do not have a safe and legal place to consume it. Public consumption spaces, or "lounges," are sometimes permitted, but otherwise, the customer is on their own to determine where they can consume. *See Part II: Dispensary Models* for more information about budtending in a consumption lounge.

Track-and-Trace

"Track-and-trace" software is used to prevent the diversion of legal products to the illegal market. A tracking tag is placed on the plant when it is rooted and follows it through to sale as an end product.

Security

Licensed cannabis businesses are usually required to have security cameras that cover the entire premises. They are likely to have these cameras for security reasons, but budtenders should be aware that the footage could be made available to government regulators at any time.

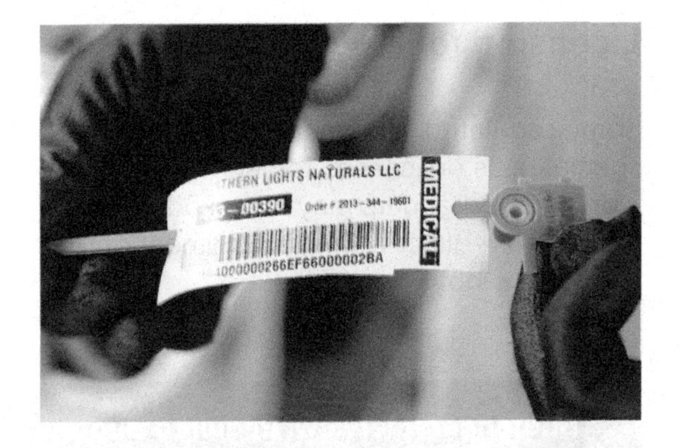

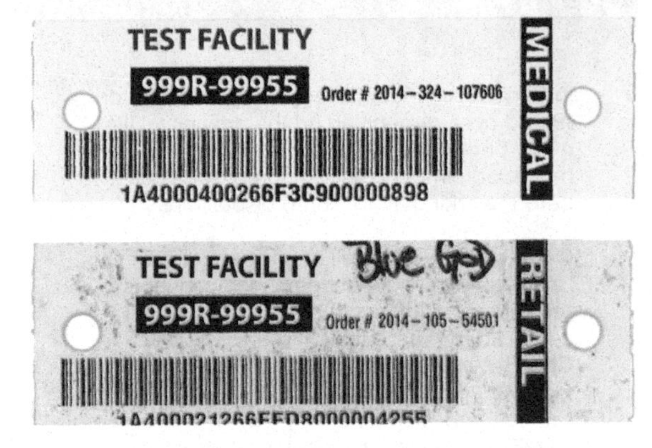

Radiofrequency identification (RFID) tags are used to track cannabis as it moves through the supply chain.

Budtender Interview

"Utah is a medical-only state, and budtenders here are called 'pharmacy agents.' There are a lot of rules. For instance, patients cannot put 'flame to flower' and must only vaporize cannabis if they want to inhale. Edibles are restricted to 'gelatinous cubes.' Patients must get certified by a qualified medical provider, 'QMP,' and their authorization is only valid for three months the first time. It has to be renewed every six months. Dispensaries are called 'pharmacies,' and they are required by law to employ a pharmacist. The first time someone comes into a dispensary they have to have a first-time consultation appointment with the pharmacist, which usually takes about a half hour. The pharmacist passes information through electronic records to the pharmacy agent, who takes over and shows them what to purchase based on the cannabinoids, terpenes, and ingestion method. A lot of people seeking cannabis have no idea what to do, and that is where pharmacy agents come in."

— **Blake Silva,** former budtender in Layton, Utah

Licensing for Industry Workers

Some regulated cannabis markets require special tests or licenses for industry workers. Budtenders may be asked to take a test and register with a government entity to secure a job.

Most Product is Regional or Local

In the US, commercial markets are relegated to within the states due to federal law. This means that although brands can set up franchising in other states, there are no national producers because products

Budtender Interview: Required Budtender Training in Canada

In Canada, cannabis is legal for persons 18 or 19 and over, depending on the province. Like every budtender in Ontario, CJ "Zesty" Daipan had to obtain CannSell Standard Certification before working at a Toronto dispensary.

Ontario law requires all employees of cannabis retail stores, store managers, and cannabis retail license holders to complete CannSell certification before their first day of work. CannSell was developed in partnership with Mothers Against Drunk Driving (MADD) Canada and is approved by the Alcohol and Gaming Commission of Ontario. The goal is to educate retail employees and store owners on how to sell cannabis responsibly.

"Our training is adamant that we know we are not licensed medical professionals. We are technically educators. I can tell customers about my experiences and educate them on the product, but we are technically not allowed to make recommendations," CJ says.

While medical cannabis is administered through Health Canada with tax deductions, health assessments, and rigorous testing, CJ works in an adult use dispensary. Still, she often sees consumers seeking relief from symptoms like epilepsy, arthritis, and pain.

"I cannot tell them which item to choose, but I can tell them, 'we have a selection of plants that might suit your liking,'" she says. "At that point, I go into educator mode. I explain their options to them so that they can compare." CJ then shares and explains the menu. "They are technically making their choice, but I have given them deeper feedback on the products without telling them what they should get."

CJ "Zesty" Daipan, budtender in Toronto, Ontario.

In Canada, even adult use cannabis is treated like a pharmaceutical product, she says. The packaging is plain with a government sticker. Edibles are limited to 10mg packets, and advertising is strictly regulated.

"They are very concerned about things being advertised to children, whereas in the States, advertising is heavy on the visuals and the nostalgia feels," she says.

cannot travel over state lines. Licensed dispensaries in each state will only carry products produced legally in that state.

The same applies to countries concerning international policies; even if cannabis is legal in neighboring countries, it is likely still a crime to transport it over an international border. A few countries allow the import and export of cannabis. Some countries do not license cultivation and production and require products to be imported.
Once federal policy changes in the US, products will likely be sold nationwide. As more nations' laws change, some products may become consistently available on international markets. For more information about legalization policies, see *Appendix A: Advocacy.*

Free vs. Limited Markets

Regional cannabis markets vary in the diversity of products available. Some regions only authorize a few producers and retailers, while others have free markets with no caps on licensing and lower barriers to entry. The difference is significant as far as products available for purchase.

In states with free markets, many varieties, products, and product types are available, and different products are at different dispensaries. In states with limited markets, there is very little price or product competition, and dispensaries often carry the same brands and products.

Some laws restrict the types of products sold, particularly raw flowers or products designed for inhalation. In some places, THC content is heavily restricted, further limiting available products.

Home Grow

It is legal to cultivate personal gardens in some medical and adult use markets. Dispensaries may sell seeds and starter plants (**clones**) in these regions. Budtenders are not required to be cultivation and plant variety experts. However, they should be aware of legal purchasing limits and basic home grow regulations if they work in a dispensary that sells these products.

Starter plants (called "clones") are available in dispensaries in regions where home cultivation is legal. (Left) Photo by Matthew Sichkaruk via Unsplash.com. (Right) Photo Oaksterdam Archives.

Budtender Interview

"Where I am from, cannabis is taboo, and not only that, it is dangerous. Law enforcement is not educated, and not all of them appreciate it. It is actually really dangerous to be a budtender and be in the cannabis industry in Texas. It is a daily fear, but at the same time, it is rewarding to see cannabis help people."

— **Quinten Neely,** Texas

Traveling

Budtenders are not responsible for knowing all cannabis laws everywhere. However, they should be able to make customers aware of local possession limits, where cannabis can and cannot be consumed, and how it should be stored. It is imperative to make travelers and tourists aware of these local regulations.

Never attempt to travel over international borders with cannabis. Even in places where it is legal on both sides of the border (such as between Washington State and British Columbia, Canada),[84] transporting cannabis over that border is considered a serious drug trafficking crime. The same applies within the US. Although it may be legal in two bordering states, crossing state borders with cannabis is still technically a federal crime.

Some regions are accommodating to people traveling with cannabis. Travelers are subject to local possession limits when they travel within a region where it is legal. Airports in legal states or Canada may even have formalized policies stating acceptable possession limits. Cannabis possession through international airports could lead to lengthy prison sentences. Travelers should be aware that even if they are allowed to possess it while boarding a flight in a legal state or country, they will be subject to the laws where they land. More importantly, bringing cannabis on an airplane is committing drug trafficking under US federal law, even when flying within a fully legal state like California.

Penalties

Cannabis is still illegal by international treaty and under most national and regional laws. Penalties for breaking the law vary by jurisdiction. In countries and regions where cannabis is still completely prohibited, penalties for simple use or possession are still punishable by prison and sometimes even death.[85] Even in places with regulated commercial markets, breaking the law is usually punishable by fines or loss of license and, in certain circumstances, could result in incarceration.

Budtenders should be familiar with local possession limits, rules about how products are packaged when they leave the dispensary, where cannabis can be legally consumed, and how to store products once seals are broken so they can pass this information to customers when appropriate. It is not a budtender's responsibility to determine whether customers will travel with cannabis. However, if they mention it, they should make them aware that possession laws vary, and traveling over state and international boundaries could result in harsh penalties.

In regulated commercial markets, there may be steeper penalties for business owners or employees who knowingly break the law. In Colorado, budtenders were arrested and faced felony charges for helping customers exceed daily purchase limits,[86] and the dispensary's owners went to prison for one year. Public consumption of cannabis is never legal but may be tolerated in some places. For example, many Northern California cities have "lowest priority" laws that discourage police from using resources on cannabis as opposed to other crimes. Budtenders should make customers aware that the legality of the products they buy varies based on their jurisdiction, and so do the places they can consume them.

Policy & Advocacy

Regardless of the law, people will grow, process, and consume cannabis, but

Protests outside the raid of Oaksterdam University, 2012. Photo Oaksterdam Archives.

the worldwide trend is towards regulated commercial markets. Budtenders are the face of the industry to customers and will continue to shape policy and the industry's future.

The laws that regulate cannabis are constantly changing and will continue to determine the role of a budtender and how they interact with customers. By simply participating in the cannabis industry, a bias is expressed that cannabis should be legal and regulated. This acknowledges that there is a political nature to cannabis, and history shows how crucial policy is to shaping humans' experiences with it. *See Appendix A: Advocacy* for more information about how to become an effective advocate.

(Top Right) Proposition 64 legalized adult use cannabis in California. Photo Oaksterdam Archives. (Bottom Left) Photo Oaksterdam Archives. (Bottom Right) Proposition 19 was the first adult use initiative of the modern era. Photo Oaksterdam Archives.

Part I Review

- Cannabis has been used throughout millennia on every populated continent as a food, fiber, medicament, and entheogen.
- Modern cannabis Prohibition effectively started in the United States through the Marihuana Tax Act of 1937 and spread worldwide via the United Nations Single Convention of Narcotic Drugs in 1961.
- Patient-led citizen advocacy paved the way for today's legal, commercial cannabis markets.
- As a result of the plant's complicated history, budtending in modern dispensaries requires navigating contradictory and confusing policies, misinformation, and the constantly evolving landscape of cannabis brands and byproducts.

Part II

Budtending Foundations

Lessons in Budtending Foundations:

- Skills & Qualifications
- Roles & Responsibilities
- Dispensary Models
- Security & Chain of Custody

Learning Outcomes:

- Understand the core roles and responsibilities of a budtender.
- Know which skills to have or develop to be an effective budtender.
- Be prepared for regulatory compliance and the unique safety challenges of the cannabis industry.

Photo courtesy of Sun Provisions.

Part II Overview

In the 1990s, commercial markets for medical cannabis were established by voter initiative but largely remained unregulated until the 2010s. As a result, the modern cannabis marketplace is diverse and unstandardized.

Navigating rapidly changing regulatory policies, plant varieties, and products can be overwhelming. The budtender's job is to help customers find products that meet their needs. Everyone's needs are different, and customized guidance is crucial to ensure customers have positive experiences, especially if they are trying cannabis for the first time.

Budtending is essentially a customer service job, but it also requires a connoisseur's knowledge of the products, attention to regulations and legal compliance, proficiency in product handling protocols, seed-to-sale tracking, lab testing, and product labeling, as well as at least a basic understanding of safety and therapeutic effects.

This section of the book provides a high-level overview of the job of a budtender, standard safety and compliance regulations, the basics of retail operation, and the unique facets of customer service required to work in a cannabis dispensary.

Skills & Qualifications

Budtending is a crash course in the cannabis industry, but beyond cannabis-specific knowledge, the primary skillset required for a budtender is similar to any other customer service job.

Although budtending is an entry-level position, it allows one to understand the industry, policies, and markets more comprehensively than any other job. Budtenders with attention to detail and computer skills can advance to management positions.

In a small dispensary, a budtender may be asked to wear many hats. While this can be challenging, it is an excellent opportunity to understand all facets of the retail cannabis industry before moving into other roles.

In large dispensaries, budtenders can advance to inventory managers. With experience working with seed-to-sale tracking software and dispensary operations, inventory managers can advance to compliance managers or private compliance consultants, which are well-paying and in-demand occupations. A budtender who advances to inventory management and has experience with transport and logistics is qualified to work in distribution.

Customer Service

Customer service is undoubtedly the highest priority and an essential qualification of a budtender. Maintaining a friendly and helpful demeanor with customers, especially difficult ones, is essential. Budtenders must always uphold high standards of professionalism and do their best to ensure customers have a positive experience in the dispensary and while using the products they purchase.

The term "budtender" is derived from bartender, and both jobs require the same basic skills. Good bartenders and budtenders are personable, can carry a friendly conversation, put customers at ease, and communicate clearly. They must also quickly assess customers' needs and preferences and efficiently keep the line moving.

Although cannabis knowledge is a key qualification for the job, due to Prohibition policies, even the most basic concepts and terms are subject to debate. For example, many in the industry avoid using the term "marijuana" because of the negative association with racist Prohibition campaigns. Others feel there is no problem with the term when it is not being used to villainize people and especially because it is often used in the context of medical marijuana statutes. (*See Part I: The Origins of Prohibition*).

In reality, pre-existing knowledge may not be as crucial as one might think. Many employers prefer to provide the same cannabis education to their budtenders so the entire team is on the same page. Of course, deep knowledge of and passion for cannabis is a plus. However, it is much easier and quicker for an employer to train people on cannabis than customer service, which can take years of experience to master.

Good customer service involves more than just relating with the customer — an experienced customer service professional is also aware of how many customers are waiting to be served. Queue management is a critical component of good customer service, and all budtenders should know when it is slow enough to have a more in-depth conversation with a customer and when they need to keep the line moving.

While customers should never be rushed out the door, the budtender should be conscious of the amount of time spent with each customer while others are waiting and avoid long conversations on topics unrelated to cannabis consumption or the transaction. They should also avoid personal conversations with friends and co-workers while serving customers.

Budtender Interview

"Cannabis is relationships. Everything we do is based on if people like us and trust us. There are so many brands, and customers make good choices when the budtender makes them feel comfortable, works with them, and educates them. Education is key.

— Alex Almodova, budtender in Burbank, California

Preventing Emotional Burnout

An essential skill for anyone in customer service to master is dealing with feelings of emotional burnout. Customer service can be draining, particularly for a budtender. It is exhausting to go from trying to help a rude or irate customer to one with a serious illness who wants medical advice and guidance the budtender cannot provide. Both situations are frustrating and can be aggravated or alleviated depending on how the budtender handles their emotions.

Burnout is real and damaging to customers, the business, and the budtender themselves. It is easy to take on a bad mood after a negative interaction and more difficult to quickly mitigate the emotions and start fresh with the next. Budtenders should develop strategies to cope with the heavy emotions customers may bring into the store. Some good options include:

- **Take Breaks:** Recognize when it is important to take a break between customers to get composed and ready for the next one. A good manager will account for these necessary breaks from customer interaction and offer tasks such as restocking products to provide the opportunity.
- **Incorporate Mindfulness Practices:** Stretching, meditation, yoga, exercise, and short walks can mitigate emotional burnout.

Required Knowledge

The effects of cannabis, methods of ingestion, products, the basics of plant varieties (aka "strains"), and legal compliance are vital knowledge for a budtender. These topics are covered in greater detail in later chapters of this book.

Some dispensaries will also sell seeds and starter plants (clones) in regions where home cultivation is legal. Seeds and clones are kept separate from other cannabis products, and some dispensaries will employ specially-trained staff with experience in cultivation to assist customers.

While it is beneficial for budtenders to understand the plant's botany and horticulture, it is not essential. When customers have questions about seeds, clones, and available varieties, it is best to refer them to the breeder or cultivator, who will have the most accurate information.

Discretion & Healthcare Privacy Laws

Budtenders must be discrete. Discretion is imperative even when helping a celebrity, politician, or other well-known person. All customers must be afforded the same privacy.

Although it is not required by law, many "medical only" dispensaries follow The Health Insurance Portability and Accountability Act (HIPAA),[87] which protects patient privacy. The same privacy and discretion should be afforded to all dispensary customers. *(See Roles & Responsibilities for more information about HIPAA).*

Dispensary privacy policies vary. Many have rules prohibiting cell phone use and taking photos inside the store, while some allow the press to take photos or record footage. Customers must be aware of and consent to be recorded. The dispensary may want to consider using a sticker or armband that customers can put on to make it clear to the press that they do not want to be photographed.

Showcasing Skills & Qualifications

When prospective budtenders apply for a job, they should list the following qualifications on resumes and interviews:

- Customer service experience, regardless of whether it is cannabis-specific
- Experience as a consumer, which demonstrates an understanding of products and services
- Cannabis-specific trainings and certifications
- Any cannabis or cannabis industry experience, from home to commercial production

Discretion isn't required, but it's imperative

"There is no law around discretion. There is no HIPAA in our industry. We make an oath not to 'out' people. If I had my doctor as one of my customers, I would not even talk to him if I met him 'in the wild.' Even for pick-up orders, we have our own system. We do not write names because this lifestyle could ostracize people from their work and families. We treat it like it is very sensitive. Someday we are going to live in a world where we do not have to, but it is not today."

— **Helen Sun,** budtender in Decatur, Michigan

Roles & Responsibilities

Customer Safety

Like a bartender, budtenders are responsible for customer safety. Although budtenders likely have no medical training, they are often expected to fulfill the role of a pharmacist, nurse, or even a doctor for their customers. **Budtenders should never dispense medical advice, even when customers request it. They cannot state that any product treats a disease or suggest protocols or treatment regimens.**

It is crucial, however, that the budtender ask the right questions to identify the customers' needs and provide them with all the information available to guide them to the right products. Customers look to the budtender to guide them to positive experiences and help them avoid negative ones. This means giving them information about how methods of ingestion, varieties, and product features contribute to the effects they may feel as far as onset, duration, and potency.

In addition to customer safety, budtenders are responsible for deeply understanding the products available, consulting the customer to gauge their specific needs, and protecting privacy.

Check-In

The process for welcoming customers into a dispensary and verifying their age or doctor's recommendation varies widely across jurisdictions. Some budtenders may be expected to perform this function, but it is usually performed by a separate employee who acts as a general receptionist. In some dispensaries, the budtender is responsible for intake, consultation, and making the sale once the customer passes through security.

In adult use dispensaries, the only credential a customer needs to present is a valid government-issued ID showing they are 21 or older. Sometimes the dispensary will capture more information for marketing purposes that is not required to enter. In medical-only dispensaries, stricter rules are in place for verifying identification and medical authorization. An employee responsible for intake welcomes the customer, checks their identification, and verifies medical cannabis authorization documents in a medical-only dispensary, such as a government-issued cannabis card. This process usually happens at the entry before the customer gets to the sales floor. Employees who review these credentials should be trained in the proper procedure to verify them and double-check everything to ensure they are legal, valid, and not expired. Once the customer is checked in, they are directed to the sales floor.

Consultation & Making the Sale

Budtenders are the customer-facing ambassadors of the dispensary and the industry at large. The customer's experience is defined by their interaction with the budtender, who should be able to speak intelligently about all products on the menu and provide guidance.

Some medical dispensaries refer to this as a "patient consultation." In adult use dispensaries, customers also consult the budtender when choosing products.

Critical Thinking: Could the Budtender Have Prevented This?

New York Times columnist Maureen Dowd traveled to Denver to report on the rollout of Colorado's first-of-its-kind legalization law in 2014. As a novice cannabis consumer, Dowd assumed that eating a bar of cannabis chocolate would be her best option.

Alone in her hotel room, Dowd ate a couple bites of chocolate and waited a few minutes. Nothing happened, so she ate more. When the chocolate finally hit her bloodstream, she became paranoid, immobile, and terrified for the next eight hours. This negative experience became the topic of her article[89] and sparked debate in and out of the industry about safety.

Had Dowd known that the effects of cannabis are more potent when eaten, the onset takes longer, and what a good starting dose for a novice consumer like her would have been, she might have enjoyed her experience. How could a budtender have prevented this? *(See Part V: Products & Methods of Ingestion.)*

Photo by Elsa Olofsson via Unsplash.com.

Budtenders are responsible for educating customers about the differences between products, the variety of delivery methods, and how they affect most people.

First, the budtender assesses the customer's needs by asking questions. The most important information to glean is whether or not the customer has prior experience or tolerance to cannabis. By doing so, the budtender immediately assesses how much information the customer needs to make informed purchasing decisions.

A good budtender will know how to speak to a diverse range of customers with different comfort and experience levels with cannabis. It is their responsibility to meet them where they are rather than talk over their head or talk down to them. By doing so, they develop strong relationships with customers that keep them coming back.

Part of making sales is also the "unmaking" of sales, or customer returns. The budtender should be familiar with return policies and be prepared to answer questions about them, particularly when recommending a new product. For instance, do products need to be unopened to be returned? Can only certain types of products be returned? Are returns only good for store credit or cash back? Hopefully, there will not be many returns to process, but understanding the process and potential legal limits is still essential.

Understanding Product Labels & Lab Testing Results

Laboratory testing allows a budtender to provide honest answers and assurances about product safety and potency. Lab testing is required in all commercial cannabis markets, albeit regulations about types of tests and lab methods vary. The two most common tests are for contaminants and cannabinoid potency.

Contaminants include pesticides, residual **solvents**, mycotoxins, bacteria, heavy metals, and foreign materials. Some regions also require potency testing for terpenes, but usually, this is an optional test required to make product claims about terpene content.

A product's test results are found on a certificate of analysis (COA) from the lab that conducted the testing. Information that appears on the product's label is derived from this COA. Usually, only some of the information from the COA is displayed on the label; most commonly, just the potency of the major cannabinoids present (i.e., THC and CBD). If a product has failed

The Evolution of Cannabis Consulting with Goose Duarte

Goose Duarte has worked at the forefront of the legal cannabis industry since its emergence in the San Francisco Bay Area in the early 2000s. He has helped define the role of a budtender in the world's pioneering dispensaries. Today he is the director of operations at Oaksterdam University.

Goose Duarte

Goose worked in almost every position at Harborside Health Center in Oakland, from inventory, stocking, product displays, check-in and registration, budtender, and management.

Harborside created and followed strict procedures that have served as a model for other dispensaries around the globe. During a decade rising through the ranks at Harborside, Goose helped establish innovative practices that have been adopted by the growing industry and embedded in international dispensary culture.

Goose outlines Harborside's six-step consultation and sale process:

- **Assess demeanor:** "You can tell a lot about customers by how they approach the counter. Observe whether they are in a hurry and seem to know exactly what they want or if they appear confused and overwhelmed."
- **Ask about experience:** New consumers will have a lower tolerance and possibly negative perceptions of cannabis. Others will be long-time users or connoisseurs. "If you are a first-time consumer, we will explain things differently than if you are an avid consumer and you have used it all your life."
- **Determine needs:** "Once you know a consumer's experience level, you can find out what effects they seek. That helps assess whether to encourage them to try edibles or flowers, and eventually vaporizer pens, drinks, patches, or tinctures. We would give them a little tour of the display case, show them what kind of products we have, how to identify them, and how to read the labels."
- **Ask how much they would like to spend:** Some consumers want quantity, while others seek quality. Show them a selection of products based on the price they can afford.
- **Let them make their selections:** Once questions have been answered and products described, give them time to choose.
- **Ring them up:** The final step is to close the transaction. Make sure every item is properly scanned and bagged, collect payment, and count change accurately.

contaminant testing, it should not even be on dispensary shelves. Sometimes the product includes a QR code on the product label that links to the full COA.

While understanding all of the information on a typical COA is ideal, a budtender should focus on reading product labels to make sense of them for customers. Although all products are tested, testing thresholds and requirements can differ depending on the product category. For example, some pesticides, like myclobutanil (Eagle 20), are hazardous if inhaled but not that dangerous when ingested, which is why it is commonly used on edible plants like grapes or cherries. Some customers may want to see the full COA, so the dispensary should have those readily available, and the budtender should be ready to talk them through it if they need help.

Labels for edible products can be somewhat tougher to understand and explain to customers. A Canadian study[88] conducted in 2020 found that "few consumers can understand and apply quantitative THC labeling" on edible products. In other words, labels that only list the THC content in milligrams do not tell the consumer much about how the product will affect them. The researchers found that labels that "provide 'interpretive' information, such as descriptors, symbols, or references to servings, have greater efficacy" in conveying the actual effects. This research stresses the importance of understanding and explaining product labels to customers.

How to Read a COA

Not all certificates of analysis (COAs) look the same or are presented in the same order, but they do contain all the same basic elements: product and tracking information, and legally required testing results for potency, pesticides, heavy metals, and other contaminants. Not all regions require the same testing, but most labs offer producers the ability to purchase testing that is not required.

Product Type	Potency	Pesticides	Mycotoxins	Residual Solvents	Heavy Metals	Microbials	Foreign Material	Water Activity	Moisture Content
Non-inhalables (solid)	✓	✓	✓	✓	✓	✓	✓	✓	
Non-inhalables (liquid)	✓	✓	✓	✓	✓	✓	✓	✓	
Flower/Trim	✓	✓	✓		✓	✓	✓	✓	✓
Concentrate	✓	✓	✓	✓	✓	✓	✓		
Pre-Roll	✓	✓	✓	✓	✓	✓	✓	✓	✓

This is a breakdown of California testing requirements. **Source:** SC Labs.

Regulatory Compliance Testing

CERTIFICATE OF ANALYSIS

DATE ISSUED 08/27/2022 | OVERALL BATCH RESULT: PASS

SAMPLE NAME: Tractor Gas
Flower, Inhalable

CULTIVATOR / MANUFACTURER
Business Name: Brand ABC, LLC
License Number: C12-0000000-LIC
Address: 98765 Any St
Any City, CA 95824

DISTRIBUTOR
Business Name: BRAND XYZ DISTRIBUTION LLC
License Number: C12-9999999-LIC
Address: 1234 SAMPLE RD
SAMPLE CITY, CA 95824-2307

SAMPLE DETAIL
Batch Number: ABC-220820
Sample ID: 220820M030
Source Metrc UID:
1A4060300033BBE000000611

Date Collected: 04/21/2022
Date Received: 04/22/2022
Batch Size: 28.35 grams
Sample Size: 18.0 grams
Unit Mass:
Serving Size:

Scan QR code to verify authenticity of results.

Sampling Method: QSP 1265 - Sampling of Cannabis and Product Batches

CANNABINOID ANALYSIS - SUMMARY — CALCULATED USING DRY-WEIGHT

Sum of Cannabinoids: 35.08%
Total Cannabinoids: 30.87%
Total THC: 29.62%
Total CBD: 0.073%

Sum of Cannabinoids = Δ^9-THC + THCa + CBD + CBDa + CBG + CBGa + THCV + THCVa + CBC + CBCa + CBDV + CBDVa + Δ^8-THC + CBL + CBN
Total Cannabinoids = (Δ^9-THC+0.877*THCa) + (CBD+0.877*CBDa) + (CBG+0.877*CBGa) + (THCV+0.877*THCVa) + (CBC+0.877*CBCa) + (CBDV+0.877*CBDVa) + Δ^8-THC + CBL + CBN
Total THC/CBD is calculated using the following formulas to take into account the loss of a carboxyl group during the decarboxylation step:
Total THC = Δ^9-THC + (THCa (0.877))
Total CBD = CBD + (CBDa (0.877))

Moisture: 13.3%

TERPENOID ANALYSIS - SUMMARY — 39 TESTED, TOP 3 HIGHLIGHTED

Total Terpenoids: 4.242%

Myrcene 10.349 mg/g **Limonene 9.754 mg/g** **β-Caryophyllene 8.575 mg/g**

SAFETY ANALYSIS - SUMMARY

Pesticides: PASS
Mycotoxins: PASS
Heavy Metals: PASS
Microbiology: PASS
Foreign Material: PASS
Water Activity: PASS

These results relate only to the sample included on this report.
This report shall not be reproduced, except in full, without written approval of the laboratory.

Sample Certification: California Code of Regulations Title 16 Effect Date January 16, 2019. Authority: Section 26013, Business and Professions Code. Reference: Sections 26100, 26104 and 26110, Business and Professions Code.

Decision Rule: Statements of conformity (e.g. Pass/Fail) to specifications are made in this report without taking measurement uncertainty into account. Where statements of conformity are made in this report, the following decision rules are applied: PASS - Results within limits/specifications, FAIL - Results exceed limits/specifications.

References: limit of detection (LOD), limit of quantification (LOQ), not detected (ND), not tested (NT)

All LQC samples were performed and met the prescribed acceptance criteria in 4 CCR section 1730, as attested by:
Michael Pham
Date: 08/27/2022

Approved by: Josh Wurzer, President
Date: 08/27/2022

SC Laboratories California LLC. | 100 Pioneer Street, Suite E, Santa Cruz, CA 95060 | 866-435-0709 | sclabs.com | C8-0000013-LIC | ISO/IES 17025:2017 PJLA Accreditation Number 87168

 CoA ID: 220820M030-001 Page 1 of 4

All of the most essential information is found on the summary analysis page of a COA. **Source:** SC Labs.

Product Information

The product's name and the company that grew the raw cannabis are listed first. This COA is from California, where a distributor is a required intermediary between the producers and retail and is responsible for handling third-party lab analysis. All companies' addresses and license numbers are listed here. Often the license number is verifiable through a government website. At the bottom of this COA, applicable regulations are cited, and the document is signed by staff responsible for processing and certifying the sample.

Sample Information

Batch refers to a single production run of a cultivar or product, and the batch number is created internally by the producer to track it. Each batch must be tested before it is available for sale. The lab creates the sample ID to track the batch's movement through testing. The METRC ID is the track and trace number attached to the plant when it started as a seed or rooted clone. This ID will follow the product through its sale at a licensed dispensary. METRC is the system required in California and other regions, but not all regions use METRC as their seed-to-sale tracking software. The sample information also includes the date the sample was collected from the batch, the date the lab received it, the size of the whole batch created by the producer, the size of the sample provided to the lab, and the size of the sample tested. The most relevant information to highlight for customers is that this is a legal, licensed product that has been tested for safety and certified by a lab, and every operator in the supply chain who touched it is legal, licensed, and regulated.

QR Verification Code

Not all COAs include QR verification codes, but they are a feature that has appeared in markets where illicit products modeled to look like licensed companies produced them have become common. Scanning this code allows the consumer to verify that the product is authentic, and the QR code will often appear on the product's label.

Summary Analyses

The rest of the first page of this COA provides summaries of the more detailed content that appears in the rest of the document.

The Cannabinoid Analysis section summarizes the most abundant cannabinoids in the sample. The "total cannabinoids" refers to the percentage of cannabinoids tested in the plant material. THC and CBD occur in the highest quantities in most plants and are summarized here. The term "total" refers to the fact that before they are heated, most THC and CBD in the raw plant are THCa or CBDa. The simple act of lighting or heating the material for inhalation will convert these cannabinoids to THC and CBD, respectively. Therefore, the total THC and CBD summarized here account for this conversion. These numbers are usually displayed on the product packaging. (*See Part III: Cannabis Compounds & the Endocannabinoid System* for more information about the process of "decarboxylation.") At the top of this section, the blue word "pass" means the lab has verified claims about cannabinoid content on the label.

The Safety Analysis summarizes the legally required tests to detect pesticides, heavy metals, and other contaminants. This summary shows that all required tests were conducted, and no contaminants were detected. If the product does not pass all these tests, it should not be available for sale.

The Terpenoid Analysis may not appear on most COAs because the testing is optional in most places. Producers can request terpene tests and should be able to produce a COA showing they tested for them if they make product claims about terpene content. On this COA, the lab tested for 39 terpenes and listed the three that occurred in the highest quantities.

Regulatory Compliance Testing

CERTIFICATE OF ANALYSIS

TRACTOR GAS | DATE ISSUED 08/27/2022 | OVERALL BATCH RESULT: PASS

CANNABINOID TEST RESULTS - 08/26/2022

Tested by high-performance liquid chromatography with diode-array detection (HPLC-DAD). Calculated using Dry-Weight. **Method:** QSP 1157 - Analysis of Cannabinoids by HPLC-DAD

TOTAL CANNABINOIDS: 30.87%
Total Cannabinoids (Total THC) + (Total CBD) + (Total CBG) + (Total THCV) + (Total CBC) + (Total CBDV) + Δ⁸-THC + CBL + CBN

TOTAL THC: 29.62%
Total THC (Δ⁹-THC+0.877*THCa)

TOTAL CBD: 0.073%
Total CBD (CBD+0.877*CBDa)

TOTAL CBG: 0.78%
Total CBG (CBG+0.877*CBGa)

TOTAL THCV: 0.153%
Total THCV (THCV+0.877*THCVa)

TOTAL CBC: 0.24%
Total CBC (CBC+0.877*CBCa)

TOTAL CBDV: ND
Total CBDV (CBDV+0.877*CBDVa)

COMPOUND	LOD/LOQ (mg/g)	MEASUREMENT UNCERTAINTY (mg/g)	RESULT (mg/g)	RESULT (%)
THCa	0.04 / 0.24	± 10.589	329.88	32.988
CBGa	0.1 / 0.4	± 0.40	7.4	0.74
Δ⁹-THC	0.1 / 0.4	± 0.21	6.9	0.69
CBCa	0.1 / 0.4	± 0.18	2.7	0.27
THCVa	0.05 / 0.17	± 0.041	1.75	0.175
CBG	0.2 / 0.5	± 0.09	1.3	0.13
CBDa	0.06 / 0.22	± 0.027	0.83	0.083
Δ⁸-THC	0.05 / 0.50	N/A	ND	ND
THCV	0.07 / 0.21	N/A	ND	ND
CBD	0.1 / 0.3	N/A	ND	ND
CBDV	0.1 / 0.3	N/A	ND	ND
CBDVa	0.02 / 0.22	N/A	ND	ND
CBL	0.1 / 0.4	N/A	ND	ND
CBN	0.07 / 0.20	N/A	ND	ND
CBC	0.1 / 0.2	N/A	ND	ND
SUM OF CANNABINOIDS			350.8 mg/g	35.08%

MOISTURE TEST RESULT

13.3%
Tested 08/26/2022
Method: QSP 1224 - Loss on Drying (Moisture)

TERPENOID TEST RESULTS - 08/27/2022

Terpene analysis utilizing gas chromatography-flame ionization detection (GC-FID). **Method:** QSP 1192 - Analysis of Terpenoids by GC-FID

COMPOUND	LOD/LOQ (mg/g)	MEASUREMENT UNCERTAINTY (mg/g)	RESULT (mg/g)	RESULT (%)
Myrcene	0.007 / 0.025	± 0.3664	10.349	1.0349
Limonene	0.005 / 0.016	± 0.3180	9.754	0.9754
β-Caryophyllene	0.004 / 0.013	± 0.4613	8.575	0.8575
Linalool	0.009 / 0.030	± 0.1158	2.946	0.2946
α-Humulene	0.009 / 0.031	± 0.1520	2.826	0.2826
α-Bisabolol	0.008 / 0.026	± 0.0752	1.748	0.1748
β-Pinene	0.004 / 0.015	± 0.0478	1.481	0.1481

TERPENOID TEST RESULTS - 08/27/2022 *continued*

COMPOUND	LOD/LOQ (mg/g)	MEASUREMENT UNCERTAINTY (mg/g)	RESULT (mg/g)	RESULT (%)
Terpineol	0.008 / 0.025	± 0.0742	1.213	0.1213
Fenchol	0.009 / 0.029	± 0.0394	1.070	0.1070
α-Pinene	0.005 / 0.015	± 0.0298	0.832	0.0832
β-Ocimene	0.005 / 0.018	± 0.0178	0.453	0.0453
Borneol	0.004 / 0.014	± 0.0103	0.220	0.0220
Camphene	0.004 / 0.014	± 0.0070	0.217	0.0217
Fenchone	0.008 / 0.026	± 0.0058	0.154	0.0154
trans-β-Farnesene	0.008 / 0.028	± 0.0084	0.147	0.0147
Caryophyllene Oxide	0.011 / 0.038	± 0.0077	0.130	0.0130
Terpinolene	0.008 / 0.027	± 0.0015	0.099	0.0099
Valencene	0.010 / 0.033	± 0.0035	0.067	0.0067
Citronellol	0.003 / 0.010	± 0.0019	0.066	0.0066
Geraniol	0.002 / 0.007	± 0.0026	0.049	0.0049
Sabinene Hydrate	0.007 / 0.022	± 0.0009	0.024	0.0024
γ-Terpinene	0.005 / 0.018	N/A	<LOQ	<LOQ
Nerol	0.003 / 0.011	N/A	<LOQ	<LOQ
Sabinene	0.004 / 0.014	N/A	ND	ND
α-Phellandrene	0.006 / 0.019	N/A	ND	ND
Δ³-Carene	0.005 / 0.018	N/A	ND	ND
α-Terpinene	0.006 / 0.019	N/A	ND	ND
p-Cymene	0.005 / 0.015	N/A	ND	ND
Eucalyptol	0.005 / 0.018	N/A	ND	ND
Isopulegol	0.004 / 0.013	N/A	ND	ND
Camphor	0.005 / 0.015	N/A	ND	ND
Isoborneol	0.003 / 0.011	N/A	ND	ND
Menthol	0.008 / 0.025	N/A	ND	ND
Pulegone	0.003 / 0.010	N/A	ND	ND
Geranyl Acetate	0.004 / 0.012	N/A	ND	ND
α-Cedrene	0.005 / 0.017	N/A	ND	ND
Nerolidol	0.006 / 0.020	N/A	ND	ND
Guaiol	0.011 / 0.035	N/A	ND	ND
Cedrol	0.009 / 0.032	N/A	ND	ND
TOTAL TERPENOIDS			42.420 mg/g	4.242%

Here the summary Cannabinoid and Terpenoid Analyses from the first page are broken down in more detail. Every cannabinoid and terpenoid that was tested for is listed here with the percentage that was detected in the sample. "ND" stands for "none detected." An ND result does not always mean that the tested cannabinoid or terpenoid did not occur in the sample, just that if it did, the concentration was too low to be detected. Other cannabinoids or terpenoids may occur in the sample in small amounts but are not represented unless the lab tests for them.

Regulatory Compliance Testing
CERTIFICATE OF ANALYSIS

TRACTOR GAS | DATE ISSUED 08/27/2022 | OVERALL BATCH RESULT: PASS

CATEGORY 1 PESTICIDE TEST RESULTS - 08/27/2022 PASS

Pesticide and plant growth regulator analysis utilizing high-performance liquid chromatography-mass spectrometry (HPLC-MS) or gas chromatography-mass spectrometry (GC-MS). *GC-MS utilized where indicated. **Method:** QSP 1212 - Analysis of Pesticides and Mycotoxins by LC-MS or QSP 1213 - Analysis of Pesticides by GC-MS

COMPOUND	LOD/LOQ (μg/g)	ACTION LIMIT (μg/g)	MEASUREMENT UNCERTAINTY (μg/g)	RESULT (μg/g)	RESULT
Aldicarb	0.03 / 0.08	≥ LOD	N/A	ND	PASS
Carbofuran	0.02 / 0.05	≥ LOD	N/A	ND	PASS
Chlordane*	0.03 / 0.08	≥ LOD	N/A	ND	PASS
Chlorfenapyr*	0.03 / 0.10	≥ LOD	N/A	ND	PASS
Chlorpyrifos	0.02 / 0.06	≥ LOD	N/A	ND	PASS
Coumaphos	0.02 / 0.07	≥ LOD	N/A	ND	PASS
Daminozide	0.02 / 0.07	≥ LOD	N/A	ND	PASS
Dichlorvos (DDVP)	0.03 / 0.09	≥ LOD	N/A	ND	PASS
Dimethoate	0.03 / 0.08	≥ LOD	N/A	ND	PASS
Ethoprophos	0.03 / 0.10	≥ LOD	N/A	ND	PASS
Etofenprox	0.02 / 0.06	≥ LOD	N/A	ND	PASS
Fenoxycarb	0.03 / 0.08	≥ LOD	N/A	ND	PASS
Fipronil	0.03 / 0.08	≥ LOD	N/A	ND	PASS
Imazalil	0.02 / 0.06	≥ LOD	N/A	ND	PASS
Methiocarb	0.02 / 0.07	≥ LOD	N/A	ND	PASS
Parathion-methyl	0.03 / 0.10	≥ LOD	N/A	ND	PASS
Mevinphos	0.03 / 0.09	≥ LOD	N/A	ND	PASS
Paclobutrazol	0.02 / 0.05	≥ LOD	N/A	ND	PASS
Propoxur	0.03 / 0.09	≥ LOD	N/A	ND	PASS
Spiroxamine	0.03 / 0.08	≥ LOD	N/A	ND	PASS
Thiacloprid	0.03 / 0.10	≥ LOD	N/A	ND	PASS

CATEGORY 2 PESTICIDE TEST RESULTS - 08/27/2022 PASS

COMPOUND	LOD/LOQ (μg/g)	ACTION LIMIT (μg/g)	MEASUREMENT UNCERTAINTY (μg/g)	RESULT (μg/g)	RESULT
Abamectin	0.03 / 0.10	0.1	N/A	ND	PASS
Acephate	0.02 / 0.07	0.1	N/A	ND	PASS
Acequinocyl	0.02 / 0.07	0.1	N/A	ND	PASS
Acetamiprid	0.02 / 0.05	0.1	N/A	ND	PASS
Azoxystrobin	0.02 / 0.07	0.1	N/A	ND	PASS
Bifenazate	0.01 / 0.04	0.1	N/A	ND	PASS
Bifenthrin	0.02 / 0.05	3	N/A	ND	PASS
Boscalid	0.03 / 0.09	0.1	N/A	ND	PASS
Captan	0.19 / 0.57	0.7	N/A	ND	PASS
Carbaryl	0.02 / 0.06	0.5	N/A	ND	PASS
Chlorantranilip-role	0.04 / 0.12	10	N/A	ND	PASS
Clofentezine	0.03 / 0.09	0.1	N/A	ND	PASS

CATEGORY 2 PESTICIDE TEST RESULTS - 08/27/2022 *continued*

COMPOUND	LOD/LOQ (μg/g)	ACTION LIMIT (μg/g)	MEASUREMENT UNCERTAINTY (μg/g)	RESULT (μg/g)	RESULT
Cyfluthrin	0.12 / 0.38	2	N/A	ND	PASS
Cypermethrin	0.11 / 0.32	1	N/A	ND	PASS
Diazinon	0.02 / 0.05	0.1	N/A	ND	PASS
Dimethomorph	0.03 / 0.09	2	N/A	ND	PASS
Etoxazole	0.02 / 0.06	0.1	N/A	ND	PASS
Fenhexamid	0.03 / 0.09	0.1	N/A	ND	PASS
Fenpyroximate	0.02 / 0.06	0.1	N/A	ND	PASS
Flonicamid	0.03 / 0.10	0.1	N/A	ND	PASS
Fludioxonil	0.03 / 0.10	0.1	N/A	ND	PASS
Hexythiazox	0.02 / 0.07	0.1	N/A	ND	PASS
Imidacloprid	0.04 / 0.11	5	N/A	ND	PASS
Kresoxim-methyl	0.02 / 0.07	0.1	N/A	ND	PASS
Malathion	0.03 / 0.09	0.5	N/A	ND	PASS
Metalaxyl	0.02 / 0.07	2	N/A	ND	PASS
Methomyl	0.03 / 0.10	1	N/A	ND	PASS
Myclobutanil	0.03 / 0.09	0.1	N/A	ND	PASS
Naled	0.02 / 0.07	0.1	N/A	ND	PASS
Oxamyl	0.04 / 0.11	0.5	N/A	ND	PASS
Pentachloronitro-benzene*	0.03 / 0.09	0.1	N/A	ND	PASS
Permethrin	0.04 / 0.12	0.5	N/A	ND	PASS
Phosmet	0.03 / 0.10	0.1	N/A	ND	PASS
Piperonyl Butoxide	0.02 / 0.07	3	N/A	ND	PASS
Prallethrin	0.03 / 0.08	0.1	N/A	ND	PASS
Propiconazole	0.02 / 0.07	0.1	N/A	ND	PASS
Pyrethrins	0.04 / 0.12	0.5	N/A	ND	PASS
Pyridaben	0.02 / 0.07	0.1	N/A	ND	PASS
Spinetoram	0.02 / 0.07	0.1	N/A	ND	PASS
Spinosad	0.02 / 0.07	0.1	N/A	ND	PASS
Spiromesifen	0.02 / 0.05	0.1	N/A	ND	PASS
Spirotetramat	0.02 / 0.06	0.1	N/A	ND	PASS
Tebuconazole	0.02 / 0.07	0.1	N/A	ND	PASS
Thiamethoxam	0.03 / 0.10	5	N/A	ND	PASS
Trifloxystrobin	0.03 / 0.08	0.1	N/A	ND	PASS

Here, the summary of pesticide testing from the first page is detailed. Each pesticide tested is listed separately with the amount detected and whether levels comply with state law. This sample passed all tests, meaning none of these pesticides were detected. If a pesticide was used that was not tested for, it would not be identified through lab testing on a COA.

Regulatory Compliance Testing
CERTIFICATE OF ANALYSIS

TRACTOR GAS | DATE ISSUED 08/27/2022 | OVERALL BATCH RESULT: PASS

MYCOTOXIN TEST RESULTS - 08/27/2022 PASS

Mycotoxin analysis utilizing high-performance liquid chromatography-mass spectrometry (HPLC-MS). **Method:** QSP 1212 - Analysis of Pesticides and Mycotoxins by LC-MS

COMPOUND	LOD/LOQ (μg/kg)	ACTION LIMIT (μg/kg)	MEASUREMENT UNCERTAINTY (μg/kg)	RESULT (μg/kg)	RESULT
Aflatoxin B1	2.0 / 6.0		N/A	ND	
Aflatoxin B2	1.8 / 5.6		N/A	ND	
Aflatoxin G1	1.0 / 3.1		N/A	ND	
Aflatoxin G2	1.2 / 3.5		N/A	ND	
Total Aflatoxin		20		ND	PASS
Ochratoxin A	6.3 / 19.2	20	N/A	ND	PASS

HEAVY METALS TEST RESULTS - 08/26/2022 PASS

Heavy metal analysis utilizing inductively coupled plasma-mass spectrometry (ICP-MS). **Method:** QSP 1160 - Analysis of Heavy Metals by ICP-MS

COMPOUND	LOD/LOQ (μg/g)	ACTION LIMIT (μg/g)	MEASUREMENT UNCERTAINTY (μg/g)	RESULT (μg/g)	RESULT
Arsenic	0.02 / 0.1	0.2	N/A	ND	PASS
Cadmium	0.02 / 0.05	0.2	N/A	ND	PASS
Lead	0.04 / 0.1	0.5	N/A	ND	PASS
Mercury	0.002 / 0.01	0.1	N/A	<LOQ	PASS

MICROBIOLOGY TEST RESULTS - 08/27/2022 PASS

Analysis conducted by polymerase chain reaction (PCR) and fluorescence detection of microbiological contaminants. **Method:** QSP 1221 - Analysis of Microbiological Contaminants

COMPOUND	ACTION LIMIT	RESULT	RESULT
Shiga toxin-producing *Escherichia coli*	Not Detected in 1g	ND	PASS
Salmonella spp.	Not Detected in 1g	ND	PASS
Aspergillus fumigatus	Not Detected in 1g	ND	PASS
Aspergillus flavus	Not Detected in 1g	ND	PASS
Aspergillus niger	Not Detected in 1g	ND	PASS
Aspergillus terreus	Not Detected in 1g	ND	PASS

FOREIGN MATERIAL TEST RESULTS - 08/26/2022 PASS

Visual analysis includes, but is not limited to, sand, soil, cinders, dirt, mold, hair, insect fragments, and mammalian excreta. **Method:** QSP 1226 - Analysis of Foreign Material in Cannabis and Cannabis Products

COMPOUND	ACTION LIMIT	RESULT
Total Sample Area Covered by Sand, Soil, Cinders, or Dirt	>25%	PASS
Total Sample Area Covered by Mold	>25%	PASS
Total Sample Area Covered by an Imbedded Foreign Material	>25%	PASS
Insect Fragment Count	> 1 per 3 grams	PASS
Hair Count	> 1 per 3 grams	PASS
Mammalian Excreta Count	> 1 per 3 grams	PASS

WATER ACTIVITY TEST RESULTS - 08/26/2022 PASS

Method: QSP 1227 - Analysis of Water Activity in Cannabis and Cannabis Products

COMPOUND	ACTION LIMIT (Aw)	MEASUREMENT UNCERTAINTY (Aw)	RESULT (Aw)	RESULT
Water Activity	0.65	± 0.00331	0.4802	PASS

The final page summarizes mycotoxin, heavy metals, microbiology, foreign materials, and water activity test results. Mycotoxin refers to toxic fungi, and microbiology refers to bacteria. Heavy metals in the growing environment can accumulate in the plant as it grows, which is also why specific metals are tested. Foreign materials refer to objects like sand or hairs. Finally, water activity is measured to ensure the flowers are dried properly and will not create conditions that encourage mold. These lab tests come with a "pass" or "fail" label, like pesticide tests.

Protecting Privacy

Although it is not required by law, many "medical only" dispensaries follow the Health Insurance Portability and Accountability Act (HIPAA)[90] of 1996, which protects patient privacy. The same privacy and discretion should be afforded to all dispensary customers.

HIPAA contains two main components, the Privacy Rule and the Security Rule. The Privacy Rule protects all "individually identifiable health information," including names, birthdates, social security numbers, and anything else that could be used to determine an individual patient's identity.

The Security Rule lays out requirements for health care providers to ensure the Privacy Rule is upheld. Under the rule, health care providers must:

1. Ensure the confidentiality, integrity, and availability of all electronic protected health information they create, receive, maintain, or transmit;
2. Identify and protect against reasonably anticipated threats to the security or integrity of the information;
3. Protect against reasonably anticipated, impermissible uses or disclosures; and
4. Ensure compliance by their workforce.

Technically, dispensaries are not regarded by the National Institutes of Health as a "covered entity" under HIPAA, so the rules do not apply to them. However, it is a good idea to comply with HIPAA to protect customers' privacy rights.

Universal Cannabis Symbols & Labeling Requirements

All regions have strict requirements for product labeling. All cannabis products with a THC level higher than 0.3% in the United States and Canada must display a universal symbol on the package that identifies them. They are also required to prominently display cannabinoid content on products. No standard naming conventions exist for cannabis varieties, so no region requires accurate labeling of the cultivar. *(See Part IV: Cannabis Varieties & Horticulture).*

Left to right: Universal cannabis product labels from California, Colorado, Michigan, Oregon, Washington, and Canada

Does More THC Mean Better Product?

Many novice cannabis consumers assume flowers and product with higher amounts of THC must be "better." Most cannabis flower in dispensaries tests between 15 and 30% THC, but the higher the THC number on a certificate of analysis (COA) the higher the price it can be sold for.

Higher prices for higher-THC flowers combined with a lack of regulatory standards for testing labs has resulted in some growers going "lab shopping"[91] or searching for the lab that will provide them with the highest THC number possible. Products on legal dispensary shelves have been labeled 30-40% or higher, which is not likely to be accurate.[92]

Knowing the THC level allows the consumer to choose which product is right for them and the best starting dose for their tolerance and experience. However, THC is not the best predictor of effects. Experienced consumers may not even look at the THC potency and instead rely on their senses by looking at and smelling the flowers to make a choice. *(See Part III: The Effects of Cannabis)*. Research out of Colorado[93] supports this theory and even indicates that more THC does not necessarily mean "more high."

A good way to explain this to customers is to use an analogy to alcohol. The alcohol by volume (ABV) appears on every label, from beer to hard liquor. Beer and wine range from 3–15% ABV, spirits 40–50%, and Everclear 95%. Is Everclear better than a fine wine because it has a higher alcohol content? The answer is clearly "no," as most people understand that the effects and experience of a glass of wine or a cold beer are not all attributable to their alcohol content, and they would not choose a shot of Everclear in most instances.

The quantity of THC will factor less into the cost of the product as the industry matures. Budtenders play a crucial role in educating consumers at the point of sale and can ask questions to determine what the customer seeks rather than guide them to the highest THC content on the shelf.

Product Handling Protocol

Pre-Packaged Flower vs. Apothecary Bulk Model

The "apothecary model" refers to dispensaries that weigh and sell cannabis flower from bulk containers when it is ordered. Although the apothecary model is still used in some regions, most do not allow it. Pre-weighed and packaged flowers are sold in regions that have banned or disallowed this model.

Budtenders who work at dispensaries using the apothecary model should familiarize themselves with metric and imperial conversions (found in the next section). The most important thing about the bulk apothecary model is that accurate weighing of the product is critical. Some customers will go home and use their own scale. If the package does not weigh out correctly, they will come back upset and may post negative comments on social media or review sites.

There are pros and cons to each model. The apothecary model allows customers to see the product and judge its freshness, smell, and appearance before they choose it. Pre-packaged cannabis is faster to sell and may be more sanitary because the customer can be assured that no hands have touched the product since it was sealed in the package.

In dispensaries using the apothecary model, budtenders should never pick out flowers with bare hands. They should wear gloves

Some dispensaries use the "apothecary model," which means the budtender selects buds and weighs the flowers as they are ordered. Photo courtesy of Sun Provisions, Decatur, Michigan.

and handle them as little as possible. Often they will use tongs or chopsticks to pick out the flowers and put them in a tray on a scale to weigh out. If budtenders use tongs or chopsticks, they should be careful not to damage the flowers by squeezing them too firmly.

In dispensaries using the pre-packaged model, sample containers for customers to look at and smell are often available to help them make a purchase decision. For accuracy, these containers should be fresh and from the same batch available for sale. Budtenders should ensure labels on display products are faced out so customers know what is in stock. When the product is sold, remove the samples from all display cases. A great way to lose a customer is to try and sell them something that is no longer available.

Product Weights: Metric vs. Imperial

From the 1940s to the 1970s, most of the cannabis consumed in the United States was purchased from other countries that use the metric system and was therefore sold in metric units; kilograms and grams. There are 1,000 grams in a kilogram. A gram was and still is a popular unit of measurement for small purchases. With the rise of domestic cultivation in the US and growing international markets, a blend of metric and imperial units has been adopted in most of the world using the following hierarchy; pounds (imperial), ounces (imperial), and grams (metric). While some countries are strictly metric, the majority use the following weights to sell cannabis flowers:

- Pound (16 ounces)
- Ounce (approximately 28 grams)
- Half ounce (approximately 14 grams)
- "Quarter" (one-quarter of an ounce, approximately 7 grams)
- "Eighth" (one-eighth of an ounce, approximately 3.5 grams)
- "Tenth"* (one-tenth of an ounce, approximately 2.8 grams)
- Gram

**The "tenth" is only a measurement under state law in Ohio, where "eighths" are not sold in licensed dispensaries.*

Most pre-packaged cannabis flower will come in increments of one gram or an eighth of an ounce, though sometimes half an ounce or ounce-sized packages may be available. If a customer orders a half ounce, it may be sold as four individual one-eighth packages. Where cannabis is sold pre-packaged, it is illegal to break up and sell a package into smaller weights, so eighths and grams tend to be the most commonly available package sizes. Some laws, such as in Ohio, require cannabis to be sold in one-tenth of an ounce units.

Concentrates like rosin, BHO, and **distillate** oil are usually sold in half-gram or one-gram containers or cartridges, some states also have quarter-gram cartrdiges.

Additional Guidelines for Apothecary Model Service

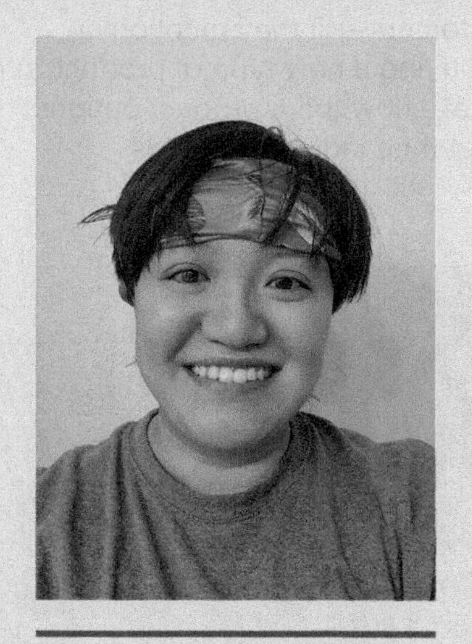

Helen Sun of Sun Provisions

Sun Provisions is a family-run small business in Decatur, Michigan, that cultivates and retails cannabis from the same location. They use the apothecary model, which they refer to as "deli style," because customers can see the color and quality before making their choice.

By regulation, dried cannabis is stored in glass jars behind the counter. If a customer wants to smell or look at the flowers, budtenders bring down the jar and tilt it in the customer's direction with the lid cracked to release the aroma. Customers can look at or smell buds from across the counter but are not allowed to touch them.

Scales are tared every morning, and budtenders must carefully and accurately weigh flowers. Once the customer makes a selection, the budtender weighs out the flower. They wear gloves and use long metal tongs to portion out flowers and weigh them in front of customers. Budtenders start with big buds, then select smaller buds to round out to the weight ordered. It takes skill and experience to weigh the buds properly, and Sun Provisions errs on rounding down in favor of the customer.

Many dispensaries shy away from the apothecary model because there is more room for error, from improper weighing to dropping buds on the floor, which must be discarded. However, at Sun Provisions, it results in empowered budtenders and repeat customers.

Maintaining Control of the Product

Many dispensaries have rules limiting how many customers a budtender can serve at once. Even if the dispensary does not have such limits, a budtender should always try to help one person at a time. If the budtender divides their attention among multiple customers, it is easier for someone to walk off with products. Aside from theft concerns, providing individualized care with more than one person at the counter is more difficult.

Never leave unattended products where customers can grab them and put them into their pockets or bags. In many jurisdictions, failing to maintain physical control of the product before a sale is complete violates the law. The budtender should limit the number of products on the counter whenever they handle them.

For example, when showing jars of pre-packaged flowers, many dispensaries and individual budtenders limit the number of jars presented at one time to just three. If a customer wants to see a different jar, the budtender puts one of the jars away before bringing another. Once the customer has made their choice, they immediately put the unwanted jars back in their storage bins out of reach of the customer to minimize the risk of theft.

Budtenders should hold onto the products while entering them into the dispensaries' point of sale (POS) system. If they are well-versed in the operation of the POS system and do not share their terminal with other budtenders, they could scan the products as they go rather than making it a separate step after the selection process.

Before finalizing the sale, confirm every product with the customer to ensure it is what they want. There is also an opportunity to try and upsell the customer on additional products. For example, if the customer buys flowers, the budtender could ask them if they need any rolling papers or a pipe. Upselling is more successful when listening to the customers — if they mention an interest in trying a new type of product, such as a **topical**, show them product options that might meet their individual needs.

Customers are checked in before they are taken to the sales floor. Photo courtesy of Glass House Brands.

Dispensary Models

There are differences between dispensaries that are open to adults of legal age and those that serve only medical patients with a doctor's recommendation. Sometimes a dispensary might be a delivery-only business that brings products directly to customers' homes and does not have a physical storefront. Each dispensary model is regulated differently.

Dispensaries differ widely regarding the store's physical design, product types, and target demographics.

Medical vs. Adult Use

Some regions only allow medicinal use of cannabis, while others allow adults to use it for any reason. Some medical-only regions require a pharmacist to be in the dispensary and consult with patients before purchasing.

Product access is the primary difference between regulations in regions with both markets. For instance, California patients (or their designated caregivers) can purchase more potent products and grow more plants at home than an adult use customer. In some countries and states, sales of flowers or products that can be inhaled are banned.

Some adult use dispensaries have separate areas for medical customers. Other areas allow medical and adult use sales at the same location but require separate purchasing lines.

Even in places that do not require separate locations or lines for medical and adult use transactions, some patients may have other special conditions which apply to them. For example, California has different tax rates for medical cannabis patients[94] who possess a Medical Marijuana Identification Card (MMIC) from a county health department.

Some regions have "reciprocity," meaning they recognize medical cannabis cards and authorizations from other regions. Sometimes there is a process for travelers to register as a patient temporarily. If a customer is visiting from outside the state or country, it is imperative that the budtender clearly explains purchase limits and other regional regulations. While it may seem like reciprocity is less important in the age of adult use, medical patients often have higher possession limits and can even have a legal defense if stopped by police.

Delivery

Like every other aspect of cannabis policy, every region has rules regarding the physical location where cannabis sales are allowed. Most dispensaries are actual "brick-and-mortar" stores with a physical location where customers enter to make purchases. Many of these stores also offer delivery, and some are delivery-only.

In the traditional cannabis economy, a large portion of cannabis was, and still is, dispensed through delivery. In some regions, cannabis can be dispensed solely through delivery or delivery tied to a "brick-and-mortar" storefront. In rural areas, customers may rely exclusively on delivery.

Unless the dispensary is a small business where employees wear many hats, budtenders do not deliver cannabis orders. When an order reaches the customer, they have already made their choices and do not need consultation or guidance from the budtender.

Two primary delivery models are associated with the dispensary: the "pizza model" and the "ice cream truck" model. Depending on the model, customers may still interact with a budtender.

The "ice cream truck" model refers to mobile dispensaries that look and function like ice cream trucks. They have a smaller menu and a single counter where consultations and sales are made. The ability of a dispensary to use this model depends on local regulations and is relatively uncommon. The "pizza model" refers to a system with one central location where orders are processed before a driver delivers them to the customer.

The pizza model is the most common form of delivery today. In some cases, customers will place orders over the phone and will likely require a budtender's consultation. Usually, customers order online or through cell phone applications, and no consultation is required. The budtender may pack the order and need to indicate in the system that it is available for pickup or delivery.

Customers who choose delivery often know what they are looking for and do not need consultation, but they may call the dispensary with questions about the software. Budtenders should familiarize themselves with the system their dispensary is using so they can guide customers through the process of using it and ensure they trigger tracking software as the order progresses.

Lounges

Cannabis consumption spaces are found worldwide and are as old as above-ground

Detailed Consultation for Delivery Customers

Shinnecock Hemp Growers started as a hemp-only mobile dispensary based on the Shinnecock Indian Reservation on Long Island, New York, and has transitioned to dispensing all cannabis products, regardless of THC content. They cultivate their own source material using sustainable and organic practices and process products using traditional herbalist methods. Products often contain other herbs, and this culture of herbalism is ingrained into the business.

Shinnecock's business has transitioned primarily to delivery since the Covid-19 pandemic, so the bulk of the customer consultation and budtender work now happens over the phone. Founder Rainbow Chavis says that people often look for specific instructions to cure and treat diseases, and she uses these questions to educate them about herbalism.

"It's a plant medicine, and because it does heal so many different things, people are hopeful... I've been dealing with plant medicines my entire life. What I do is educate them on what the plant can do, and hopefully, it matches what they're looking for," she says.

Photo of **Rainbow Chavis** by Nasha Hill courtesy of Shinnecock Hemp.

Rainbow attributes customer loyalty to these detailed education and consultation sessions.

"Our clients always come back, and ... the stories they share with us are incredible. It's amazing to be part of someone's healing process," she says. "I spend a lot of time with people before they even make a purchase to let them explain what is going on with them and what they need."

commercial markets. There are various models for consumption spaces, and they are often (but not always) attached to retail dispensaries where commercial cultivation and sales are legal. Some budtenders will not just sell cannabis to customers but will also be there while they consume it, which presents them with other opportunities, tasks, and responsibilities.

The original commercial cannabis spaces of the modern era originated in Amsterdam. Like most countries, The Netherlands signed the UN Single Convention on Narcotic Drugs in 1961[95] and listed cannabis in Schedule I when they classified substances[96] a decade later, in 1972. Although cannabis is technically illegal, sales of small amounts have essentially been decriminalized. In Amsterdam, coffee shops have openly sold and permitted on-site consumption since the 1970s. *(See Part I: History & Policy).*

Cannabis is still consumed informally in social settings in parts of Afghanistan and the Middle East. Private collectives with social consumption spaces exist in Barcelona, Spain, and the United States of America.

In the United States, lounges originated in San Francisco alongside local and state medical cannabis laws. Like Amsterdam, the City of San Francisco already had a no-enforcement policy for cannabis when Dennis Peron opened the first storefront dispensary in the early 1990s. Customers had to become members of Peron's collective, making the space and any gatherings in it private.

As of 2023, some regions in the US and Canada license retail dispensaries with on-site consumption spaces. Depending on other regional regulations, they may or may not be allowed to sell food or drinks. They all prohibit the use of alcohol and tobacco. Some may allow smoking on the sales floor, some may be vaporizer-only. While many are simply spaces attached to retail dispensaries where consumption is allowed, others are spas, restaurants, salons, music venues and more.

While much of the budtender's job is the same in these spaces, the primary difference is that the interaction extends to the customer consuming the products the budtender recommended. This allows them to refine their recommendations because they can see how customers respond to the products in real-time. It also comes with far more responsibilities.

On-site consumption lounges often offer smoking devices, such as pipes, grinders, and rolling papers. Photos courtesy of Cultivating Spirits.

Budtender Interview

"What really drew me to working at Harborside was owner Steve DeAngelo's reputation as an activist. When I first started working there, we had an activism station where patients would write letters to politicians or prisoners of the Drug War. There are many different types of stores with different themes, and I definitely encourage people to research the dispensary they want to work at and learn about the company culture so they can make sure they match with it."

— **Mitchell Colbert,** former budtender and Oaksterdam budtending course instructor in Oakland, California

Budtenders are responsible for ensuring all patrons are safe and understand the rules. In places with shared pipes, bongs, or vaporizing devices, it may also be the budtender's responsibility to ensure they are cleaned and sanitized between uses. Water should always be free and readily available, and budtenders should ensure it is always easily accessible.

The budtender has a responsibility to prevent unsafe driving when possible. Judging safety to drive is subjective, and like a bartender, budtenders must remain aware of how much people have consumed and signs of over-use. Not doing so could open budtenders and businesses to criminal liability. Under so-called "dram shop laws,"[97] a bartender or other person responsible for selling alcohol can be held liable for over-serving a patron or selling more liquor to someone who is clearly impaired and poses a threat to public safety, such as attempting to drive a car.

Cannabis lounges are relatively new to regulated markets. However, in the absence of similar "gram shop laws," budtenders working in establishments that serve cannabis should use their best judgment to serve customers as if these laws are already in place. Some regions (like Nevada)

Alcohol and Cannabis Do Not Mix

Arturo Cano, budtender in Las Vegas Nevada

Arturo Cano works at a busy dispensary on the Las Vegas strip, where he meets tourists from all over the world. Most tourists come from places where cannabis is still illegal. Cano says he sees everything from "medical refugees" who move to or visit Nevada for safe access to people who want to have fun and maybe try something new.

"We don't allow *any* drinks inside the store," he says. "If you are drunk or buzzed, it's just a 'no.' A lot of people are understanding, but there have been occasions where they want to speak to the manager or argue."

As a former bartender, Cano is trained to identify intoxication and will not sell cannabis to customers who have been drinking. Las Vegas dispensaries are strict about not allowing customers to mix the two substances. Even experienced consumers may feel dizzy and nauseous from mixing.

Budtending in a Barcelona Cannabis Club

Helga Bucher works at High Class Social Club in Barcelona, one of the hundreds of private consumption lounges that have cropped up in the city despite Spanish laws prohibiting them. "It is not like a dispensary in the United States," Bucher says. "One of the most important rules is we cannot say the word 'buy' or 'sell.' Everything is 'interchange.'"

Helga greets guests in the reception area, takes information from their photo identification (passports for tourists), and snaps their photos. Most importantly, she explains the rules. "Nobody can be outside the club waiting for you. They have to come in with you or go to another place completely," she says.

Helga Bucher, budtender in Barcelona, Spain

Customers must also purchase credits that they use within the club. According to Helga, products are limited to what is available in the gray market, but High Class often collaborates with cannabis brands to offer wider options. Helga shows people around the large facility, which can be overwhelming for first-time visitors and tourists who flock from surrounding countries like Germany and Morocco.

"High Class is big, beautiful, and really modern, with fancy sellers. They are a little bit lost, so we make the tour, show where the soda is, where the coffee is, where we do movie nights, and have a station with papers and grinders," she explains. "Then we explain all the edibles or hash we have, and then we show the menu."

There is comfortable furniture and tables where people chill, socialize and work. All guests must remain on the premises for at least 20 minutes, but many stay all day. When they leave, it is not legal to take cannabis out with them. "If you take your weed with you, it is your responsibility," she says.

have "reverse gram and dram shop" laws, immunizing budtenders and bartenders from liability.

Staff and management of consumption lounges should be prepared to ensure all patrons have safe transportation and do not pose a risk to public safety. They can offer taxi cab phone numbers, public transportation maps, and vouchers to pay for transit, taxis, or rideshare to mitigate the possibility of patrons driving when it is unsafe.

Themed Dispensaries

In legal commercial markets, more dispensaries are opening with "themes," such as the Superette retro-grocery-store themed dispensaries in Canada, the herb shop and dispensary Home Grown Apothecary in Portland, Oregon, the "Burning Man of Weed Dispensaries" Planet 13 in Las Vegas, or Jay Z's New York kosher deli-themed dispensary in Southern California.

The applicant's experiences should be relevant to the theme when applying for a job at a themed dispensary. For example, it would be helpful to have been to Burning Man or a similar music festival when applying at one of the dispensaries with that theme. It would be helpful to be familiar with Jay Z's music when applying to his NY Deli dispensary or even to have real-world deli experience.

Security & Chain of Custody

The first priority of a budtender is customer safety, both in the store and after they head home with their purchases.

Although the dispensary should have dedicated security staff, everyone on site should be security-focused. In the United States, almost every dispensary is still a cash-only operation. Extra caution should be taken with all currency received, and safety protocols for handling cash should be employed and understood by all staff.

A budtender is also responsible for maintaining control of the products they sell to prevent diversion into unregulated channels and access to children.

Using the Point-of-Sale (POS) System

Selling products and taking payments from customers is only half of the transaction. The other half is accurately recording those sales. All states require "seed-to-sale" tracking, and every transaction in the dispensary must be recorded and reported to state regulatory officials. Seed-to-sale systems track the chain of custody of all cannabis material from each plant and show that the material has only been handled by authorized individuals and entities with the appropriate licenses.

The dispensary's point-of-sale system helps maintain compliance with daily purchase limits. Photo courtesy of Light Sky Farms.

The task of seed-to-sale tracking is almost universally handled by a point-of-sale (POS) system. Various POS systems are used in dispensaries today, but they almost always sync with the "track-and-trace" software used by regulators. METRC and BioTrackTHC are the two most common systems used by regulatory agencies in the US.

The POS system is the dispensary-facing side of compliance software, and the track-and-trace software is the regulator-facing side. The POS tracks the required information from the retailer, and the track-and-trace system makes it available to regulators.

Data from the dispensary's POS is also used to help maintain compliance with daily purchase limits for individual customers. Violations of purchasing limits result in steep fines for the dispensary. More severe violations such as "looping," in which the dispensary staff intentionally allows customers to exceed purchase limits through multiple transactions, can result in jail time for the business owners and even the budtender.

In medical-only states, customers can only purchase cannabis for themselves unless designated as a caregiver to an authorized patient. In adult use states, it is often legal to purchase cannabis to "gift" to another person over the age of 21. Purchase limits and the ability to "gift" or share purchases vary by jurisdiction.

One potential snag that can arise in working with POS systems is an unexpected power outage. Dispensaries should inform staff of policies to continue tracking purchases if they are made when the system is down. Although paper record-keeping is time-consuming, no products can be sold without proper tracking. Once the power comes back up, budtenders should enter these paper records into the electronic system.

Silence

Discretion is key to safety in a dispensary. Cannabis still has a high value on illegal markets, so dispensaries full of product and cash are major targets for theft. For the safety of all employees and the viability of the business, staff must not repeat security procedures or discuss cash and product-handling procedures with people who do not work at the dispensary.

Handling Currency

Federal law prohibits banks and other financial service providers from working with cannabis businesses in the United States. As a result, budtenders in the US are likely to handle a lot of cash, and proper handling procedures are required.

Budtenders Arrested for Illegal "Looping"

Every cannabis regulatory scheme limits the amount a single person can purchase in a given period. "Looping" is when budtenders allow customers to exceed purchase limits by conducting multiple transactions. In 2017, 13 Colorado budtenders were arrested[98] and five faced felony charges after selling an undercover officer the one-ounce limit up to 16 times in one day.

The dispensary should ensure all budtenders have a clear understanding of the law and comply with it. Business owners could lose their licenses. Owners, managers, and budtenders involved could all face prison time.

Tip Jars

Many dispensaries keep "tip" jars near the cash registers in the United States. No suggested tip or percentage of the transaction is considered standard, like in other industries. Budtenders should not assume or expect customers to tip, although many will drop their change in the jar or leave extra cash as a token of appreciation for their service.

Outside the US, tipping is uncommon in any industry and is sometimes viewed as an inadequate subsidy for unfair wages. Dispensary owners should pay fair wages rather than expecting customers to supplement them through tips. Budtenders in the US should also be aware that any tips received are taxable and must be reported to the government. It is considered wage theft[99] if dispensary owners or managers take any amount of the tips left for budtenders.

Tips are not standard in dispensaries, but some do put out jars. Photo by Sam Dan Truong via Unsplash.com.

Various software programs that interact with the POS allow dispensaries to accept debit card payments, and the budtender should understand how the dispensary is accepting card payments if it does. Some dispensaries have "workarounds" to accept debit card payments from customers. For instance, if the customer's total comes to $57, they may run a debit card as a cash ATM withdrawal for $60 and provide the customer with $3 cash in change from the register. If the charge on the customer's bank statement will not match the name of the dispensary, the budtender should inform the customer to avoid any confusion later. If cannabis banking bills are passed in the US Congress, customers can purchase cannabis with credit and debit cards without workarounds. To learn more about how to support advocacy efforts for banking, see *Appendix A: Advocacy.*

An important cash-handling skill is accurate counting—incorrect counting results in charging customers incorrectly and an unbalanced cash register. When collecting payment, keep all the bills visible on the sales counter so the customer, and more importantly, the cameras, can see them. Do the same when counting out change. Count twice and count out loud so that both the budtender and the customer can verify that the correct change is given.

Many dispensaries have a drop-safe where cash is secured when the registers get too full of large bills. The drop-safe is outfitted with a small, bill-sized door at the top, and budtenders "drop" cash into it for safekeeping until management moves it into the main safe. If the dispensary uses a drop-safe, budtenders should be trained on how and when to use it. There is usually a limit to what can be kept in the register, so large bills are "dropped" periodically while small bills are kept in the register to make change. Instead of using a drop-safe, other dispensaries will have managers periodically remove large bills from the registers, leaving just enough to make change.

Situational Awareness & Security Culture

At the most basic level, customer safety means controlling the flow of people coming into the dispensary and moving about on the sales floor. Many stores have policies establishing how many people can be inside the store at the same time or a rule that limits budtenders to serving just one customer at a time. Make sure visitors are aware of and follow the dispensary's rules.

According to STRATFOR,[100] a non-governmental geopolitical intelligence platform, situational awareness is defined as "being aware of one's surroundings and identifying potential threats and dangerous situations," which is "more of a mindset than a hard skill." In a dispensary, this mindset helps keep customers safe from potential threats. There are three primary elements of situational awareness:

1. Cultivate a mindset that threats exist and could exist in any place, at any time. Denial, apathy, or complacency can result in serious harm.

2. Recognize the imperative need to take responsibility for security.

Identifying Counterfeit Currency

The ability to identify counterfeit currency is a crucial skill. Budtenders must be familiar with the security features of the currency they handle.

The US Currency Education Program's "Know Your Money" guide[102] describes the security features used to detect counterfeits in the United States. Relying on counterfeit detection pens is helpful, but they are not always accurate. According to Cornell University,[103] the pens detect "the presence of starch" in the paper and often show a false positive result when the bill is counterfeit. The pens also can produce a false negative if the bills are worn down or have been through the wash. A pen test is better than nothing, but other senses should also be used. Cornell offers this advice, "Look for differences, not similarities. Counterfeit bills, if they are any good at all, will be similar to real ones in many ways, but if a bill differs in just one way, it's probably fake."

Every country or region has a guide for handling currency and detecting counterfeits. In Canada, this is the Bank of Canada/Banque du Canada.[104] For countries in the European Union, this is the European Central Bank.[105] Even if the dispensary is in a country that accepts debit and credit cards for cannabis purchases, the budtender must be familiar with procedures to detect counterfeit currency.

Source: United States Secret Service.

Budtender Interview

"A big part of the budtender's job during a robbery is to make sure no one— customer or staff — tries to be a hero. Human life is irreplaceable, but money and cannabis can be replaced."

— **Mitchell Colbert,** former budtender and Oaksterdam budtending course instructor in Oakland, California

3. Learn to trust intuition. The subconscious is amazing at pattern recognition and can see things the conscious mind does not.

Many facets of on-site safety are beyond the budtender's control, and it is essential to be particularly aware of these vulnerabilities. For example, facility design is a major factor — all outdoor areas (especially parking lots) should be well-lit and adequately covered by security cameras. Security cameras should also cover the entirety of the sales floor. If the dispensary is located in a crime-prone area, consider asking a security staff member for an escort to vehicles during nighttime hours.

Cannabis dispensaries in the United States can be particularly vulnerable to robbery due to the need to operate in cash. Dispensary owners and managers should ensure all staff is aware of the possibility, safety protocols, panic buttons, and all procedures to respond.

Budtenders should keep an eye on the sales floor and stay constantly aware of the possibility of a robbery.

Robberies & Raids

Staff should be trained to respond in a raid or robbery, but customers are not likely to have the same training. Managers and owners should have a plan, and budtenders should follow their lead.

Panic alarms are one of the most valuable tools in the event of a robbery. These are buttons discretely placed near cash registers that can be pressed in the event of a robbery to alert security and law enforcement.

Never challenge attackers during a robbery. During a law enforcement raid, the same is true. Do not challenge law enforcement. For the safety of everyone in the store, be compliant with their demands. Money and cannabis are replaceable, human lives are not.

Law enforcement raids are uncommon for licensed businesses. The 2012 raid of Oaksterdam University[101] was perhaps one of the last significant police actions against a legal cannabis business in the US. It proved to be an absolute catastrophe for law enforcement because it drew resources away from a mass shooting nearby that killed seven people.

Some jurisdictions do not require people to show their identification to law enforcement, but it is a good idea for everyone to at least verbally identify themselves. Not providing identification when requested can make law enforcement more suspicious, but the reality is that law enforcement is not raiding a dispensary to harass and arrest the budtenders. Their main concern is to secure evidence and deal with the business owners. *(See Appendix B: Know Your Rights).*

Part II Review

- Budtending is ultimately a customer service job.
- Customer service jobs can be emotionally and physically draining.
- Required knowledge about cannabis, products, brands, and regulations is vast and constantly evolving.
- Factors such as state medical or adult use laws, consumption lounges, themes, and delivery services shape a dispensary's culture and the role of the budtender in it.
- Despite medical and adult use legalization laws, additional safety concerns for dispensary employees must be factored into day-to-day operations.

Part III

The Effects of Cannabis

Lessons in the Effects of Cannabis:

- Cannabis Compunds & the Endocannabinoid System
- Safety & Research

Learning Outcomes:

- Understand the basics of how the phytocompounds in cannabis interact with the human body.
- Identify the boundaries between product guidance and unqualified medical advice.
- Be familiar with current research on the effects of cannabis.

Photo by Girl with red hat via Unsplash.com.

Part III Overview

Governments that license and regulate cannabis usually separate customers and licensed retail businesses through “medical” and “adult use” (or recreational) designations. While this separation bifurcates the market, how it is regulated, and the product types available, the lines are not always clear regarding actual human use. Customers in a “recreational” store are often seeking therapeutic effects. Customers in a “medical” store often seek products that help them relax or enjoy themselves. Regardless of the official reason for use, all customers seek specific effects from cannabis.

The budtender’s job is to understand the products available for sale and the effects they can produce so that they may assist in guiding the customer to the selection that best meets their needs. They should never attempt to diagnose or treat conditions or prescribe the use of products.

In order to make recommendations customized to a customer’s needs or expectations, a budtender needs to have a basic understanding of how cannabis interacts with the human body to produce its effects and a general understanding of current research regarding side effects and contraindications. A knowledgeable budtender can quickly learn to gauge customers’ needs, and present them with options and information.

This section overviews how cannabis interacts with the human body to produce the effects people seek.

Cannabis Compounds & The Endocannabinoid System

In 1964, an Israeli research team led by Dr. Raphael Mechoulam isolated and identified what they thought to be the "active ingredient" in the cannabis plant: Δ^9-tetrahydrocannabinol (THC). As a result of this discovery, THC became the basis of research, regulation, and the market value of the plant. Today there is a mountain of research[106] on synthetic or isolated THC, competing hemp and cannabis markets arbitrarily divided by THC content,[107] and the majority of plant varieties are very high in THC.

Dr. Raphael Mechoulam. Photo Wikimedia Commons.

More recently, there has been a similar singular focus on CBD, driving research, investment, and innovation in both the cannabis and hemp markets. Despite a focus on isolates in research, many researchers, herbalists, and consumers say it is the sum of all the parts that matters more than any individual constituent.

What is usually referred to as the "**entourage effect**" is a theory postulated in 1998[108] by Dr. Mechoulam that the effects of cannabis are a result of a synergy of all the naturally-occurring plant compounds in cannabis (or other herbs) as opposed to any isolated ingredient within it. Many experts, including Oaksterdam University, now prefer the term "**ensemble effect**," which implies harmony among all phytocompounds, as the term "entourage" can imply that one cannabinoid is more important than the others.

Although the entourage effect is still technically a theory, substantial evidence supports it.[109] THC[110] and CBD[111] are both FDA-approved pharmaceutical drugs in the form of proprietary patented isolates. These pharmaceutical products have done little to stem the demand for "**full-spectrum**" products that contain as much of the natural plant profile as possible.

As well-known cannabis researcher Dr. Ethan Russo put it,[112] *"The plant does it better."*

The Human-Cannabis Interaction

Dr. Mechoulam's industry-defining research[113] began in the 1960s but has continued until his death in March, 2023. His work studying the constituents of cannabis led to the discovery of the **endocannabinoid system (ECS)** in 1988.

The ECS acts as a regulatory modulator in the human body. Many experts believe that it exists to promote homeostasis, a state of physiological equilibrium necessary to maintain optimal health. The ECS is a network of receptors located on cells throughout the body that regulates numerous biological processes, including humans' emotional well-being, pain response, immune response, bone density, and reproductive activities.

The ECS consists of various receptor sites, the best known being CB1 and CB2. CB1 receptors[114] (named as such because they were discovered first) are predominantly located in the brain, particularly in the regions that regulate mood, emotions, cognition, memory, and movement control. CB2 receptors[115] are predominantly located in other parts of the body and regulate immune response, among other functions.

> *Endocannabinoids and the CB1 and CB2 receptor sites are collectively known as the endocannabinoid system (ECS).*

These receptors interact with chemical compounds naturally produced by the human body known as endocannabinoids (endo means "coming from within"). Endocannabinoids are "agonists" that initiate a physiological response when combined with a receptor.

The two best-known endocannabinoids are anandamide and 2-arachidonoylglycerol (2-AG).[116] New ones are still being discovered (like pentadecanoylcarnitine, PDC),[117] and there could be others, such as virodhamine, noladin ether, and palmitoylethanolamide,[118] but none have been as widely accepted. Endocannabinoids and the CB1 and CB2 receptor sites are collectively known as the ECS. Anandamide and 2-AG are endogenous cannabinoid agonists because they are produced naturally by the

The "Bliss Molecule"

The Sanskrit word "ananda" translates roughly to the English "bliss," which is why Dr. Mechoulam's team chose the name when they identified it. Anandamide is thought to be responsible for the "runner's high,"[119] or that blissful feeling people experience after aerobic exercise. Anandamide is often thought of as "the body's THC,"[120] although it does not actually have that large of an impact[121] at CB1 receptors (which causes the THC "high").

आनंद

Ananda in Sanskrit

Get a Closer Look

Phytocannabinoids: Origins & Biosynthesis

Although cannabinoids got their name from the plant that led to their discovery (cannabis), they are found in other plants as well. This overview[122] breaks down current research (as of 2020) on plant-sourced cannabinoids.

Care & Feeding of the Endocannabinoid System

In 2014, well-known cannabis researchers John M. McPartland, Geoffrey Guy, and Vincenzo Di Marzo reviewed[126] the available scientific literature on the ECS in a study titled "Care & Feeding of the Endocannabinoid System."

The review identified factors that either up- or down-regulate the ECS, such as diet, sleep, hydration, exercise, stress management, pharmaceutical drugs, cannabis, alcohol, tobacco, and complementary and alternative medicinal treatments such as acupuncture, massage, and herbs. The findings support plant-rich whole-food diets, proper sleep and hydration, regular exercise, and abstinence from alcohol and tobacco to promote homeostasis (balance) in the ECS.

The researchers concluded that further study is warranted so the healthcare profession can better integrate an understanding of the ECS into clinical practice.

Flavonoids, or pigmentation chemicals, are responsible for the bright colors of cannabis varieties. "Purple" cannabis varieties are high in the flavonoid anthocyanin, which also makes blueberries blue. Photo by Diyahna Lewis on Unsplash.com.

human body to stimulate the ECS and other receptor systems to elicit a physiological response. Anandamide is a neurotransmitter that acts upon CB1 receptors to regulate mood, memory, movement control, and cognition, among otherfunctions. 2-AG also acts upon the CB1 receptor system. Human bodies fluctuate the amount of endogenous cannabinoids produced in response to different factors.[123]

Plants also produce **cannabinoids** that interact with the ECS. Other well-known plant chemicals (phytochemicals) that are thought to contribute to the human experience with cannabis are **terpenes**, and **flavonoids**.

Cannabinoids are tasteless and scentless chemical compounds produced by cannabis and other plants. There are over 100 known cannabinoids, and this total has continued to grow with modern research. The best-known are THC and CBD, considered the "primary" cannabinoids because they occur in the most significant quantities in the plant. Most cannabinoids are considered "minor," although research[124] is revealing more about their outsized influence.[125]

Terpenes are essential oils or aroma molecules responsible for the smells cannabis and almost all other plants produce. They are known to have therapeutic properties, although the bulk of research on them, like cannabinoids, has been on isolated individual terpenes. They are thought to factor significantly into the range of effects of cannabis varieties.

Flavonoids are the pigment molecules responsible for the range of colors of cannabis varieties and other colorful fruits and vegetables. Although less is known about cannabis flavonoids compared to cannabinoids and terpenes, research on non-cannabis plants points to a range of therapeutic benefits.

Clinical "Endocannabinoid Deficiency"

A functioning ECS is necessary for survival. In preclinical studies,[127] animals genetically modified to lack specific ECS receptors suffered from "failure-to-thrive" syndrome, among other maladies. In humans, subjects taking a synthetic drug designed to block ECS activity experienced appetite loss, depression, and other ill effects.

In 2001, a decade after the ECS was discovered, veteran cannabis researcher Ethan Russo proposed[128] that a deficiency could cause many common conditions for which patients seek pharmaceutical assistance. Russo called this condition "Clinical Endocannabinoid Deficiency" (CED), in which the body produces abnormally low amounts of endocannabinoids. In 2004 he followed up with a study[129] that found "migraine, fibromyalgia, [irritable bowel syndrome] and related conditions display common clinical, biochemical and pathophysiological patterns that suggest an underlying clinical endocannabinoid deficiency."

A 2014 study[130] by Smith and Wagner confirmed that "underlying endocannabinoid deficiencies indeed play a role in migraine, fibromyalgia, irritable bowel syndrome, and a growing list of other medical conditions." Russo released another study[131] on CED in 2016 that included an updated and exhaustive list of conditions believed to be factors, including post-traumatic stress disorder (PTSD), glaucoma, cystic fibrosis, bipolar disease, and even phantom limb pain.

In addition to these primary chemical classes, the cannabis plant also produces alkaloids, aldehydes, ketones, amino acids, and other minor chemicals.

Most dispensary customers will be primarily interested in cannabinoids and, increasingly, terpenes. Very few will knowingly express preferences for specific flavonoids, although they may express preferences for varieties with a specific color, for example, "purple" varieties.

There is no exact science or methodology to predict how specific cannabis varieties will affect different customers. Budtenders can gauge preferences and use what they know about the smell, appearance, and laboratory results of the cannabis flowers and products they sell to make helpful suggestions to customers.

A look at each of the best-known and sought-after compounds provides some guidance into the potential effects of available products.

Cannabinoids

Tetrahydrocannabinol (THC)

THC is not a single chemical but a suite of isomers, or variations on the same molecular structure. The best known are Δ^9-THC ("delta 9"), THCa, and 11-hydroxy-THC.

Δ^9-THC is the most well-studied of all phytocannabinoids and is known to have various documented therapeutic effects in human subjects and preclinical models. In human trials, Δ^9-THC is most well-established as an:

- Antiemetic (treats nausea and vomiting)
- Appetite stimulant
- Mood elevator
- Analgesic agent (painkiller), particularly in the treatment of neuropathy
- Anti-inflammatory

Δ^9-THC molecule

- Bronchodilator
- Alleviator of intraocular pressure (such as in glaucoma)

In preclinical (animal or cellular) models, THC has been shown to possess additional therapeutic properties, including:

- Antioxidant: slows damage to cells
- Neuroprotectant: in animal models, THC administration can slow the progression of aggressive brain diseases, such as ALS or Alzheimer's disease
- Antibacterial/antifungal agent: cannabis compounds have been tested against MRSA and malaria

Anticancer properties have also been identified. THC promotes apoptosis (programmed cell suicide) on malignant cancer cells and slows the progression of cancerous tumors by inhibiting the formation of new blood vessels to support the tumor (angiogenesis). These effects have been documented consistently in animal and cellular models, but they have yet to be replicated in controlled human trials.

FDA-approved medicines based on the THC compound are available by prescription: dronabinol (oral synthetic THC capsules sold as Marinol® or Syndros®) and nabilone (oral synthetic THC capsules sold as Cesamet™). These drugs are typically far more expensive than herbal cannabis, but their existence and use are an acknowledgment by the FDA of the relative safety and efficacy of THC.

THC has proven to be effective for sufferers of certain types of chronic pain, particularly neuropathic pain. A 2012 study[132] published in the journal *Pain* described the effects of THC as a pain distractor (as opposed to a typical painkiller), meaning that though pain signals were still sent along the nerves, they were less noticeable to people feeling them. Multiple studies[133,134] show that THC can benefit people suffering from pain, even at low doses, and other studies[135] show that THC relieves pain by acting as an analgesic agent. THC also acts as an anti-inflammatory, prevents gastric hemorrhages,[136] and helps mice suffering from colitis.[137]

The first patient who received cannabis from the federal government was Robert Randall, a man who had suffered from glaucoma for over a decade. (*See Part I: The Origins of Legalization*). In 1972, he had

The US Government Acknowledges Medicinal Use of Cannabinoids

The US Department of Health and Human Services currently holds a patent on the therapeutic use of phytocannabinoids as antioxidants and neuroprotectants (patent #6,630,507[138]). While this patent is the source of much controversy,[139] it does not preclude the availability or use of cannabis if it were to become federally legal.

been told he would be blind in five years. Randall did not go blind in five years and lived longer and better than his doctors predicted, largely thanks to THC's proven ability to reduce intraocular pressure (IOP). Several studies have demonstrated THC's ability to lower IOP.[140,141,142]

Tetrahydrocannabinolic acid (THCa)

Before the plant is heated or aged, most of the THC it contains is tetrahydrocannabinolic acid (THCa).[143]

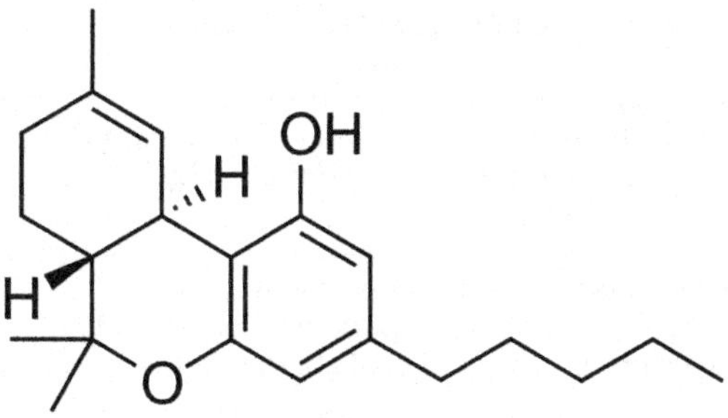

THCa molecule

Psychoactive or Psychotropic?

A substance is "psychoactive" if it crosses the blood-brain barrier and affects the mind and functioning of the nervous system.

Although the term "psychoactive" has come to be understood as feeling "high," the term "psychotropic" is more accurate. "**Psychotropic**" is defined[150] as "affecting mental activity, behavior, or perception," or the feeling of "being high." "**Psychoactive**" is defined[151] as a substance that affects mental processes.

Technically speaking, CBD is psychoactive. CBD crosses the blood-brain barrier and affects neurological conditions such as epilepsy. It is psychoactive but not psychotropic. Coffee, tea, chocolate, tobacco, and many other substances are also technically psychoactive.

Once decarboxylated, THCa becomes Δ⁹-THC. The process of decarboxylation begins once a plant is cut, and the drying and curing process will further it along. THCa is non-psychotropic, meaning it does not produce a "high," but it has otherwise similar effects to THC; it is anti-inflammatory, encourages appetite, anticancer, combats insomnia, and is antispasmodic.

Research shows[144] that THCa shares a mechanism with THC to protect dopaminergic neurons against cell death, which could be promising in treating cancer. While THC is a potent anti-emetic, one study[145] suggests that "THCa may be a more potent alternative to THC in the treatment of nausea." Anecdotal research by California-based Dr. William Courtney[146] shows that THCa from the juicing of fresh cannabis[147] may aid people with autoimmune conditions.

11-Hydroxy-Δ^9-Tetrahydrocannabinol (11-Hydroxy-THC)

When cannabinoids are consumed orally, they are digested and pass through the liver, where they are subjected to "the first-pass effect."[148] When THC is ingested through food, it experiences significant first-pass metabolism[149] and much of it is converted into the psychotropic metabolite 11-hydroxy-THC.

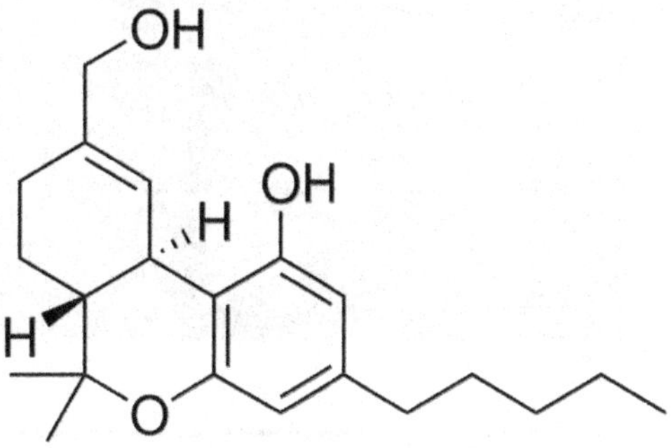

11-hydroxy-THC molecule

Compared to inhalation, research shows[154] that when THC is orally ingested, a "much higher concentration of 11-hydroxy-THC was produced."

Another study found that 11-hydroxy-THC seemed to have an enhanced ability to cross the blood-brain barrier.

Decarboxylation

Decarboxylation is a chemical process in which a carboxyl group is released as carbon dioxide. In simpler terms, it is a process that uses heat or aging to convert cannabinoids such as THC-acid and CBD-acid (THCa and CBDa) into their "active" forms, THC and CBD, or convert THC to CBN.

When cannabis is smoked or vaporized, the heat that creates the smoke or vapor causes the conversion. Cannabis is usually decarboxylated before it is added to edibles, topicals, or tinctures.

Decarboxylation happens at different rates and for different reasons. The four main drivers are exposure to UV light (sunlight), exposure to oxygen, exposure to heat, and the passage of time. When it comes to preserving cannabis long-term, except for time, all these factors can be controlled by storing it somewhere airtight, out of direct light, and away from heat sources.

Research indicates that decarboxylation is not limited to cannabinoids, but terpenes can also be converted through this process. A 2014 study[152] was the first to show that the terpene myrcene could be converted to the novel terpene "hashishene" through exposure to heat and sunlight during the drying and curing process of hash making.

UNDERSTANDING MEDICAL CANNABIS

Cannabinoids and Their Relationships

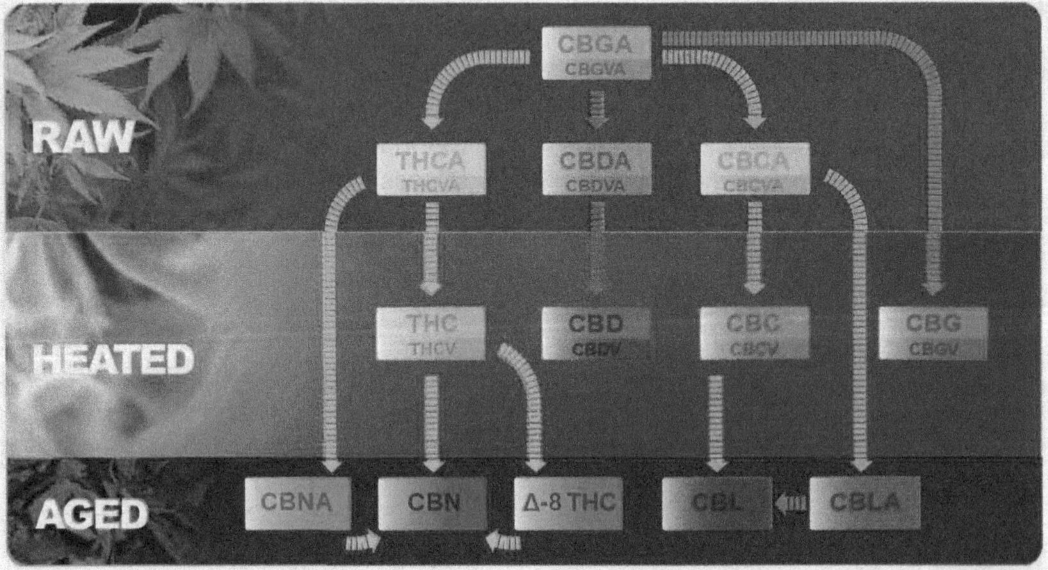

Source: "Understanding Medical Cannabis"[153] by Elemental Wellness and Steep Hill Labs.

The conversion to 11-hydroxy-THC in the liver explains why edible products have a stronger ability to affect the brain and cause a powerful and long-lasting effect.

Tetrahydrocannabivarin (THCV)

Tetrahydrocannabivarin (THCV)[155] is a molecule structurally related to THC but produces different effects. Whether or not it is psychotropic is debatable; while Steep Hill Labs has referred to THCV's purported psychotropicity as making it "the sports car of cannabinoids," SC Labs postulates[156] that it may be dose-dependent. SC Labs reported that THCV blocks CB1 receptors at low doses, which would prevent a psychotropic effect, but at higher doses, it binds to the receptors, doing the opposite.

THCV, like many other cannabinoids, is shown to reduce inflammation[157] in mice, and it is hoped that it can also reduce inflammation in humans. THCV is also an antioxidant with neuroprotective properties that could perhaps play a role in delaying the progress of Parkinson's[158] and other neurological diseases. One of the unique things about THCV is that it produces a "reverse munchies" effect, suppressing appetite[159] rather than stimulating it. THCV "also has been shown to regulate[160] blood glucose levels, suggesting it might be helpful in weight reduction and treating diabetes.

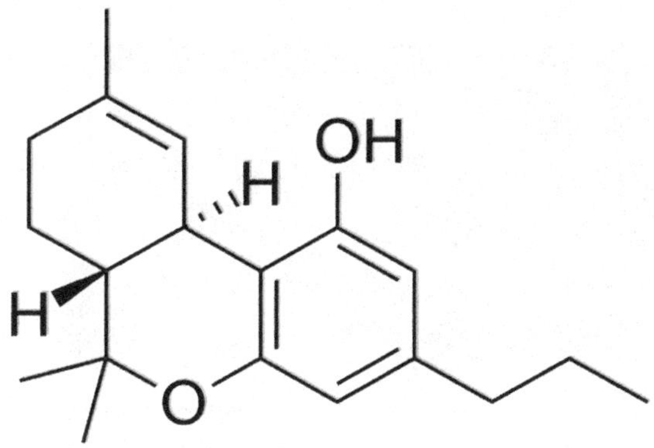

THCV molecule

Cannabidiol (CBD)

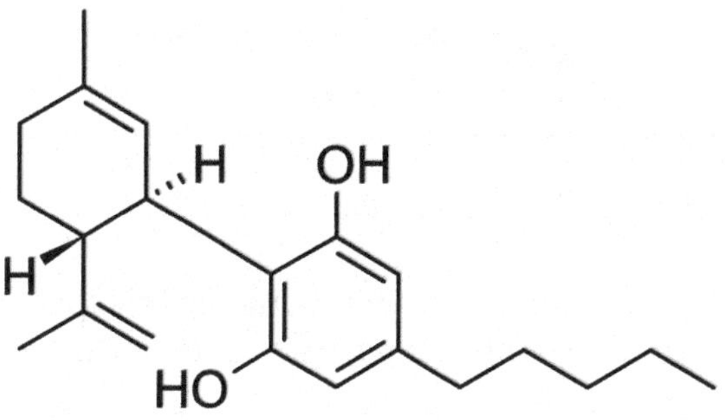

CBD molecule

CBD is the second-most studied phytocannabinoid. Because it is not a direct CB1 agonist, it is not associated with the same degree of mood alteration as THC. Regardless, it does cause anxiolytic (antianxiety) effects at certain doses. It is well-established in human clinical trials as an anticonvulsant.

A plant-derived, FDA-approved CBD medicine (Epidiolex®) is available by prescription to treat severe forms of epilepsy. It is also found in products in medical or adult use cannabis dispensaries and over the counter in a wide variety of hemp-based products. Some of these products have been identified as dubious or unsafe,[161] so it is crucial to evaluate their source and quality seriously. Hemp is legal in the US, and these products are subject to FDA regulations.[162]

Cannabidiolic acid (CBDa)

Cannabidiolic acid (CBDa)[163] is less researched than THCa. However, some information is known about its therapeutic

CBDa molecule

effects,[164] such as its anti-hyperalgesia (pain sensitivity), anti-inflammatory, and antiseizure effects. A 2012 study[165] indicated that CBDa could inhibit the migration of certain types of breast cancer in preclinical settings, including even aggressive cancers. Like THC and THCa, CBDa is shown[166] in multiple studies[167] to help prevent nausea and vomiting.

Cannabigerolic acid (CBGa)

Cannabigerolic acid (CBGa)[168] is sometimes referred to as the "mother cannabinoid" because it is the chemical precursor to THCa, CBDa, or CBCa, meaning they all start as CBGa before converting to these other forms either due to genetics or

What is the difference between cannabis and hemp?

Although "cannabis" and "hemp" are regulated separately, hemp is, in fact, also cannabis.

Traditionally, plants referred to as "hemp" or "industrial hemp" were bred to harvest their seeds and stalks, which can be manufactured into fabric, paper, biofuels, food, cosmetics, and much more. Plants bred for their leaves and resinous flowers, specifically the density of therapeutic compounds they contain, have traditionally been referred to as "marijuana."

Legally, however, it is the overall content of the psychotropic cannabinoid Δ^9-tetrahydrocannabinol (THC) that distinguishes "hemp" from "marijuana."

Although this distinction is arbitrary and confuses traditional understandings of cannabis varieties, plants that contain less than 0.3% THC are legally considered "hemp" in the United States and much of the world, and those that contain greater than 0.3% THC are considered "marijuana" or "cannabis." This arbitrary THC line can fluctuate up to 1% in different countries or regions, but THC is still used to make the distinction.

(Left) Industrial hemp field in the United Kingdom. Photo by Adrian Cable via Wikimedia Commons. (Right) True industrial hemp crops produce very few flowers because growth is concentrated on seeds and stalks. Photo by Adrian Cable via Wikimedia Commons.

The Latest Research on Cannabinoids and Cannabinoid Acids

The commercial cannabis boom has allowed more researchers to look deeper at individual cannabinoids beyond THC and CBD. The scientific review "Minor Cannabinoids: Biosynthesis, Molecular Pharmacology and Potential Therapeutic Uses,"[169] published in 2021 breaks down what peer-reviewed research has uncovered thus far.

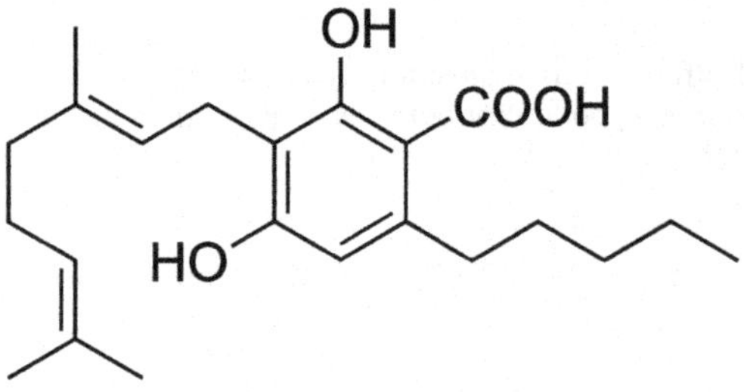

CBGa molecule

through maturation or heat. Research is just beginning to reveal its therapeutic properties, including antiseizure,[170] anti-inflammatory, antiviral,[171] and antioxidant.[172]

Cannabigerol (CBG)

In 2000, research showed that CBG has anti-inflammatory and analgesic effects.[173] Studies show[174] that CBG could have antidepressant,[175] anti-inflammatory, and analgesic (painkilling)[176] properties and reduce intraocular pressure in glaucoma patients.[177] According to a 2022 literature review,[178] preclinical studies have indicated that CBG also possesses anti-oxidant and anti-cancer properties.

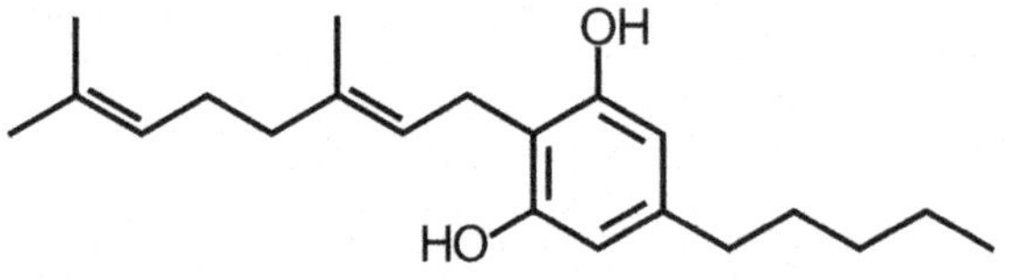

CBG molecule

Cannabichromene acid (CBCa) & Cannabichromene (CBC)

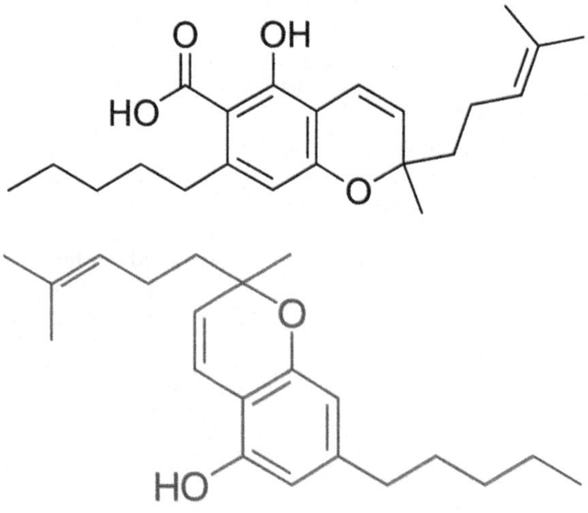

(Top) CBCa, (Bottom) CBC

CBGa converts to THCa, CBDa, and CBCa. CBC[179] and CBCa are the least-studied cannabinoids of the three. Research is emerging about the therapeutic properties of these compounds alone and in combination with other cannabinoids. One study[180] looking at CBD and CBC's effects as painkillers found they both "might represent useful therapeutic agents with multiple mechanisms of action." In addition to its painkilling effects, CBC is shown to be an anti-inflammatory,[181] antidepressant,[182] and potentially promote neurogenesis[183] in mice.

Scientific Chemotype Classification

"**Chemotype**" is a system of classifying plants by the phytochemicals they produce. So far, researchers have identified five core cannabis chemotypes.[184] These classifications are used mainly by researchers and rarely in dispensaries by customers. Budtenders may, however, encounter a savvy customer using these terms and should be able to interpret the reference. The five cannabis chemotypes are:

- **Type I: THC-dominant**
  The vast majority of products sold in dispensaries come from Type I plants.
- **Type II: Both THC- & CBD-dominant**
  Type II plants have varying ratios of THC to CBD, but both occur in significant quantities. Many landrace plants (the building block of modern varieties) are Type II. Products with equal ratios of THC and CBD may be a good starting point for new users.
- **Type III: CBD-dominant**
  Type III plants are often legally considered hemp (based on low-level THC content) and are the basis for most CBD products.
- **Type IV: CBG-dominant**
  Type IV plants are used to make CBG-rich products, a newer and smaller segment of both hemp and cannabis commercial markets.
- **Type V: Little to no cannabinoid content.**
  Very little is known about Type V cannabis, but researchers have identified[185] other phytocompounds that are of interest by researching Type V plants. Type V products will not be available in dispensaries

Cannabinol (CBN)

THCa can be decarboxylated into THC, and THC can be further decarboxylated to become the mildly psychotropic CBN.[186] It was previously suggested that it has the most potent sedative effects out of any known cannabinoid, making it an ideal sleep aid, but expert opinions are mixed.[187] The lack of clear scientific evidence has not slowed down marketing of CBN as a sleep aid. CBN demonstrates the same unique method of making pain receptors less sensitive to pain signals as THC. Also, like THC, CBN is shown to increase appetite.[188] Like many cannabinoids, CBN is demonstrated to have anticancer effects.[189] In preclinical models, the cannabinoid has also been shown to possess antibacterial properties.

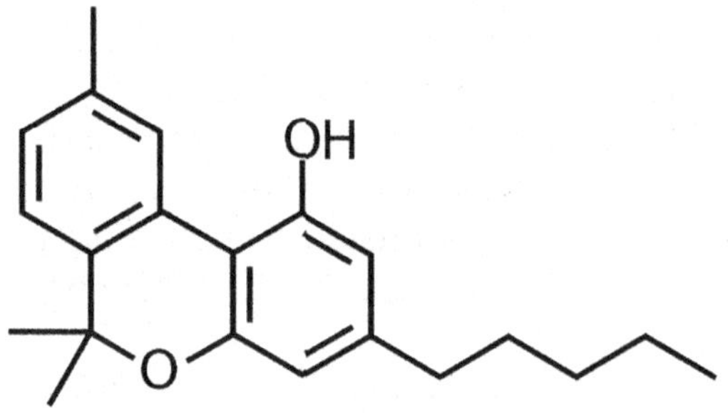

OH
O

CBN molecule

What are synthetic and designer cannabinoids?

Synthetic cannabinoids are manufactured in a laboratory instead of being naturally synthesized by the cannabis plant. There are two different types of synthetic cannabinoids. The first type is FDA-approved pharmaceuticals such as dronabinol (Marinol®, synthetic THC). The second refers to various unregulated "designer" mixtures, like "Spice/K2,"[190] sold in convenience stores and smoke shops, which are dubiously legal, and sometimes dangerous. These do not contain classic cannabinoids or have the same safety profile.

So-called "minor" cannabinoids are now being synthesized in large quantities from hemp waste. Synthesized cannabinoids use chemical processes to convert hemp-sourced cannabinoids such as CBD and THC into THCO, Δ^8-tetrahydrocannabinol (Δ^8-THC), and other cannabinoids that naturally occur in the plant in minimal quantities.

In particular, Δ^8 is being marketed as a "legal high" by unscrupulous hemp producers because it is mildly psychotropic. In February 2023, the DEA classified Δ^8, THCO and other synthesized cannabinoids not naturally occurring, even if they are derived from hemp plants, as Schedule I, and therefore illegal.

Cannabis researchers have raised concerns[191] about their use and safety in new products sold on the hemp market. Products containing high levels of Δ^8-THC are synthetically manufactured using unregulated manufacturing processes that may involve the use of dangerous household products. They are often inaccurately labeled for potency and may contain cutting agents or heavy metals. The adverse effects[192] of these products have been reported to the US Food & Drug Administration (FDA). Budtenders should be aware that if Δ^8-rich products are available in the dispensary, they are synthetic, not naturally occurring.

Photo by Elsa Oloffson via Unsplash.com

Terpenes

Cannabis has been extensively bred for the unique aroma profiles it produces. Some have speculated that terpenes likely play a significant role in the ensemble effect and may be responsible for people's diverse experiences when they consume different varieties of cannabis. More research is needed to better understand the effects caused by natural phytochemical synergies. However, a large body of research on the potential therapeutic effects of terpenes already exists due to their ubiquity in other plants.

Plants do not produce terpenes for human enjoyment but as protection against ultraviolet light, to lure pollinators, and to repel pests. Beyond their influence on the effects of cannabis, terpenes have industrial and therapeutic applications as fragrances, aromatherapy, bug repellants, cleaning supplies, and more.

Properly harvested, dried, and cured cannabis should preserve as much of the terpene profile from the living plant as possible, which will be evident to both budtenders and customers by the pungency of raw flowers' aroma. Extraction or infusion processes used to produce byproducts often alter or eliminate terpenes. However, some producers add them to final formulations as natural cannabis-derived compounds or synthetic isolates. Vaporizer cartridges are the most likely products to include added or reintroduced terpenes. Added or reintroduced terpenes should be clearly labeled on product packaging, but this usually is optional by most regulations.

The terpene content of living plants fluctuates throughout the day based on environmental conditions. While there are over 100 terpenes in the cannabis plant, like cannabinoids, some are not found as abundantly or frequently. This chapter covers the most common primary and secondary terpenes.[193]

Like THC, many of these terpenes are not a single terpene but a "suite of isomers,"[194] or varying versions of the molecule, that may act differently and result in different effects. For simplicity, this overview does not distinguish between terpene isomers. The most commonly-occurring terpenes are categorized as "primary," and notable "secondary" terpenes are listed afterwards.

Safe Dabbing

"Dabbing" refers to the vaporization of small amounts ("dabs") of extracts that are processed so as not to leave behind plant residue. Although terpenes are generally safe, research[195] shows that they can become toxic when heated at the high temperatures sometimes used to "dab." Safe dabbing[196] uses temperatures high enough to make cannabinoids and terpenes inhalable but low enough to prevent this conversion.

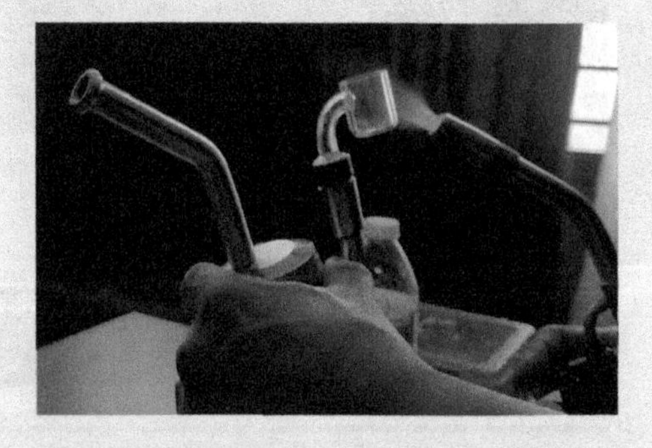

It is difficult to control dabbing temperatures when heating with a blowtorch. Photo by Angela Bacca.

Primary Terpenes

(Top) Mangoes. Photo by Mahak Agrawal via Unsplash.com. (Bottom) Mycrene molecule.

Myrcene

Myrcene[197] is the most abundant[198] terpene in cannabis plants, accounting for potentially more than half of the total terpene content. It is partially responsible for the sweet and tropical smell of some hops and ripe mangoes. A pervasive myth in the cannabis industry is that eating a ripe mango before intaking cannabis will cause the consumer to get higher[199,200] However, there are no scientific studies to back up that claim. Myrcene is shown across multiple studies to be an analgesic[201] and an antinociceptive[202] painkiller. In cannabis, myrcene is believed to be responsible for the "couch lock" effect of heavily sedating varieties, in which consumers are so relaxed they feel stuck to their couch. Studies support the sedative effects of myrcene.[203,204]

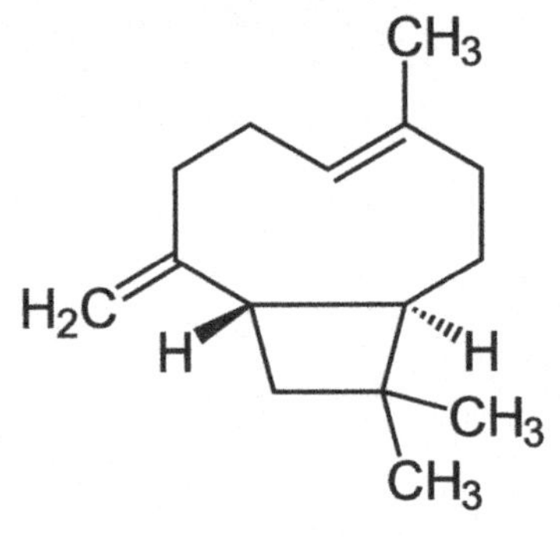

(Top) Black pepper. Photo by Anas Alhajj via Unsplash.com. (Bottom) β-Caryophyllene molecule.

β-Caryophyllene

β-caryophyllene[205] is the terpene responsible for the spice of black pepper. Caryophyllene is also recognized as a dietary cannabinoid[206] because it interacts with the CB2 receptor. So far, it is the only terpene known to interact with any CB receptor site. Caryophyllene has been shown to potentially reduce voluntary alcohol consumption[207] in mice. It has also been shown to protect against liver fibrosis[208] in mice and lab models. Multiple studies on rodents have shown it to work as an anesthetic[209,210] Other benefits of caryophyllene include reducing anxiety and depression,[211] treating symptoms of inflammatory bowel disease,[212] and fighting cancer.[213,214] Perhaps what is most impressive is that caryophyllene can improve the stress response[215] in worms, leading to increased longevity, which could indicate similar benefits for humans.

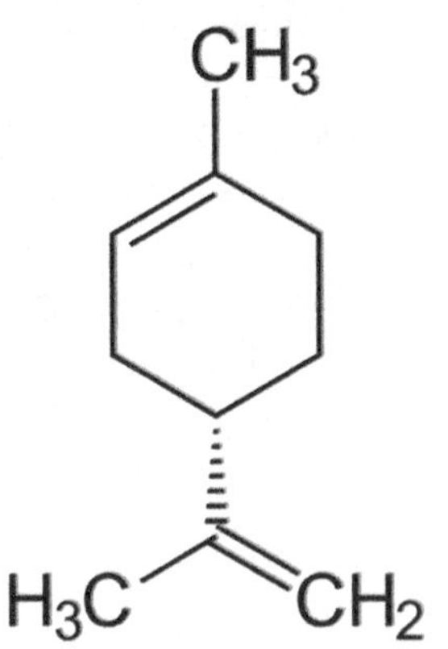

(Top) Citrus fruits. Photo by Bruna Branco via Unsplash.com. (Bottom) Limonene molecule.

Limonene

Limonene[216] is what gives citrus fruits their signature aroma. It has been shown to have anti-anxiety effects[217] in murine models. Multiple studies on human cells[218,219] have shown it to have anti-inflammatory effects, including some that specifically benefit gut health.[220] So many studies have shown limonene to have anti-cancer effects[221,222,223,224] that it was the subject of a Phase 1 FDA-approved trial.[225] The researchers found that a "favorable toxicity profile supports further clinical evaluation," but no follow-up studies occurred. In cannabis, limonene is usually associated with uplifting varieties.

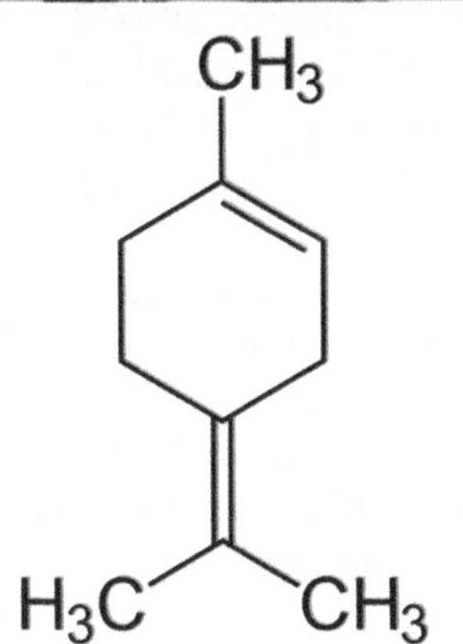

(Top) Sage plant. Photo by Paulina H. via Unsplash.com. (Bottom) Terpinolene molecule.

Terpinolene

Terpinolene[226] is commonly found in conifers, rosemary, sage, nutmeg, and apples. Studies on mice have indicated that it has a sedative effect, is an antioxidant, and has anticancer properties.[227,228]

α-Pinene

Pinene[229] is responsible for the fresh scent of pine needles. In mice, pinene has been shown to protect against pancreatitis,[230] and several additional studies on mice[231,232,233] have revealed various anticancer effects. Like limonene, pinene also has well-documented anti-inflammatory effects.[234,235] A traditional folk remedy for tuberculosis involved sending people to sanitariums, many of which were often surrounded by pinene-rich pine trees.[236] More recent research on pinene shows it to be a bronchodilator (an agent that widens the main passageway into the lungs and alleviates respiratory difficulty). It is also beneficial to the upper airway[237] and effective in combating the bronchitis virus.[238] In cannabis, pinene is usually associated with uplifting varieties.

(Top) Pine needles. Photo by Andy Beecroft via Wikimedia Commons. (Bottom) α-pinene molecule.

Ocimene

Ocimene[239] is commonly found in kumquats, other citrus, and herbs like basil, mints, and bay leaves. More recently, it has been identified as a primary terpene in cannabis, and many "tropical" smelling[240] varieties produce higher levels. According to a review study by well-known cannabis researchers Ethan B. Russo and Jahan Marcu in *Advances in Pharmacology* (2017),[241] ocimene likely has anti-inflammatory,[242] anticonvulsant, and antifungal properties and is "a volatile pheromone important for the social regulation of honeybee colonies."

(Top) Kumquats. Photo by Elianna Friedman via Unsplash.com. (Bottom) Ocimene molecule.

(Top) Lavender plants. Photo by Alexander Grey via Unsplash.com. (Bottom) Linalool molecule.

Secondary Terpenes

Linalool

Linalool[243] has a distinct floral aroma and it is commonly found in lavender and citrus fruits. Lavender oil has been used for millennia as a folk remedy for sleep, depression, anxiety, and cleansing. Recent research substantiates these benefits[244,245] Linalool has also been shown to be a painkiller,[246] an anticonvulsant,[247] and have anti-inflammatory properties[248] in mice and rat models. In cannabis, linalool is usually associated with relaxing varieties.

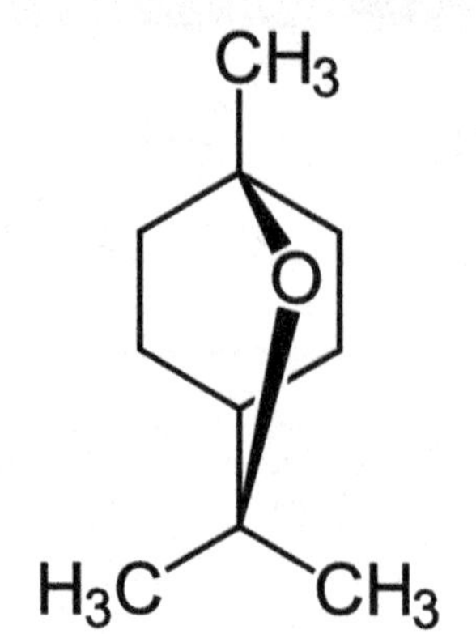

(Top) Eucalyptus leaves. Photo by Jessica Irani via Unsplash.com. (Bottom) Eucalyptol molecule.

Eucalyptol (Cineole)

Eucalyptol is responsible for eucalyptus trees' distinct, pungent, and astringent aroma. It is sometimes called cineole and is a common ingredient in mouthwashes and cough suppressants.[249] It also is used as an eco-friendly insecticide[250] and repellent. Eucalyptol is shown to possess "good antibacterial activity"[251] as well as benefits against the symptoms of Alzheimer's disease,[252] tuberculosis,[253] asthma,[254] and gastrointestinal issues.[255] Like most terpenes and cannabinoids, eucalyptol has been shown to be an anti-inflammatory agent[256,257] and to have anticancer effects, specifically on leukemia[258] and colon cancer.[259]

Humulene (α-Caryophyllene)

Humulene (also known as α-caryophyllene)[260,261] derives its name from the *Humulus lupulus* plant (hops), which produces it in abundance. Cannabis and hops are "plant cousins" as they are both members of the *Cannabaceae* family. Humulene has a pungent, herbal aroma. The research on humulene has primarily been in vitro and animal studies, showing its potential as an anti-inflammatory and painkiller[262] with demonstrated antitumor activity.[263]

(Top) Hops. Photo by Markus Spiske via Unsplash.com. (Bottom) Humulene/ α-caryophyllene molecule.

Hashishene

Hashishene[264] is a decarboxylated form of myrcene that was first named in 2014[265] because it is almost uniquely found in traditionally pressed "charas," or hashish. The therapeutic properties of hashishene are unknown as it has not been thoroughly investigated and researched.

Classic pressed hash. Photo by Hakuna Matata via Unsplash.com.

Flavonoids

Flavonoids are plant pigments (colors) with well-known antioxidant and anti-inflammatory properties. They are found abundantly in colorful, nutrient-dense foods. Cannabis contains flavonoids like quercetin and luteolin that are well-studied because of their abundant production in other plants. Cannabis also contains a relatively unique class of flavonoids, the cannflavins, that research is only now beginning to elucidate.

Flavonoids protect plants from various stresses, have powerful therapeutic properties in humans, and have a wide range of industrial applications.

Plants synthesize flavonoids[266] to regulate cell growth, attract pollinators, and protect against biotic and abiotic stresses.[267] Biotic stress refers to attacks from natural living things: pests, fungi, bacteria, herbivores, and weeds. Abiotic stress refers to climatic factors such as temperature, solar radiation, drought, or flood.

Flavonoids are used in the food industry as preservatives and coloring agents.[268] Their antioxidant properties are also utilized by the cosmetics and pharmaceutical industries.

When humans ingest flavonoids, they have been shown to be powerful antioxidants and have anti-inflammatory, anti-cancer, anti-aging, cardioprotective, immunomodulatory, antibacterial, antidiabetic, and antiparasitic properties.[269] These therapeutic properties are why flavonoids are the cornerstone of anti-inflammatory diets[270] recommended for cardiovascular diseases, diabetes, and other conditions.

Flavonoids are abundant in richly-colored foods[271] like carrots,[272] blueberries,[273] red cabbage, grapes, and kale. For instance, the well-known flavonoid resveratrol is found in grapes and extracted for use in anti-aging face creams[274] and is behind the theory that a daily glass of wine may have positive health benefits.[275] According to Project CBD,[276] resveratrol increases the expression of CB1 and CB2 receptors on the cell surface and interacts directly with CB1 receptors, although its effect is unclear.

Although these individual compounds have known therapeutic activity, their bioavailability[277] (the amount of the substance made available to the body when ingested) is low and the subject of ongoing research.[278] Flavonoids are safer and may be more bioavailable[279] when consumed in whole plants as opposed to synthetics or isolated supplements.

More than 20 flavonoids have been identified in cannabis,[280] the most abundant being luteolin, quercetin, anthocyanins, and cannflavins A, B, and C, which are (mostly) unique to cannabis. Cannflavin A has been identified[281] in monkeyflower.

Quercetin

Quercetin[282] is the most abundant flavonoid in the human diet and it is found in a wide range of foods including[283] onions, apples, grapes, berries, broccoli, citrus fruits, cherries, green tea, coffee, and red wine grapes. Quercetin is a popular natural supplement that has been touted by some to improve immune function, fight inflammation, and combat allergies[284,285,286] Quercetin can increase[287] the body's expression of CB1 cannabinoid receptors.

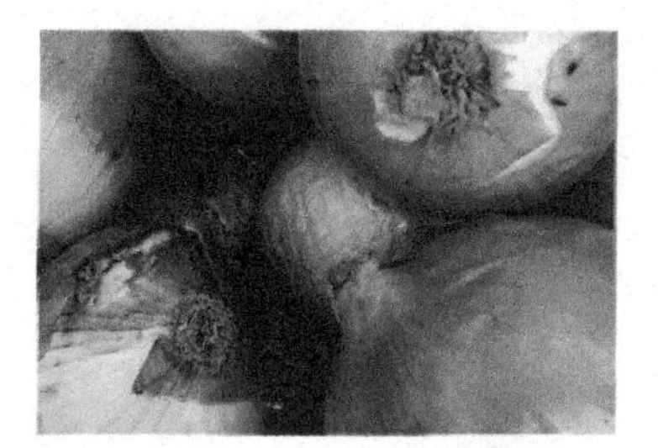

(Top) Chartreuse onions. Photo by Leonita Yuliana Sriyanto via Unsplash.com. (Bottom) Quercetin molecule.

Luteolin

Luteolin is abundant[288] in celery, parsley, broccoli, onion leaves, carrots, peppers, cabbages, apple skins, and chrysanthemum flowers. Luteolin-rich plants have been used[289] in traditional Chinese medicine to treat hypertension, inflammation and as an anticancer agent for thousands of years. Contemporary research has shown luteolin to be beneficial for a wide range of applications,[290] including mitigating brain fog, inflammation, and obesity.[291] It has been studied in the treatment of diabetes, specifically insulin resistance.[292]

(Top) Broccoli. Photo by Bozhin Karaivanov via Unsplash.com. (Bottom) Luteolin molecule.

Anthocyanin

Anthocyanin[293] is responsible for the coloring associated with purple varieties of cannabis. It is abundant in red, purple, and blue fruits, vegetables, and herbs[294] such as red onions, purple cauliflower, purple corn, eggplant skins, blueberries, bilberries, raspberries, grapes, and ube (purple yam), among others. Anthocyanins have an affinity[295] (meaning they bind easily) to both the CB1 and CB2 receptors. Cell cultures, animal models, and human clinical trials have shown anthocyanins to have antioxidant, antimicrobial, anti-inflammatory, anticancer, and brain-supporting properties. Although anthocyanin is available in supplements, it may be more bioavailable[296] when consumed in foods.

(Top) Purple cauliflower. Photo by Massimo Virgilio via Unsplash.com. (Bottom) Anthocyanin molecule.

Cannflavins

Cannflavins A, B, and C are a group of flavonoids seemingly unique to the cannabis plant. Although there is a growing body of research on common flavonoids found in other plants, researchers are still scratching the surface regarding cannflavins. It is still unknown why the plant synthesizes them, their effects on humans (both natural and isolated compounds), and their role in the ensemble effect.

Preclinical studies indicate cannflavins have anti-inflammatory,[297] neuroprotective,[298] antiparasitic, antiviral, antimalarial,[299] and anti-cancer effects.[300,301,302]

It is also known that the plant's production of cannflavins, like cannabinoids and terpenes, increases with stress. A 2020 study[303] on cloned plants grown at different elevations shows that the production of cannflavins A, B, and C increases at higher elevations.

(Top) Cannflavin A. (Bottom) Cannflavin B.

Making Product Recommendations

The available research on cannabinoids, terpenes, and flavonoids is exciting. It is also essential to understand it in context. Very few studies have examined the synergy of these agents and how they work together to produce the broad range of effects people feel when they consume cannabis products. More research is also needed to understand bioavailability based on ingestion method. Studies involving isolated molecules cannot be extrapolated to make medical statements, guarantees, or predictions of how cannabis products will affect the customer.

Plants are like people. Even within a family, every unique plant has its own unique DNA. The array of compounds varies not just between plant varieties but also between individual plants—the final chemical profile results from the plant's genetics and the garden's environmental conditions. Even flowers picked from different parts of the plant will have varying phytochemical profiles due to factors[304] like uneven exposure to light. Furthermore, humans are different from one another, and factors like sleep, diet, hydration, stress, and medications may result in inconsistent effects, even with the same cannabis product and on the same day.

Although there is no scientific method to predict how a product will make a customer feel, the available information about plant compounds guides the budtender to make recommendations that best meet the customer's needs. For instance, if a customer is seeking a flower that produces uplifting effects, the budtender may present options of citrus-smelling cannabis, which is known to be higher in limonene. More detail on cannabis varieties can be found in *Part IV: Cannabis Varieties & Horticulture.*

Great budtenders ask about preferences. Photo courtesy of Glass House Brands.

Safety & Research

Budtenders are not expected to be experts on medicine or human and plant biology, but they should understand the current state of research, why some customers with medical-use authorization may seek certain products, and the boundaries of what statements can and cannot be made about a product's effects.

Due to the plant's illegality, initial waves of clinical research were mostly limited to isolated molecules in lab or animal models. However, there has been a significant increase in the number of trials assessing whole-plant cannabis, not just its isolated components. Whole-plant cannabis and other products sold in dispensaries have not been rigorously tested in humans and they have not been approved by the FDA as medicine prescribed to treat any diseases or conditions. In fact, under current US regulations, scientists cannot legally access state-legal cannabis products in clinical trial settings.

It is the budtender's responsibility to be as informed as possible about the overall safety of cannabis products, how their effects vary by method of ingestion, and the reasons people want to use cannabis so they can provide the education consumers need to make the right decisions.

Scientific Research

A pervasive myth about cannabis is that there is just "not enough research" to support its general safety or medicinal use. Upon closer inspection, however, this claim rings hollow.

Unlike pharmaceutical medications, cannabis has an extensive history of human use. (*See Part I: The Origins of Modern Prohibition*). This alone provides ample empirical evidence of the plant's relative safety and efficacy, but this history does not guide current policies.

A cursory review of the available scientific evidence finds the "not enough research" position to be either woefully or willfully ignorant. In fact, a keyword search on the PubMed database,[305] the repository for all peer-reviewed scientific research published worldwide, identifies over 40,000 papers specific to the cannabis plant, its active constituents, and its effects. The totality of this evidence is far greaterthan the total number of studies dedicated to many conventional medications, including ibuprofen,[306] Ritalin,[307] and hydrocodone.[308]

So what does all this research say about the safety of cannabis? A review of the relevant literature identifies cannabinoids to be uniquely safe for human consumption:

"Marijuana, in its natural form, is one of the safest therapeutically active substances known to man. By any measure of rational analysis, marijuana can be safely used within a supervised routine of medical care." — DEA Chief Administrative Law Judge Francis Young, September 6, 1988[309]

"Except for the harms associated with smoking, the adverse effects of marijuana use are within the range of effects tolerated for other medications." — US National Academy of Sciences, Institute of Medicine, 1999[310]

"The acute toxicity of cannabis is very low. There are no confirmed cases of human deaths from cannabis poisoning in the world medical literature." — World Health Organization, 1995[311]

"Based on evidence currently available, the Schedule I classification is not tenable; it is not accurate that cannabis has no medical value, or that information on safety is lacking." — Open Journal of Neurology, 2012[312]

Clinical Trials

Healthcare professionals rely on clinical trials to guide the treatment of their patients. Clinical trials[313] are studies that test treatments like behavioral interventions, surgeries, and new drugs on people. These often only occur after testing has been conducted in lab or animal models.

To date, several hundred controlled clinical trials have evaluated the safety and efficacy of cannabis and cannabinoids in patient populations. By contrast, many conventional medicines are granted market approval based on only one or two pivotal clinical trials.

Scientists' interest in studying cannabis has grown exponentially[314] in recent years. To see firsthand the type and number of cannabis-specific studies taking place throughout the world, one can visit the website ClinicalTrials.gov. Developed in part by the US Food and Drug Administration (FDA), Clinical Trials is a government database of privately and publicly funded clinical studies conducted worldwide. It identifies several hundred involving the cannabis plant in various stages of recruitment. (Search: marihuana, marijuana, cannabis, hemp).

Clinical trial data affirms the efficacy of cannabis for pain relief, particularly in treating neuropathic pain. Many clinical trials also establish the therapeutic use of cannabis and cannabinoids in patients suffering from nausea, appetite loss, multiple sclerosis, epilepsy, and gastrointestinal disorders, among other debilitating conditions.

Cannabinoids act as palliative agents, meaning they provide temporary symptomatic relief. Research is beginning to illuminate[315] how cannabis may modulate or alter the progression of certain autoimmune diseases, neurodegenerative disorders, HIV, MRSA, neurotoxicity, neurotrauma, and cancer.

Clinical Applications for Cannabis & Cannabinoids: A Review of the Recent Scientific Literature by Paul Armentano

This report is a primer for patients and their physicians and an introduction to the broad range of therapeutic applications for cannabis and its various compounds.

Cannabis Health Index by Uwe Blesching

This comprehensive sourcebook combines evidence-based insights and consciousness research to present a case for the healing effects of cannabis on over 100 chronic symptoms and diseases.

Under the current federal Prohibition system, there is no legal pathway[316] for a botanical substance like cannabis to go through the standard FDA review process. The FDA primarily evaluates patented, synthetic products developed by private companies. Because cannabis remains federally illegal, no private companies can produce cannabis for drug development purposes yet. Nonetheless, numerous studies exist assessing the safety of cannabis and cannabinoids against the same metrics of safety that the FDA uses to assess conventional drugs (e.g., risk of lethal overdose, dependence liability, etc.) These studies consistently show that cannabis either meets or exceeds these standards.

Defining Safety

Although what customers do in their homes is not a budtender's responsibility, it is their responsibility to provide all the information customers need to avoid adverse outcomes with products they purchase. In extreme cases, an unpleasant experience with edibles might make the customer feel the need to go to a hospital.[317]

Thousands of years of human use and decades of study have proven the relative safety of cannabis. However, defining therapeutic agents as "safe" does not mean they lack any potential for causing harm. The reality is that conventional medicines that are considered safe often cause significant adverse side effects, including death. Cannabis also can cause side effects.

Conventional therapeutic agents are determined to be either safe or unsafe largely depending on three criteria:

- Their potential to cause significant adverse side effects
- Their dependence liability
- Their risk of lethal overdose

Side Effects

Although cannabinoids possess a unique safety profile compared to many other prescription drugs, they may cause side effects. Typically, these effects are dose-related, meaning that the larger or more potent the dose, the greater likelihood of more acute effects. Also, these effects are more prevalent in naïve consumers who have yet to develop a tolerance.

Some of the more common and less severe side effects that can be caused by cannabis include:

- Euphoria
- Inhibition of or increased anxiety
- Paranoia
- Alteration or magnification of perceptions
- Distortion of time perception
- Dry mouth
- Red eyes
- Drowsiness
- Inability to drive or operate heavy machinery

Less common and more serious side effects are:

- Panic attacks
- Increase in blood pressure
- Tachycardia
- Cough/increased risk of chronic bronchitis
- Cannabinoid hyperemesis syndrome (cannabis-induced vomiting)
- Inability to drive or operate heavy machinery
- Hallucinosis or temporary feelings of psychosis (especially at high doses)

Driving

Cannabis can influence psychomotor performance.[318] That is why experts in the field recommend waiting for at least three to four hours[319] after cannabis inhalation (and longer times following oral administration) before operating a motor vehicle. Cannabis ingestion can delay reaction time, increase subjects' propensity to weave while driving, increase brake latency, and interfere with one's ability to integrate multiple stimuli and respond accordingly (so-called "divided attention tasks").

Although studies consistently show that the consumption of alcohol, even at legal limits, increases one's risk of a motor vehicle accident in a manner greater than that of cannabis, it is not accurate to opine that drivers under the influence of cannabis are safer drivers than sober motorists. In reality, studies[320] show that THC-positive drivers possess an estimated 20 to 30 percent greater risk of motor vehicle accidents than drug-negative drivers.

Biphasic Properties of Cannabinoids

Even with **full spectrum** cannabis, some cannabinoids, including THC[321] and CBD,[322] have been shown in rodent studies to have "biphasic" effects.[323,324] Low doses of THC or CBD may produce different, perhaps even opposite, effects than higher doses. For example, many people use CBD as a non-psychotropic sleep aid. However, research shows[325] that CBD produces an alerting effect (like caffeine) at low doses and only acts as a sedative at much higher doses. Other studies indicate[326] that CBD possesses antianxiety effects at specific doses but no significant effect on anxiety at other doses. THC at low doses may be calming and relaxing in some instances, but higher doses may induce feelings of dysphoria.

By comparison, research by investigators with the US National Highway Traffic Safety Administration reports that those who operate a vehicle with levels of alcohol in their system below legal limits possess an estimated 400 percent increased risk of an accident.

The FDA does offer some guidance on this issue. They indicate that driving following the ingestion of THC may be safe when a person develops a tolerance. Pure synthetic THC has been available as a Schedule III prescription drug since the mid-1980s. Dronabinol, name brand Marinol®, is prescribed to increase appetite and treat nausea and vomiting in cancer patients. The FDA states that, "MARINOL can cause and may impair the mental and/or physical abilities required for the the performance of hazardous tasks such as driving a motor vehicle or operating machinery. Concomitant use of other drugs that cause dizziness, confusion, sedation, or somnolence such as central nervous system depressants may increase this effect (e.g., barbiturates, benzodiazepines, ethanol, lithium, opioids, buspirone, scopolamine, antihistamines, tricyclic antidepressants, other anticholinergic agents, muscle relaxants). Inform patients not to operate motor vehicles or other dangerous machinery until they are reasonably certain that MARINOL does not affect them adversely."

Cognition (IQ)

The consensus of the available literature finds that cannabis exposure does not cause lasting adverse events on either cognition or intelligence quotient (IQ), even in those whose brains are still developing. Longitudinal studies of twins find no differences[327] in IQ attributable to cannabis use. More recently, the first quantitative review and meta-analysis of scientific literature regarding cognitive function in adolescents and young adults[328] further support this consensus.

After reviewing 69 cross-sectional studies comprising 2,152 cannabis consumers and 6,575 comparison participants, the analysis found: "Association between cannabis use and cognitive functioning in cross-sectional studies of adolescents and young adults are small and may be of questionable clinical importance for most individuals. Furthermore, abstinence of longer than 72 hours diminishes cognitive deficits associated with cannabis use. [...] results indicate that previous studies of cannabis in youth may have overstated the magnitude and persistence of cognitive deficits associated with use. Reported deficits may reflect residual effects from acute use or withdrawal." — J. Cobb Scott, Ph.D.; Samantha T. Slomiak, M.D.; Jason D. Jones, Ph.D.; et al.

For more information on cannabis and cognition, see NORML's Fact Sheet: Marijuana Exposure and Cognitive Performance.[329]

Psychosis

Overall, observational data[330] have identified that so-called "cannabis-induced psychosis" incidences are relatively rare[331] — on par with those associated with alcohol.

Those predisposed to psychosis or other psychiatric disorders may be at higher risk for adverse events following cannabis exposure, which may, in some cases, exacerbate disease symptoms. It remains premature at best and sensational at worst to claim a causal relationship between cannabis use and the onset of psychiatric disorders, particularly among those not predisposed to the condition.

Dependence Liability

The concept of dependence liability refers to whether or not those exposed to a

Cannabis, Mental Health & Context

Fears that chronic cannabis use may be positively associated with various mental illnesses, particularly schizophrenia, are long-standing. Researchers investigating the use of cannabis and its impact on mental health reported that those who use cannabis in moderation, even long-term, will not suffer any lasting physical or mental harm. For more information, read the full report "Cannabis, Mental Health and Context: The Case for Regulation," by Paul Armentano at NORML.org.[332]

controlled substance will eventually go on to use it habitually (this is not the same as the likelihood of addiction). While it is generally agreed upon by experts in the field that cannabis possesses some degree of dependence liability, it is relatively low compared to many other substances.

Specifically, researchers affiliated with the National Academy of Sciences, the US National Institute on Drug Abuse, and others acknowledge[333] that fewer than ten percent of adults who consume cannabis ever become dependent upon it. This percentage is estimated to be higher for those who begin their cannabis use as adolescents. This figure is similar to the percentage of adults who exhibit dependence on caffeine and is well below that of adults who exhibit dependence on alcohol (14 percent) or tobacco (32 percent).

While some federal agencies, like the US Centers for Disease Control, have alleged[334] that a far higher percentage of cannabis consumers suffer from so-called "cannabis use disorder," this claim is misleading. Data published in the *Journal of the American Medical Association* (JAMA) refuted this claim, finding[335] "no increase in the prevalenceof marijuana use disorder." Data finds that in recent years, incidences of so-called CUD have significantly declined[336] among both adolescents and young adults.

Overdose

Alarmist headlines about "poisonings" or "overdoses" that lead to hospitalization are frequently reported in mainstream media. Such language provides the impression that the overdose risk potential of cannabis is similar to other controlled substances like alcohol, which can be lethal. This is not the case.

High doses of THC — particularly when consumed by inexperienced consumers — can lead to various adverse effects, including rapid heartbeat, paranoia, distortions in time perception, and dysphoria. When these effects are severe, people may visit the emergency room for observation and treatment. Such incidents are relatively infrequent[337] and non-life-threatening. In most cases, when people go to the ER after consuming too much cannabis, they are only provided nominal interventions,[338] such as administering fluids or anti-anxiety medications like benzodiazepines.

Budtenders can help prevent overdose and adverse effects by advising customers, particularly those with less experience, to abide by the "start low, go slow" principle. Urge customers to consider limiting their ingestion of high-strength edible products until they can tolerate their effects.

Budtenders can help prevent overdose and adverse effects by advising customers, particularly those with less experience, to abide by the "start low, go slow" principle. Urge customers to consider limiting their ingestion of high-strength edible products until they can tolerate their effects. (See Part V: Dosing Guidelines).

"Start low and go slow" is especially crucial advice concerning the ingestion of edible products. Cannabis ingested in an edible form causes a delayed onset, often prompting people to take a higher dose than needed, which results in the uncomfortable feeling of being "too high."

CBD may counteract those effects. Anecdotal evidence supports this claim,[341, 342] although little clinical research exists to substantiate the phenomenon. Some sources[343] claim that CBD must be administered before THC to achieve this effect, which means it does not work as a cure for a THC "overdose" but rather as a preventative measure. While research on this direct effect is limited, there are mechanical[344] reasons to assume CBD will calm the effects of THC.

Other home remedies for feeling "too high" include the supplement citicoline,[345] eating a meal, drinking water, drinking

(*See Part V: Dosing Guidelines*). This advice is similarly appropriate for the use of concentrates or dabs.

Some severe instances of cannabis-related hospitalizations have been reported[339] in scientific literature. They are rare and typically specific to young children's inadvertent consumption of THC products. Although not typical, the support of a ventilator has been reported[340] as necessary for treating these patients. For these reasons, adults should never store any cannabis products, especially high-THC edible products, where children can access them. Further, such products should always be stored in childproof packaging, and the contents should always be prominent on the label to avoid accidents.

Adults should never store any cannabis products where children can access them.

Budtenders should assess when a customer is new to cannabis, new to a particular method of ingestion, or has a very low tolerance. Experienced consumers know how to "**titrate**" or assess the right dose for them by consuming a small amount and waiting to feel the effects before consuming more.

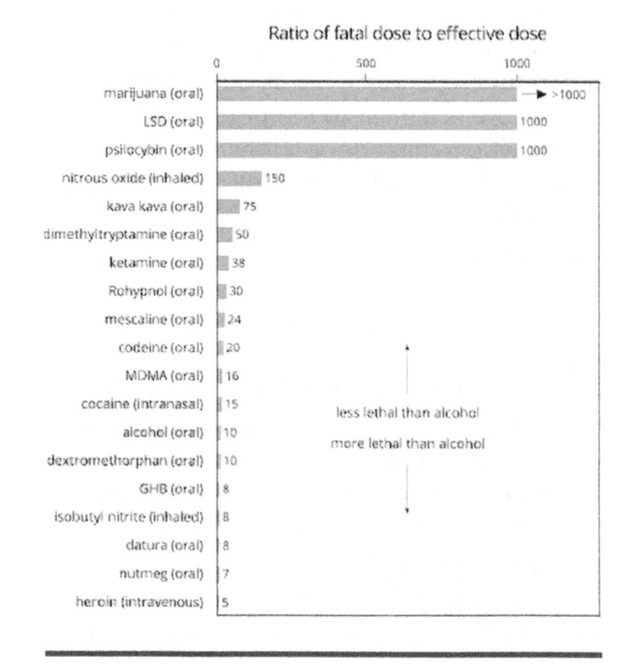

Gable, R. S. (2006). Acute toxicity of drugs versus regulatory status. In J. M. Fish (Ed.), Drugs and Society: US Public Policy, pp.149-162, Lanham, MD: Rowman & Littlefield Publishers.

a caffeinated beverage, or taking a nap. It is important to remember that the feeling will pass and the effects are not lethal, even if they are uncomfortable.

Ingesting too much cannabis is not fatal. "LD50" is an abbreviation for "lethal dose, 50%" or median lethal dose. This number refers to the estimated amount or dose of a substance required to cause a lethal drug overdose in 50% of subjects. Most therapeutic agents have lethal overdose potential. By contrast, the ingestion of phytocannabinoids has no history of causing lethal overdose in humans, regardless of the quantity consumed. However, the ingestion of certain unregulated, synthetically derived cannabinoids has been associated with toxic side effects.

Budtender Interview

"When I was budtending in medical-only dispensaries, and a patient was looking for CBD, I would mention in a non-threatening way that CBD has some potential drug interactions. The handy thing is that CBD's drug-to-drug interactions are very similar to those that interact with grapefruit juice. If a medicine has a warning about interacting with grapefruit juice, chances are it will interact with CBD in a similar fashion. Of course, if there were potential interactions, we recommended they discuss it with their doctor or the medical professional who recommended cannabis."

— **Mitchell Colbert,** former budtender and Oaksterdam budtending course instructor, Oakland, California

Prescription Drug Interactions & Contraindications

Although cannabis is relatively safe, it is not safe to consume cannabis while impaired by alcohol or other drugs. Those taking pharmaceutical medications should consult a knowledgeable medical professional to prevent potential drug interactions.

There is limited data substantiating drug interactions with cannabis, although some exceptions exist. For example, data indicate cannabis may be contraindicated with some antiplatelet and anticoagulant agents,[346] such as Warfarin.[347] FDA guidelines for dronabinol (Marinol) warn[348] that THC can lead to severe drowsiness if consumed with a central nervous system depressant. It also can put patients at a higher risk of tachycardia when taken with antihistamines.

CBD,[349] and to a much lesser extent THC and CBN, inhibits the production of certain liver enzymes. Any disruption to these enzymes could significantly impact how drugs affect the body. The FDA warning for Epidiolex also warns[350] of a risk of elevated liver enzymes.

While budtenders are unlikely to discuss conventional medical treatments with customers, some may disclose that they are on medications. Budtenders must always direct the customer to consult with a medical professional, although they can share information about these known drug interactions if they have concerns.

Opiates

Many people turn to cannabis instead of prescription opiates and opioid street drugs. Numerous studies[351] document that large percentages of those prescribed opioids tend to taper or cease their use of these painkillers following the initiation of cannabis therapy.

For instance, a 2017 study[352] of a pain patient cohort enrolled in New Mexico's medical cannabis program determined that subjects were more than twice as likely to reduce their use of opiates and more than ten times as likely to eliminate them as compared to matched controls (pain patients who did not utilize medical cannabis).

A 2020 assessment[353] of trauma patients in Colorado concluded that oral THC was associated with a "nine-fold greater reduction in opioid consumption" compared to similarly matched controls. A recent observational trial[354] from the University of Kentucky also reported that CBD is associated with reductions in opioid use in nearly one out of two patients.

Clinical trials assessing the concomitant use of cannabis and opioids provide some insight into the cause of this phenomenon. A study[355] led by researchers at the University of California at San Francisco reported that the administration of vaporized cannabis augmented the analgesic effects of opioids in patients with chronic pain, thereby decreasing overall pain scores and potentially allowing "opioid treatment at lower doses." A 2018 clinical trial performed by Columbia University investigators reported[356] that the combined administration of otherwise sub-therapeutic doses of both opioids and smoked cannabis produced "analgesia comparable to an effective opioid analgesic dose."

In addition to these analgesic and opioid-sparing effects, it is also possible that cannabis may reduce cravings for opiates.[357] Such effects have only been demonstrated in preclinical (animal) models. Many states now explicitly permit physicians to recommend cannabis for this purpose.

In all, this data suggests that patients who use opioids may be able to obtain effective treatment from cannabis at extremely low doses and, as such, may consider integrating it. Some patients should be cautioned that various pain-maintenance programs continue to look disparagingly toward cannabis and may oust[358] participants who test positive on a clinic-mandated drug test.

High Risk & Special Needs Customers

As with any substance, cannabis may not always be appropriate for everyone. Certain populations could be at greater risk of more serious adverse effects following consumption or exposure. Some of those higher-risk populations include:

- Individuals with a history of heart attack, stroke, or other cardiovascular diseases
- Individuals with a history of psychosis, schizophrenia, or other psychiatric conditions
- Individuals using pharmaceutical drugs that are metabolized by the liver
- Seniors
- Children

Cardiovascular Conditions

Cannabinoids can influence blood pressure regulation and modulate an array of cardiovascular effects.

Nationally representative population studies evaluating cannabis use and cardiovascular risks have yielded inconsistent outcomes – potentially because of confounding variables. While some studies have identified[359] an association between cannabis smoking and an increased risk of either stroke or myocardial infarction, other similarly designed studies have identified no independent risk[360] between cannabis use and adverse cardiovascular events. A 2021 longitudinal study assessing the safety of cannabis use over a 20-year period in over 3,200 middle-aged subjects reported[361] that a history of tobacco smoking was "strongly associated" with atherosclerosis (hardening of the arteries) but that the cumulative use of cannabis alone was not. A 2021 study[362] of a nationally representative cohort of 57,000 adults reported "a decrease in the prevalence of cardiovascular events with marijuana use" once authors controlled for potential confounders such as body mass index, tobacco smoking, and alcohol use.

Most recently, a review[363] of over 46 randomized clinical trials of either purified or synthetic cannabinoid products (e.g., dronabinol or nabilone) reported that the short-term use of these products in clinical trial settings was not associated with any "serious cardiovascular events." That said, some subjects reported tachycardia and/or hypotension following their ingestion of cannabinoids.

While naïve subjects often report experiencing a temporary increase in heart rate and blood pressure[364] following cannabis consumption, most people quickly develop tolerance to these physiological effects. Among older subjects with diagnosed hypertension, medical cannabis treatment has been associated with[365] "reductions in systolic and diastolic blood pressure, as well as heart rate."

Several other studies[366] looking at CBD's impact on cardiovascular health have also shown potential for positive effects. In a blog[367] written for *Harvard Health Publishing*, cannabis researcher Peter Grinspoon (the son of the late legendary cannabis researcher Lester Grinspoon)[368] discusses the therapeutic effects and potential risks of CBD use, and heart issues were not among the very few risks associated with CBD.

Mental Illness

Scientific data is largely unsupportive[369] of the notion that cannabis exposure causes psychosis or other psychiatric conditions in otherwise healthy individuals. However, data is more convincing that those predisposed to such conditions may have them exacerbated by high-THC cannabis products. By contrast, some limited data indicates that high concentrations of CBD may possess clinically significant[370] antipsychotic properties in some patients with schizophrenia. Therefore, those who have or may be predisposed to these conditions should be discouraged from using THC-dominant cannabis products.

Children

Children may be eligible to consume cannabis under medical cannabis laws. However, their legal guardian is more likely to be the customer in the dispensary. Children who have been recommended cannabis usually have serious conditions like cancer, epilepsy, autism, and other rare and damaging conditions.

Budtenders assisting parents and guardians of minor patients should make sure medical professionals are working with them on a care plan and that the budtender is not being asked for medical advice. Budtenders should encourage guardians to monitor and document the child's responses to products they use and share results with a medical professional and the budtender to guide future purchases. Budtenders should be mindful to avoid recommending **tinctures** that contain alcohol to pediatric customers.

Seniors

Some have expressed concern that older subjects may be vulnerable to experiencing adverse events from cannabis. In response to these concerns, several studies and reviews have recently assessed the safety of either whole-plant cannabis or cannabis-derived products in people over 65. Most of these studies evaluated the side-effect profile of synthetic oral THC (dronabinol) in elderly patients. In most instances, reported adverse effects were relatively mild. Commonly reported effects[371] among older subjects include "sedation, dizziness, dry mouth, and impaired motor function." That said, the duration of many of these trials was relatively short.

By contrast, longitudinal data from Israel, where doctors may prescribe cannabis flower to qualified patients, documents few significant adverse events. In a cohort of several thousand elderly medical cannabis patients who consumed cannabis for several months, the most commonly reported adverse effects were dizziness and dry mouth. The authors concluded,[372] "The therapeutic use of cannabis is safe and efficacious in the elderly population."

The extended use[373] of medical cannabis in older patients is not associated[374] with negative cognitive performance or an increased risk[375] of serious mental health issues (among those without a prior psychiatric history). Some data indicate[376] that "older adults may be less sensitive to the effects of THC on cognitive and affective measures," and others have even speculated[377] – primarily based upon preclinical findings – that cannabis "use in old ages may be associated with improved brain health, in accordance with the known neuroprotective properties of several cannabinoids."

Budtender Interview: Guiding Caregivers

Mars Anderson

Marisa "Mars" Anderson, a "patient care specialist" at Green Thumb Industries in Joliet, Illinois, often helped the parent and caregiver of a young child with a medical cannabis recommendation. The child was five years old and suffered from a condition that caused seizures every few minutes.

"It was shocking at first because in the moment I did not know how to mitigate or handle that," Mars said.

Anderson relied on her training to stay within the scope of a budtender. She stated that she was "not a doctor" and left the child's treatment plan to the parent and doctor while she focused on helping select the right products based on the guidelines the parent provided. This parent chose a full extract cannabis oil with a high ratio of CBD to THC to minimize psychotropic effects.

Mars invited them to step out of the queue or the building for fresh air if needed. She also brought stickers and the child's favorite lollipops to take the edge off the taste of the oil.

"I did what I could to make the experience not so daunting for the patient," Mars says.

Mars says focusing on medicinal cannabis patients was fulfilling, "You really feel like you're helping someone and giving back in some way, which is why I'm still in the industry today," she says.

Nurse Toni Explains Cannabis Health Equity

According to the World Health Organization, **health equity** "is the absence of unfair, avoidable or remediable differences among groups of people."

Although all adults have equal access to cannabis where it is legal—there are no explicit barriers to specific groups of people—access to retail storefronts, information, and cannabis products are not equitable. Addressing access barriers such as money and transportation are out of the budtender's control. However, budtenders can provide critical access to information and education to new consumers.

Nurse Toni

Nurse Toni is an Oakland, California-based clinical nurse who incorporates preventative, holistic, and natural wellness practices in patient care and advocates for health equity in the cannabis industry. She advises the National Cannabis Industry Association's education committee on the subject.

She says opening cannabis stores without education and guidance is ultimately detrimental to new consumers, particularly older people and people of color. "They are privy to access but lacking education, that is a setup for failure for the community and the industry."

She uses an analogy of an apple tree to describe how equal access does not necessarily mean equitable access when it comes to information and opportunities in the cannabis industry.

"There is a big apple tree, and everyone can access it. You can't see that the tree is leaning over to one side, so no matter how many underserved people are invited to get some apples, they may remain out of reach. It is equal opportunity to the apples, but access and structures are different."

Nurse Toni says most important thing a budtender can do to promote equitable access to cannabis information is to continually educate themselves about cannabis history, policy, science, and social-cultural issues so that they can meet customers where they are and support them. Budtenders cannot solve all health equity issues, but they can provide equitable access to cannabis information in the retail dispensary.

Nonetheless, because many older customers may be consuming cannabis for the first time – or for the first time in many years – budtenders should recommend taking a "start low, go slow" approach to cannabis products. *(See Part V: Dosing Guidelines)*.

Pets

Almost all animals[378] have an endocannabinoid system. Therefore, it is presumed that common house pets, like dogs, cats, birds, or even fish, may experience cannabis similarly to humans. Like humans, pets are susceptible to disease and illness, particularly when they age. With the rise of legal hemp CBD products, many pet owners have been purchasing cannabis and hemp products for their pets. Dogs have more THC receptors in their brains[379] and are incredibly THC sensitive, even more so than cats.

Customers looking to use cannabis in their pet's treatment should speak to a veterinarian. Budtenders should recommend that pet owners start with low or no-THC products at small doses, potentially increasing the dose incrementally after observing how the pet responds. For more information on cannabis for pets, see the American Veterinary Medical Association's web page.[380] Veterinarians can also join organizations such as the Veterinary Cannabis Society.[381]

Photo by Resilience CBD on Unsplash.com.

Association for Cannabis Health Equity and Medicine (ACHEM)

Want to learn more about cannabis equity? ACHEM is a professional medical association serving the needs of BIPOC healers and healthcare professionals to advance health equity.

ACHEM believes that to "get equity right," a comprehensive and shared understanding of what exactly equity is, what it must holistically do, and what roles everyone must play to achieve it must be developed. ACHEM also believes there is an opportunity to leverage cannabis policy, the cannabis economy, and the evidence-backed agricultural, industrial, medical, and nutritional uses of cannabis to address many of the medical and socio-ecological problems plaguing impacted communities as a direct result of their systemic divestment of access to wellbeing.

Visit ACHEM[382] to access information and tools and learn more about how to promote cannabis equity.

Part III Review

- Cannabis produces cannabinoids, terpenes, and flavonoids, which cause the therapeutic effects customers seek.
- The effects of different cannabis varieties and preparations are likely a result of the synergy of cannabinoids and other plant compounds. This theory is known as the "entourage effect" but is more appropriately referred to as the "ensemble effect."
- Cannabis is generally very safe, but some customers need guidance for appropriate and efficacious use.
- The practice of medicine is heavily regulated and strictly defined, and budtenders are not medical professionals qualified to dispense advice.
- Botanical products do not interact with the body similarly to standardized pharmaceutical products. Budtenders cannot suggest doses, products, or regimens for medical treatment.

Part IV

Cannabis Varieties & Horticulture

Lessons in Cannabis Varieties & Horticulture

Basics of Cannabis Cultivation

Cannabis Varieties

How to Make Recommendations

Learning Outcomes:

Understand the basic life cycle and growing processes of the cannabis plant

Discuss the basis for cultivar (strain) identification and the lack of standardization in labeling

Know how to guide customers to products that produce the effects they seek

Photo by CRYSTALWEED via Unsplash.com.

Part IV Overview

Before becoming extracts, edibles, topicals, or tinctures, all products start as a seed or clone. The seeds are sprouted or the clones are rooted, grow stalks and leaves, and then flowers. Once the flowers mature, they are harvested, dried, and cured. Dried flowers are often the finished product, but are increasingly being used to extract or infuse a variety of end products like extracts, vaporizer cartridges, edibles, topicals, patches, tinctures, and more. Yet, the vast majority of product sales are still dried flowers.

According to New Frontier Data,[383] cannabis flowers were still the number one product in 2022, comprising 44% of the market share. Budtenders will find that a lot of the job is helping customers navigate flower varieties. Budtenders should know the basics of the cannabis plant's life cycle and common cultivation practices because it helps them identify and communicate quality indicators with customers.

A basic understanding of plant biology and horticulture gives the budtender a basis to discern quality indicators on dried flowers and how to best guide customers to the varieties they seek. In states where home cultivation is legal, starter plants (clones) may be available for sale, and budtenders may be asked for information about how they grow best.

The vast majority of the public, and even many budtenders, do not clearly understand cannabis varieties and their effects. This section breaks down the plant's biology and horticulture and explains how to communicate about effects of varieties as accurately as possible.

Basics of Cannabis Cultivation

The Cannabis Grower's Handbook (2021) by Ed Rosenthal with Dr. Robert Flannery and Angela Bacca

Cannabis Grower's Handbook is the definitive guide for all cultivators. First-time home growers will learn how to get started and enjoy a successful first harvest. Experienced growers will find new information about lighting, flowering, outdoor CO_2 supplementation, stimulating growth, and harvesting. Author Ed Rosenthal has been educating cannabis growers for over 50 years, including as a horticulture professor at Oaksterdam University. The content in this edition of his book was reviewed and edited by Oaksterdam horticulture professors Joey Ereñeta and Jeff Jones.

Cannabis is an annual plant, meaning it completes its entire life cycle within one year. Outdoors in the Northern Hemisphere, seeds germinate in the late winter or early spring. The stalks and leaves grow until the summer solstice. Flower growth occurs throughout the summer, and the plant is mature and ready to harvest in the fall.

Most flowers are monoecious, meaning they are both male and female and can self-pollinate. Cannabis, however, is usually dioecious, meaning male and female plants are separate. The finished, unpollinated, dried female flowers are the most desired product because they contain large amounts of cannabinoids, terpenes, flavonoids, and other botanical compounds with therapeutic properties. (*See Part III: The Effects of Cannabis*).

If male pollen is nearby, the female flowers will capture it and produce seeds. However, unpollinated (seedless) female flowers are the most desirable and valuable product, so most cannabis cultivators exclusively grow and cultivate female plants. Male plants are identified and eliminated because they have no commercial value except for breeding and seed production.

Life Cycle of the Cannabis Plant

Vegetative Growth Stage

Cannabis is a **photoperiodic** plant, meaning its growth responses are triggered by the daily ratio of uninterrupted darkness and light.

In nature, seeds sprout and grow roots in the spring as the climate warms and the daylight hours progressively get longer. Once the seed has taken root, it will continue "vegetative growth" until the summer solstice. During vegetative growth, the plant establishes its infrastructure: a network of roots, a strong central stalk, lateral branches, and large **"fan leaves"** that catch sunlight to power photosynthesis (growth).

A plant in the vegetative growth stage. Photo by Nate Hammer of Homegrown Cannabis Co.

The summer solstice is the "longest day" of the year, meaning it has the most hours of sunlight. It occurs in late June in the Northern Hemisphere and late December in the Southern Hemisphere. The progressively longer hours of darkness after the solstice trigger the plant to grow flowers.

Reproductive (Flowering) Stage

Cannabis reproduces by growing flowers that develop seeds that can lie dormant through the winter and germinate in the spring. During the reproductive stage, the plant grows dense clusters of flowers called racemes (or inflorescences) around their stalks, known colloquially as **"buds."** Near the top of the branches, these buds may cluster together to make tight collections of racemes, often referred to as **colas**. Buds and colas can vary significantly in size, from a dime's diameter to the size of a football.

The central stalk becomes covered with flower clusters in the shape of a tail, or "cola." Photo by Nate Hammer of Homegrown Cannabis Co.

The Triumph of Seeds by Thor Hanson

This book tells the riveting tale of the world of seeds in a way that provides insight into the human-plant interaction. It is a great educational resource for budtenders in regions where it is legal to cultivate at home and purchase seeds in a dispensary.

Cannabis: A Beginner's Guide to Growing Marijuana (2018) by Danny Danko

This is a novice marijuana grower's handbook that guides readers through the absolute essentials of cannabis horticulture.

As the flower matures, the stigmas become darker and turn shades of brown and orange. Photo by Nate Hammer of Homegrown Cannabis Co.

These flowers, and the leaves and stems close to them, are covered in thousands of tiny, hair-like glands called **trichomes**. Sometimes called "crystals," trichomes are visible to the naked eye. They secrete the plant's resin, which gives cannabis flowers their pungent stickiness. Trichomes contain the sought-after cannabinoids and terpenes. (*See Part III: The Effects of Cannabis*).

Unpollinated female flower clusters are heavier and have the highest volume of trichomes. When separated from the flowers and leaves, the trichomes (resin) are collected and concentrated to make **kief**, **hash**, and other extracts.

Ripening & Harvest

Determining peak harvest time varies depending on the cultivator, plant variety, climate, and desired end product. Growers look for three criteria to determine when to harvest: trichome color, stigma maturation, and flower bract fullness or density.

After harvest, fan leaves are stripped off the plants before cutting branches from the stalk. Flowers are either dried on the branches or cut from the stems and dried on screens. The "sugar leaves" are trimmed to shape the finished dried buds, either before or after drying. Drying will typically take five to ten days under proper conditions. Once dried, flowers can be cut from the stem and placed into a sealed container to begin the curing process.

Curing is the process of aging dried flowers to equalize moisture content and allow the sugars to degrade to chlorophyll, which connoisseurs believe improves the flavors, texture, and overall quality. Curing typically lasts between two weeks and two months before the flowers are ready for long-term storage.

Properly cured flower clusters should feel dry to the touch yet retain some sponginess. When bent sharply, the inner stem should snap in the middle. Cured buds should be stored in an air-tight, cool, and dark container. For long-term storage, oxygen purging technologies are used to avoid oxidation. Properly dried, cured, and stored cannabis maintains freshness for many months (or even up to several years) without any noticeable loss in quality.

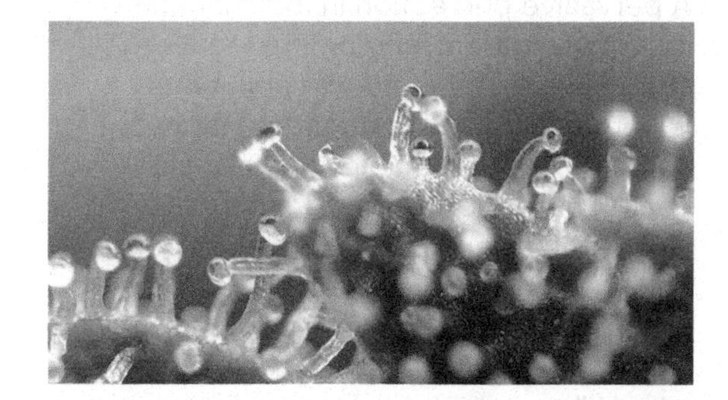

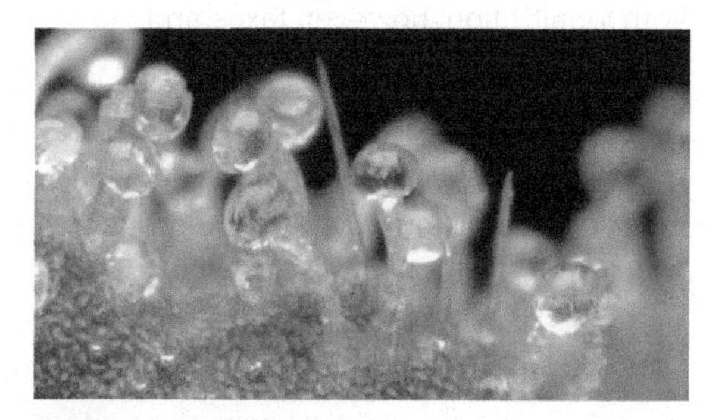

(Top Left and Right) As the flowers mature the trichomes change from clear, to cloudy, to amber. Photos Oaksterdam Archives. Photo Oaksterdam Archives. (Middle) A pollinated female plant growing a seed. Photo by Angela Bacca. (Bottom Left) A mature male plant covered in pollen sacks. (Bottom Right) A female plant in the early stages of flowering. Photos Oaksterdam Archives.

Growing Environments

Cannabis growers have used what they know about the plant's life cycle and basic needs to design ideal environments indoors. During full Prohibition, growing indoors helped cultivators hide their gardens from law enforcement and thieves. Over time, innovative cannabis farmers have shaped mainstream indoor horticultural practices.

With legalization, however, taxes and market prices have pushed more farms outdoors and into greenhouses, where using the sun as a lighting source lowers overhead costs. Although outdoor cannabis has historically been associated with lower quality, modern cultivators have proven that high-quality cannabis can also be grown under the sun.

Some customers will have strong preferences for cannabis flowers based on how they were grown. Some may prefer indoor or organic and sustainable farming practices. Some customers will purchase solely on price, while others will zero in on quality or a specific phytochemical profile. Budtenders should understand the basic farming practices employed to produce cannabis to properly guide discerning customers to the products that meet these preferences.

Outdoors

Outdoor cultivators typically produce one harvest a year in the fall. In mild climates, light deprivation and autoflowering varieties can be utilized to produce multiple harvests a year.

Autoflowering plants are genetically triggered to produce flowers based on time instead of the ratio of darkness to light (**photoperiod**). They finish faster than traditional varieties, allowing cultivators in mild climates to produce two to three (or more) crops per year outdoors.

Light deprivation is another technique employed to produce more than one harvest outdoors. Cultivators use tarps or other coverings to control the light the plants receive and manipulate them to flower and harvest earlier, by the middle of the summer.

A pervasive perception in the cannabis marketplace from long before legalized storefronts is that outdoor cannabis is lower quality. Although outdoor farmers do not have the same level of climate control as indoor growers, high-quality cannabis can and is produced outdoors. Still, the myth is so pervasive that pricing is consistently lower for outdoor cannabis versus indoor. Cost-conscious customers who still seek high quality may find outdoor cannabis is the best choice.

Large plants are grown on outdoor cannabis farms. Photo Oaksterdam Archives.

Indoors

Indoor cultivators use artificial lighting to control their plants' vegetative and flowering cycles. To trigger a flowering response, they adjust their light timers to shorten the light hours and extend the darkness their plants receive each day.

Beyond control over the plant's life cycle, indoor cultivators design and customize the entire growing environment. Indoors, all natural outdoor inputs must be reintroduced: light, carbon dioxide, airflow, temperature, humidity, and irrigation.

Indoor cannabis has long been associated with higher quality because the cultivator can create a sterile environment and fine-tune the climate and cultivars for consistency. The cost of indoor cannabis is higher than outdoor because of the quality perception and the high cost of artificial lighting and other indoor grow equipment.

As the technology continues to improve, more indoor cultivators are moving from high-intensity discharge (HID) lamps toward light-emitting diodes (LEDs). LED lights are far more efficient than HID lamps, lowering long-term overhead costs and reducing the operation's carbon footprint.

An indoor cannabis garden. Photo Oaksterdam Archives.

Indoor cultivation is required by law in some places and the only possible hospitable climate for cultivation in many others. In these markets, budtenders must help customers discern products through other quality and sustainability measures. These markets are also likely to have higher prices at the register due to the cost of the entire region's supply being grown indoors.

What is Sungrown?

The term "sungrown" was first used at Harborside in Oakland, California, in 2006. They wanted to change the public perception of crops grown outdoors by labeling high-quality outdoor products as "sungrown." The perceptions of outdoor cannabis have changed due in part to these efforts. In many legal markets, more high-quality cannabis is grown outdoors and in greenhouses. Search "The Story of Sungrown" on Youtube to learn more.

Greenhouses

Greenhouse cultivators enjoy the best of indoor and outdoor farms: they can use natural sunlight and climate to reduce overhead costs while maintaining the same climate controls as indoor growers.

Greenhouse cultivators utilize a hybrid of natural sunlight, artificial light, and light deprivation technologies. Similar to operating an indoor facility, this allows the grower to control the start and stop of the vegetative and flowering cycles.

More cultivation is occurring in greenhouses as cannabis laws change. High-quality cannabis can be grown in any of these environments. However, because of the lower overhead and higher level of cultivator control, greenhouse-grown cannabis is increasingly associated with both quality and affordability.

Cannabis colas nearing harvest in a greenhouse. Photo courtesy of Glass House Brands.

Home Grow

New cannabis plants are grown from seed or propagated from stem cuttings (clones) or tissue culture.[384] Seeds and clones are an additional product category at dispensaries in regions where home cultivation is legal. Customers buying seeds or clones may have very detailed questions about growth patterns and traits of specific varieties.

Budtenders should be familiar with the general information provided by the breeder or farm to market the variety but ultimately refer customers to the breeder or farm for more detailed or specific questions. Many dispensaries also sell cultivation books or guides.

A small balcony garden. Photo by Angela Bacca.

Seeds

There are two subcategories of seeds budtenders should be familiar with: feminized and autoflowering. Seeds may be available as both feminized and autoflowering.

Feminized

Unpollinated female plants produce the densest, most trichome-rich flowers. **Feminized** seeds have nearly a 100% chance of producing female plants. Regular

Mature cannabis seeds. Photo by Nate Hammer of Homegrown Cannabis Co.

What is "organic" cannabis?

The use of the term "organic" to sell agricultural products is strictly regulated. Products sold internationally can receive the label if they meet local organic labeling requirements and conditions set by international trade agreements.

Cannabis is not a legal crop in most parts of the world, so it does not usually receive official organic labeling. Producers can label their products as organic but cannot legally claim to be certified organic. However, many cannabis producers are choosing to cultivate in a way that would meet current national and international standards.

Some third-party certification services maintain standards for organic cannabis and certify legal farms and individual batches they produce. The first third-party organic certification available to cannabis cultivators was Clean Green,[385] founded in 2004 by an attorney who worked with the USDA on their organic inspections. Clean Green was created to provide an organic cannabis certification that mirrors the rigors of a USDA certification. Dragonfly Earth Medicine[386] was founded in 2007 to certify all farmers who employ regenerative growing practices, including cannabis cultivators. While the biodynamic certifying group Demeter[387] was founded in 1928, they did not begin to certify cannabis companies until more recently. The Cannabis Certification Council[388] was founded in 2017 to certify cannabis both as organic and sustainable. Sun + Earth Certified[389] and Certified Kind[390] have recently been launched as alternate organic certifications focused specifically on the cannabis and hemp industries.

The State of California is leading the way for government-backed organic cannabis certification. Last year, regulations were approved to begin the OCal[391] state-run organic certification program.

Not all cultivators are transparent with their growing practices. Discerning customers and budtenders can encourage dispensary management to stock products from cultivators who are transparent about their cultivation and production practices and receive third-party organic certification.

See also:

- United States Dept. of Agriculture Organic Standards[392]
- European Union Organic Standards[393]
- Canada Organic Certification*[394]
- Global Organic Certification Database[395]

*Note: Cannabis is legal for all uses in Canada and can be certified organic.

Recommended Reading

DIY Autoflowering Cannabis by Jeff Lowenfels

This book covers the history and benefits of auto flowering cannabis with step-by-step instructions.

Budtender Interview

"My budtending experience introduced me to a lot of experienced growers who not only gave me seeds but also gave me some equipment to help towards my grow. It was a really beautiful, therapeutic process."

— **Binx Taylor,** Oakland, California

seeds have a 50% chance of being male or female. Males can destroy a crop if they are not removed from the grow space in time to prevent pollination. Usually, only plant breeders utilize male plants.

Autoflowering

Autoflowering varieties initiate flower growth regardless of light patterns and grow smaller but finish faster. They are an easy option for busy or inexperienced home growers who live in mild climates and want to harvest multiple outdoor crops a year.

Clones

When cultivators identify a desirable seed cultivar they want to propagate, it is turned into a "mother plant" from which cuttings can be taken and rooted to create a consistent genetically-identical crop. Each of these plants is called a "clone." Clones are sold in dispensaries after they have already rooted, so they are further along in the grow cycle by the time the customer buys them. Some varieties are only sold as clones.

Clones may be more desirable than seeds for some home growers because the finished product is more predictable. They are guaranteed to be female, and cloning significantly reduces variation and leads to a predictive uniformity cycle to cycle, allowing the grower to fine-tune their practices. Customers may also seek specific cannabinoid or terpene profiles, which are easier to obtain from known cloned varieties.

A healthy, rooted clone. Photo Oaksterdam Archives.

Cannabis Varieties

Cannabis flowers are marketed primarily by the names on their label. Breeders often give their plants names that reflect their smells, tastes, purported effects, or growing patterns because they communicate to growers and end consumers what they can expect by buying them. It is crucial for budtenders to understand that there is no standard naming convention or process for cannabis varieties, so very few evidence-based conclusions can be reached about their effects and growing patterns based on these names.

Traditionally, the term "strain" has been used to refer to these varieties. A more appropriate term to use is "**cultivar.**" The term "strain" is appropriate to classify viruses, fungi, and bacteria. The word "cultivar" is a portmanteau derived from "cultivated variety." It refers to the flowers as a unique product of both the plant's genetics and the conditions provided by the cultivator.

Many customers will look to the budtender to help them choose a cultivar or other cultivar-specific products. Although it may not matter much to customers whether or not it is called a strain or cultivar, what matters to them is that it produces desired effects.

Do Variety Names Matter?

Many inexperienced customers may be intimidated by the multitude of unique and frequently provocative cultivar names such as Train Wreck, Blue Dream, and Jack Herer. More questions may arise when they see that most flowers are categorized further into broad classifications like **indica**, **sativa**, or hybrid. Budtenders can help customers make sense of it by first breaking down the relevance of these names.

Cultivar names have the sole purpose of branding and marketing and often are not the best measure of the effects they produce. There is no oversight body to assure that a product marketed as "White Widow" is consistent with any other "White Widow" product sold elsewhere. Sometimes, a new name may appear randomly to cash in on a fad.

Recommended Reading

The Botany of Desire by Michael Pollan

In *The Botany of Desire*, Michael Pollan elucidates the intimately reciprocal relationship between people and plants. In telling the stories of four familiar plant species—apples, potatoes, tulips, and cannabis—Pollan illustrates how they evolved to satisfy humankind's most basic yearnings—and, by doing so, made themselves indispensable.

To further complicate matters, there is nothing to prevent a grower from selling their product under any name, so a well-known variety with consistent demand, like Blue Dream, may actually be several unrelated varieties.

Sometimes these names do provide insight into the product. For instance, varieties with strong citrus scents are often associated with uplifting effects and are also often sold under names that include the words lemon, orange, or grapefruit to advertise to customers with this preference.

> *In many instances, "strain names" confuse customers because they provide little to no consistent or accurate information about the plant's history, genetics, effects, and to whom these effects are most applicable. By helping customers choose products based on the available data rather than the "strain" name, budtenders give them the tools they need to achieve their desired effects.*

In many instances, these names may confuse customers because they provide little to no consistent or accurate information about the plant's history, genetics, effects, and to whom these effects are most applicable. One analysis of over 120 cannabis samples by researchers writing in the peer-reviewed journal PLoS ONE concluded,[396] "[M]arijuana strain names often do not reflect a meaningful genetic identity."

Even the widely-accepted division between "sativa" and "indica" varieties often provides little valid guidance about the effects they produce. Though the terms remain popular colloquially, scientists have increasingly grown skeptical of claims that these labels refer to any actual distinguishing characteristic.

The narrative handed down for generations is that sativa varieties are associated with more awake, "caffeine-like" effects that make them ideal to consume during the day, whereas indica products tend to be associated with a full-body high and so-called "couchlock effects" that make them more appropriate to consume in the evening.

Nonetheless, modern analytical testing of so-called true indica versus true sativa varieties identifies few differences in the plants' analytical makeup and none responsible for these supposed disparate effects. In 2018, cannabinoid scientist Robert McPartland concluded,[397] "Categorizing cannabis as either 'sativa' or 'indica' has become an exercise in futility. ... Ubiquitous interbreeding and hybridization render their distinction meaningless."

Because the existing system of "strain" or cultivar names tells so little, budtenders should encourage customers to base their product selections on the analytical information provided on the product labels. This information should include a listing of the cannabinoids and their potency and other relevant consumer safety information. By helping customers choose products based on the available data rather than the "strain" name, budtenders give them the tools they need to achieve their desired effects. *(See the following chapter: How to Make Recommendations).*

Genetics

All natural organisms, including plants and humans, are a product of their DNA (nature) and environmental conditions (nurture). Two farmers could grow plants with identical genetics (clones) but produce two plants with different final appearances or chemical profiles. Genetics can and are being used in the cannabis industry to begin defining cultivars and **varietal** families (closely related plants). For now, cannabis genetics as a method of distinguishing the effects of cultivars is murky.

A good way to understand how convoluted cannabis genetics are and what meaning can be ascribed to them through cultivar names is to compare them to similar crops, such as grapes and well-known wine cultivars.

In the wine industry, genetic and other plant standards distinguish varietals, such as chardonnay from pinot noir. While a vintner can sell the wine under any fun or descriptive name, similar to a cannabis farmer, this is separate from the labeled varietal and is understood as marketing, while the varietal name is not.

Cannabis vs. Grapes Terminology

	Cannabis	Grapes
Species	*Cannabis Sativa* L.	*Vitis vinifera*
Strain	Fiber Hemp / High THC / High CBD	Wine Grape / Table Grape / Raisin
Cultivar	Blueberry	Cabernet Sauvignon
Chemotypes	High-THC, Myrcene, Limonene	Peppery and Fruity: Caryophyllene and Terpinolene
Phenotypes	Short, Bushy, Dense Buds, Mold-resistant	Berry Size and Firmness, Skin Color

Cannabis Evolution and Ethnobotany by Robert Clark and Mark Merlin

Cannabis: Evolution and Ethnobotany is a comprehensive, interdisciplinary exploration of the natural origins and early evolution of cannabis, highlighting its historic role in the development of human societies.

Budtender Interview

"The terms "indica," "sativa," and "hybrid" are still useful for new consumers. It's the easiest way to help them decide what they need. A lot of people associate sativa with energy and creativity and indica with rest and pain relief. If you have a new person coming in, a lot of them will say, 'I'm looking for an indica because I know it's for pain relief.' From this point you know how you can educate them by presenting and describing options. I just don't see those two terms dying anytime soon.

— **Binx Taylor,** Oakland, California

The Sativa-Indica Fallacy

According to New Frontier Data,[398] cannabis flowers account for half of dispensary sales. Budtenders rely heavily on talking about these varieties because it is the best way to distinguish them as products. Most dispensaries will divide them into three general categories: indica, sativa, and hybrid.

Although almost every dispensary uses these labels to describe effects, they have no scientific backing. The indica-sativa classification has prevailed because it served a purpose during Prohibition. In the absence of a system based on science and research, people had to find a way to categorize their perceived, subjective experiences.

The terms indica and sativa more accurately describe the plant's physiology and geographic origins. "Indica" plants evolved in the high-altitude Hindu Kush mountains. They tend to grow shorter and denser and flower faster than those that evolved in equatorial regions. "Sativa" plants are more related to modern industrial hemp, evolved closer to the equator, and are taller, lighter, and brighter in color. They also have thinner leaf blades and longer flowering cycles.

There is some biological basis for these terms, however. French naturalist Jean-Baptiste Lamarck was credited with coining the term "indica" in 1785[399] because he wanted to differentiate the psychotropic cannabis from India from the non-psychotropic "hemp" prevalent in Europe (known as *Cannabis sativa*). He derived the term "Indica" from India, and *Cannabis indica* was born.

There have been numerous rejections of Lamarck's definition of "indica," and today there are alternative interpretations of the term:

"Throughout the last few centuries, *Cannabis indica* has meant different things depending on who was using the term at that particular time. The term was originally coined as a way to distinguish the [psychotropic] plants found growing in warmer climates from their fibre-producing relatives in Europe that had traditionally been known as *C. sativa*. Despite being discarded by botanists fairly soon after Lamarck introduced it in 1785, the term indica managed to survive and thrive due to its use by various groups: physicians who wanted to use cannabis as a medicine, lawyers who tried to keep their clients out of jail, and recreational cannabis growers who wanted to market their

products. They all used the same term but may not have agreed on its actual meaning."
— Erkelens and Hazekamp, 2014.[400]

To add more confusion to the mix, the term "sativa" is still 100% correct — if, and only if, referring to the commonly accepted taxonomic name of all plants of the species, *Cannabis sativa*. This name applies to all cannabis.

There is just one indica-sativa-related term for cultivars that is still accurate — the "hybrid" label. Hybridization results from selective breeding to maximize desirable traits such as THC and CBD potency, size, or a specific terpene profile. The sheer number of hybrid cultivars is a testament to the industry's prolific use of selective breeding. Almost every cultivar found in every dispensary in North America could accurately bear this label.

Budtender Interview

"It's not always accurate to say sativa or indica will make you sleepy or energetic. In Oregon, a lot of farms will now label the terpene content on the package and we use this to discuss the products with customers."

— **Cas Czwiczynski,**
Portland, Oregon

Hemp

Hemp, marijuana, and cannabis are the same plant. Traditionally, plants referred to as "hemp" or "industrial hemp" were bred to harvest their seeds and stalks, which can be manufactured into a plethora of byproducts like paper, rope, fabric, and foods. Plants bred for their resinous flowers are referred to as "marijuana" and "cannabis."

Legally, it is the overall content of the psychotropic cannabinoid Δ^9-tetrahydrocannabinol (THC) that distinguishes "hemp" from "marijuana." With the legalization of hemp in the US and many other countries, any cannabis plant under the legal THC limit can be considered hemp. This arbitrary distinction has led to a boom in over-the-counter cannabis products that either have very low or no THC but instead are higher in cannabinoids like CBD and CBG.

Products legally produced as hemp are subject to FDA regulations and are not usually available in dispensaries selling high-THC products. There are still products produced in non-hemp medical cannabis markets that are high in cannabinoids other than THC.

Extra caution should be taken in markets that allow hemp-derived synthetic cannabinoids to be sold in products in licensed dispensaries. Compounds that may or may not naturally occur in tiny amounts in the cannabis plant (Δ^6-THC, Δ^8-THC, Δ^{10}-THC, among others) are sometimes

Interpening: The Art and Science of the Cannabis Sommelier by Max Montrose

Interpening provides a basis for budtenders and customers who want to become quality experts and convey the nuanced differences between cannabis varieties. This book teaches the reader how to evaluate and qualify every detail of cannabis flowers.

synthesized from excess THC or CBD in the hemp market and added to products. There is no research on the safety of these products, and Oaksterdam advises budtenders not to recommend them to customers. For more information on naturally occurring and synthetic cannabinoids *see Part III: Cannabis Compounds & The Endocannabinoid System.*

Variety Labeling Standards

No universally accepted naming conventions or standards exist for cannabis varieties, meaning anyone can call any plant anything they want. As a result, customers cannot repeat experiences by purchasing a cultivar with the same name, which presents a significant challenge for the budtender to use these names to guide customer purchases.

Researchers have taken samples of cultivars that bear the same name but were produced by different growers, sequenced their genetics, and compared them to other samples, similar to human DNA services like 23andMe and Ancestry.com. They often found little genetic similarity between samples labeled as the same cultivar from different sources. This result has been replicated in many studies.[401]

A 2015 study[402] from Canadian researchers found that of the cultivars analyzed, 35% shared more genetic similarity with cultivars with unrelated names than with cultivars with similar names.

In 2017, Vice[403] spoke with Sean Myles, a professor of agricultural genetic diversity who worked on this study. Myles concluded, "They call things Purple Kush, but Purple Kush does not mean anything . . . There are so many exceptions, and the correlation is so weak that putting a number on a bag and saying, 'This is a 50/50 hybrid of indica and sativa,' is highly, highly dubious. When you go into a grocery store and there is a big pile of apples labeled as Honeycrisp, you expect that they're actually Honeycrisp apples . . . You can't just throw McIntosh apples in there and sell them for $4.99 a bag. It's crazy, it's absolutely nuts . . . I mean, you couldn't run an industry like this anywhere else except for cannabis."

Customers may often complain that the flowers they purchased labeled "Gelato" look and taste nothing like the

Gelato they purchased on their last visit or from another dispensary and affect them entirely differently. The information in this chapter explains this phenomenon.

If consumers begin to insist on accurate cultivar labels, it will drive the industry to make improvements. The cannabis industry can and must achieve this same level of product awareness through consumer education, which requires budtenders to deliver the correct information and terminology to customers.

Currently, budtenders must accept that using common strain and variety labels is not a reliable way to provide recommendations. The following chapter provides guidance on how to recommend cannabis cultivars more accurately.

Products with synthetically produced Δ⁸-THC are sold over-the-counter as hemp, and although infrequently, in licensed dispensaries. Oaksterdam advises budtenders not to recommend them to customers. Photo by Elsa Olofsson via Unsplash.com.

Will there be accurate cultivar labels in the future?

Companies like Medicinal Genomics and Phylos Bioscience have worked to sequence and define the cannabis genome. They have collected genetic data from cannabis samples found in ancient tombs and off the shelves of modern-day dispensaries. The sample data is then linked to a growing genetic map of the cannabis plant, which helps trace the lineage of a particular cultivar and get a clearer picture of what it truly is.

They have concluded that they cannot and will not define cultivars based on these names because it would require them to "pick the winners" by choosing which plants can bear which names. This does not mean there will never be order in future legal markets. It simply means that using labels like "Blue Dream" to accurately talk about effects and growing patterns is unlikely to happen soon.

Licensed cultivators have the opportunity instead to use genetic and phytochemical data to define cultivars as their own individual products. One day there may be consensus on general varietal families. For instance, Phylos defines six distinct families: hemp, CBD, berry, skunk, landrace, and OG Kush. While these categories may be used in the future, cultivar names must be understood as the marketing tools they are.

When cannabis is fully legal, plant patenting[404] will become a more standard way to define some cultivars.

How to Make Recommendations

The current lack of standardization has not scared away cannabis consumers. Indeed many customers experience similar effects when using a specific cultivar or a particular ingestion method. However, there are strategies other than "strain names" that budtenders can use to guide cultivar recommendations that meet customers' needs and produce the desired effects.

These strategies rely on objective analytic data (lab testing results) and the customer's subjective experience. This information should be paired with additional research about the growers, extractors, and manufacturers of available products to learn more about their practices and track records.

Use Available Objective Data

The first step is to look at the available objective data, which are found on the product's lab testing results, called a certificate of analysis (COA). THC and CBD potency testing and labeling are required in all licensed commercial markets. Terpene potency and labeling are usually available but not required. While the accuracy of potency test results is still not necessarily guaranteed,[405] the information provided may be the only hard data available on which to base a recommendation.

Assessing a customer's prior experience with cannabis and potency test results can help narrow down which cultivar is the right one to recommend. (*See Part VI: Customer Service*). For example, selecting a high-CBD/ low-THC cultivar or one with roughly equal CBD and THC content would be a good start for new or THC-sensitive consumers.

Many consumers purchase cannabis based solely on the concentration of THC in the product. Picking the product with the highest THC number is rarely the best way to select cannabis. If a customer might be open to other suggestions, the budtender can take the opportunity to educate them about other high-quality or unique varieties they carry.

More products are becoming available containing significant quantities of CBC, CBG, and THCV. These cannabinoids could shed light on the vastly different experiences with cannabis from one person to another, and it is worth recommending them to customers interested in trying new things. (*See Part III: Cannabis Compounds & the Endocannabinoid System*).

Encourage customers to keep track of any positive or negative effects they experience from particular cultivars or products to see if they can identify any patterns. For instance, do they notice that when they have a cultivar high in CBG, they have a better-than-average experience? If so, recommend the cultivars and products that contain CBG, even if there is only a tiny amount. Because these cannabinoids are typically present at such low levels in the plant, only a tiny amount is likely needed to influence the effect.

Understanding Custom Experience

In many cases, there will be relatively little objective data to leverage when recommending a cultivar. A customer's unique senses and experiences help inform recommendations. Everyone will have a different subjective experience with every single cannabis product.

Regulatory Compliance Testing

CERTIFICATE OF ANALYSIS

DATE ISSUED 08/27/2022 | OVERALL BATCH RESULT: PASS

SAMPLE NAME: Brand-XYZ Pre Rolls
Pre-roll Product, Product Inhalable

CULTIVATOR / MANUFACTURER
Business Name: Brand-ABC LLC
License Number: C12-0000000-LIC
Address: 6789 Any Street, Any City, CA 955555

DISTRIBUTOR
Business Name: Brand-XYZ
License Number: C12-9999999-LIC
Address: 1324 Any Street, Any City, CA 95555

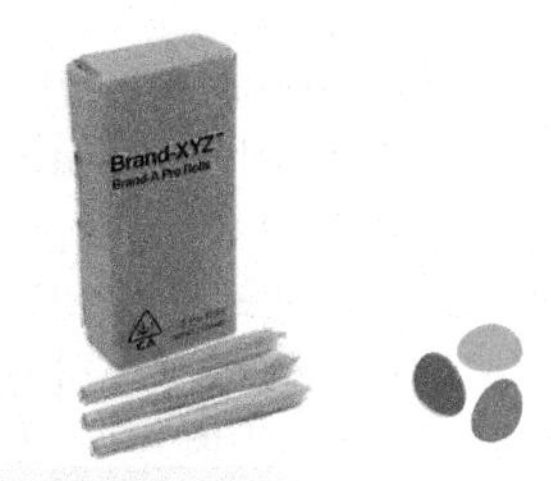

SAMPLE DETAIL
Batch Number: ABC123
Sample ID: 220101A001
Source Metrc UID: 0A0000000000000000000000

Date Collected: 08/24/2022
Date Received: 08/25/2022
Batch Size: 50000 units
Sample Size: 25.0 units
Unit Mass: 1 Grams per Unit
Serving Size:

Scan QR code to verify authenticity of results.

Sampling Method: QSP 1265 - Sampling of Cannabis and Product Batches

CANNABINOID ANALYSIS - SUMMARY PASS

Sum of Cannabinoids: 19.1140%
Total Cannabinoids: 19.0471%
Total THC: 19.0471%
Total CBD: 0.0584%

Sum of Cannabinoids = Δ^9-THC + THCa + CBD + CBDa + CBG + CBGa + THCV + THCVa + CBC + CBCa + CBDV + CBDVa + Δ^8-THC + CBL + CBN
Total Cannabinoids = (Δ^9-THC+0.877*THCa) + (CBD+0.877*CBDa) + (CBG+0.877*CBGa) + (THCV+0.877*THCVa) + (CBC+0.877*CBCa) + (CBDV+0.877*CBDVa) + Δ^8-THC + CBL + CBN
Total THC/CBD is calculated using the following formulas to take into account the loss of a carboxyl group during the decarboxylation step:
Total THC = Δ^9-THC + (THCa (0.877))
Total CBD = CBD + (CBDa (0.877))

SAFETY ANALYSIS - SUMMARY

Δ^9-THC per Unit: PASS	**Pesticides:** PASS	**Mycotoxins:** PASS
Residual Solvents: PASS	**Heavy Metals:** PASS	**Microbiology:** PASS
Foreign Material: PASS	Water Activity: NT	

TERPENOID ANALYSIS - SUMMARY 39 TESTED, TOP 3 HIGHLIGHTED

Total Terpenoids: 3.330%

β-Caryophyllene 3.054 mg/g | α-Bisabolol 1.061 mg/g | α-Humulene 0.953 mg/g

These results relate only to the sample included on this report.
This report shall not be reproduced, except in full, without written approval of the laboratory.
Sample Certification: California Code of Regulations Title 16 Effect Date January 16, 2019. Authority: Section 26013, Business and Professions Code. Reference: Sections 26100, 26104 and 26110, Business and Professions Code.
Decision Rule: Statements of conformity (e.g. Pass/Fail) to specifications are made in this report without taking measurement uncertainty into account. Where statements of conformity are made in this report, the following decision rules are applied: PASS - Results within limits/specifications, FAIL - Results exceed limits/specifications.
References: limit of detection (LOD), limit of quantification (LOQ), not detected (ND), not tested (NT)

All LOQ samples were performed and met the prescribed acceptance criteria in 4 CCR section 1730, as attested by: Mark Lotto
Date: 08/27/2022

Approved by: Josh Wurzer, President
Date: 08/27/2022

SC Laboratories California LLC. | 100 Pioneer Street, Suite E, Santa Cruz, CA 95060 | 866-435-0709 | sclabs.com | C8-0000013-LIC | ISO/IES 17025:2017 PJLA Accreditation Number 87168

 CoA ID: 220101A001-001 Page 1 of 4

The certificate of analysis provides THC, CBD, and other cannabinoid levels and confirms that the product passed all safety tests.

The most important aspect of a customer's subjective experience is their olfactory senses. The olfactory zone is the nose, ears, and mouth. If the customer likes the smell of the flower a budtender presents, there is a good chance the cultivar will produce positive effects.

This phenomenon is demonstrated when two people smell the same flower; one thinks it smells fantastic, while the other thinks it smells terrible. This reaction also illustrates why two people can consume the same flower and have vastly different effects. Just like cannabis cultivars, no two people are the same.

Terpenes are also known to produce specific physiological effects, regardless of where they occur in nature. For example, lavender's sedating and relaxing effects can most likely be attributed to the terpene linalool. Linalool is also found in floral-scented cannabis varieties. *(See Part III: The Effects of Cannabis).*

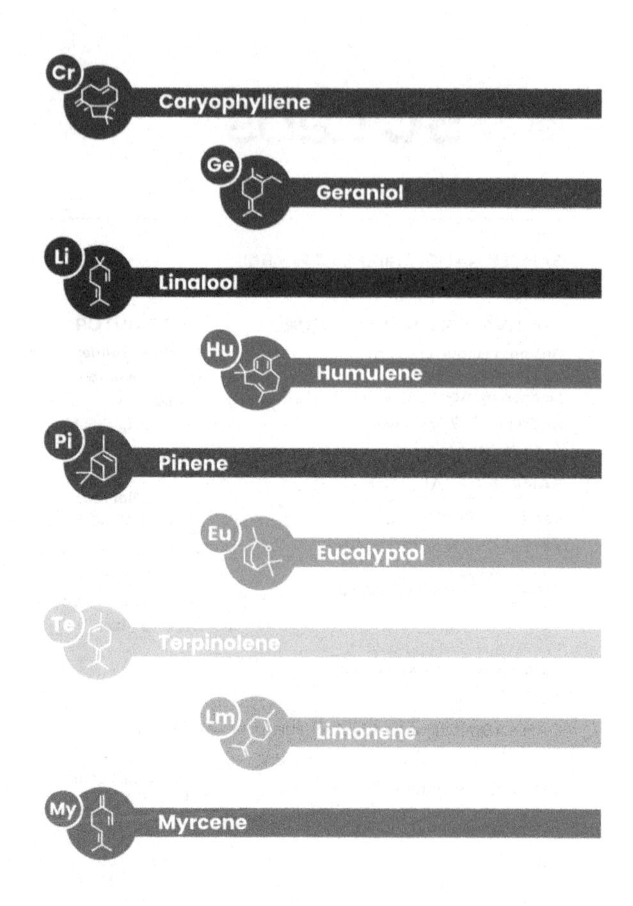

Terpenes Influence Effects

Very few jurisdictions require terpene testing and labeling. However, many savvy cultivators and dispensary owners pay extra for terpene potency lab testing because it helps them differentiate their products from the multitude of competing brands.

Popular "essential oils" are also terpenes. Terpenes are prized organic compounds

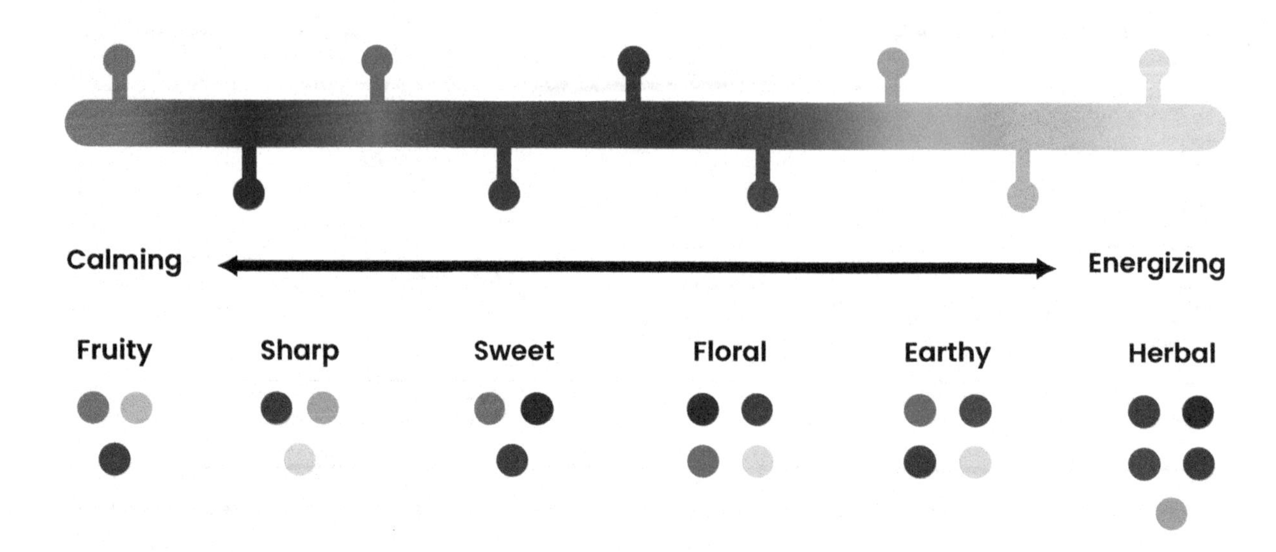

responsible for the aroma and, to a lesser extent, the flavor of a range of botanical products often identified by their smell and taste, including coffee, wine, and, of course, cannabis.

Budtenders can encourage the owners and managers of their dispensaries to push the growers and extractors they buy their products from for more lab testing of terpene content. This data is a valuable tool that helps sell products.

Know the Vendors

Until there is a universal system for tracking cultivars and quantifying their characteristics, the name on the label is not a solid enough basis to provide a recommendation. However, over time, budtenders will learn which growers produce consistent cultivars and can pass that information to customers.

Many growers maintain a cache of trusted genetics and produce and standardize their growing practices for consistency. Although the physical characteristics of the flower may still change from batch to batch, the product is relatively standard.

Most cultivators take great pride in their work, want to represent their genetics honestly, and always label their products as accurately as possible. The best way to determine whether a grower follows these principles in practice is to ask lots of questions and encourage customers to ask questions. Take every opportunity to talk to growers and learn more about their farming practices. If they value genetic fidelity, they will be happy to discuss it.

Recommending Extracts

Many extraction methods reduce flower to a single cannabinoid. For example, supercritical CO_2 extraction targets THC and strips away all or nearly all of the other compounds in the plant material, including terpenes and other cannabinoids. Sometimes these terpenes can be captured during the extraction process and re-integrated into the final product. The extractor can mix the terpenes into distillate before filling up

A vendor display at Rosemary Jane in Oakland, California. Photo by Binx Taylor.

A variety of cannabis extracts. Photo Oaksterdam Archives.

vape cartridges. This process can be costly and will not necessarily result in a product with a cannabinoid or terpene profile similar to the original plant material from which it was extracted.

Most extracted products do not contain the original plant terpenes or the full array of minor cannabinoids found in the plant. Therefore, the guidelines presented here are not useful for recommending these products, only dried cannabis flowers. The following chapter provides guidance on recommending cannabis products beyond the flower.

Many extracted products are labeled with a cultivar name. For example, a vape pen cartridge labeled Blueberry Cookies may not have been extracted from a plant called "Blueberry Cookies." The smell of blueberries and cookies associated with the cultivar may have been mimicked by including artificial terpenes. Many consumers are unaware that the terpenes found in some extracted products are synthetic or extracted from natural sources other than cannabis. However, many in-the-know consumers will demand to know if extracted products contain cannabis-derived terpenes.

There are extraction processes that preserve more of the whole plant's compounds, such as **hydrocarbon extraction** of fresh frozen cannabis that makes the popular product shatter.[406] Products produced via these processes are more likely to contain the full spectrum of cannabinoids and terpenes found in the original plant material and tend to be prized by connoisseurs in particular. Solventless extracts such as kief, hashish, and rosin are minimally processed and are most likely to contain the full spectrum. *(See Part V: Products & Methods of Ingestion).*

These full-spectrum products notwithstanding, the cultivar name should be the least important factor. Even the most dedicated extractors often have to make up new names for each batch to keep customers interested. Many extractors have to use huge quantities of cannabis to make their products and sometimes combine plant material from several (even dozens) of different cultivars to make a single extract.

So what information guides extracted product recommendations? Like flower, potency testing results for THC and CBD are on the package. If terpenes are labeled explicitly as cannabis-derived, this can also guide a recommendation but should not be the main factor. There is still not enough information about isolated terpenes and how they impact effects, and researchers are just beginning to understand their influence on the effects of whole-plant cannabis. Cultivar labeling rarely guides a consumer in purchasing an extracted product. There will always be exceptions, and many avant-garde extractors are constantly developing new methods to preserve more of the full spectrum of cannabis compounds. Some extractors also make "single-origin" extracts, suggesting that cultivar labeling might be more accurate for these products. The following section of this book breaks down how to guide customers through the world of extracted cannabis products, including vaporizers, tinctures, topicals, edibles, and more.

Part IV Review

- Cultivation techniques and processes affect the quality of the final finished flowers.
- There is no standard naming convention for cannabis varieties, so variety names are not reliable for predicting effects. Budtenders must rely on other objective information such as lab tests, farms and farming practices, and the customer's subjective experiences.
- Although the terms "indica" and "sativa" are commonly used to describe the effects of cannabis varieties as either relaxing or stimulating, they are not accurate. Nonetheless, they are still widely utilized as a general method to guide customers.

Part V

Products, Methods of Ingestion & Dosing

Lessons in Products, Methods of Ingestion & Dosing:

- Cannabis Products
- Methods of Ingestion
- Dosing Guidelines

Learning Outcomes:

- Understand how cannabis is infused, extracted, and processed into other end-use products
- Demonstrate an understanding of all methods of ingestion
- Understand the variety of products commonly available to customers and how these products vary in potency, duration, and overall effect

Photo by Terre di Cannabis via Unsplash.com.

Part V Overview

Although cannabis flowers are still the most-common end-use product, legal, commercial markets have provided an outlet for innovation, and cannabis can and is being added to just about anything, within the bounds of local regulations. The psychotropic and physiologic effects of these products vary not just due to plant variety and chemical compounds the plant produces but also by how they are ingested and processed by the body.

Cannabis is infused into tinctures, extracted into hashes, processed into cartridges for use in vaporizer "pens," added to foods, encapsulated, made into inhalers, transdermal patches, and more. Creativity and the law are the only limits.

For flowers to become byproducts, they must first be infused or extracted. Extractions are a product category with endless variety, from solventless hashes and kiefs to dabbable extracts like shatter, diamonds, badder, and more. Infusions include the butter and oils that become the base of products such as edibles, tinctures, and topicals.

Cannabis products can be vaporized, smoked, eaten, rubbed on the skin, absorbed under the tongue, and used in suppositories. Understanding how these different methods of ingestion are processed in the body to produce various effects adds a layer of complexity to how budtenders guide customers and recommend products.

How cannabis is consumed and how it is dosed often plays a more significant role than the phytochemical compounds it contains. Through concise, clear, and thoughtful communication, budtenders can help people avoid the most common adverse outcomes people experience when they consume cannabis. (*See Part III: Safety & Research*).

Cannabis Products

Humans have perfected cannabis extraction methods and practices over thousands of years. Some of these traditional methods are still widely used, but 21st-century technology and commercial legalization have resulted in an extraction renaissance that is radically reshaping the way people consume cannabis.

Extractions result in various end products with different colors, textures, consistencies, flavors, and phytochemical profiles. Some extractions are niche and connoisseur products, and some are the base for finished products made with lower-quality flowers that produce higher profit margins.

Connoisseurs will be familiar with the various products and may have more questions about companies and their production methods than the potential effects. New and naïve consumers may be looking for products that are not inhaled, and understanding how the processing alters the end product is key to making good recommendations.

Part III: The Effects of Cannabis looked at the phytochemical compounds in the resin glands (trichomes) of the leaves and flowers that produce the effects customers seek. No matter what technique or technology is used, the core goal of extraction is separating trichomes from inert plant matter. There are no magic methods for achieving this, just different applications of physical processes or organic chemistry with outcomes dictated by the process used, the skill of the extractor, and the chemical and structural idiosyncrasies of the material being extracted.

There are many ways to consume cannabis. Photo courtesy of Botaniq.

Some extraction processes, particularly the classical methods, rely solely on mechanical separation of the trichomes from the plant matter. In contrast, others largely depend on chemical interactions between the trichomes and solvents. Most contemporary methods utilize some combination of both. Product variation is generally the result of secondary and tertiary processes applied to refine and further isolate desirable compounds for a purer, more highly concentrated product.

Products & Ingestion Methods

The following chart describes the basic product categories, how they can be ingested, and the unique features or variables that differentiate products within that category.

Category	Description	Method of Ingestion	Product Differentiation
Flowers	Dried raw flowers of the cannabis plant.	Smoked or vaporized; can be juiced.	Many varieties and brands are available. Growing, drying, and curing methods alter price and end quality
Pre-Rolls	Cannabis flowers pre-ground and rolled into joints (cigarettes).	Smoked.	Size is a differentiator; pre-rolls are available from tiny (quarter gram) to large (whole gram or more). Sometimes, the tiny joints are referred to as "dog walkers" because they can be smoked quickly while taking a walk. Rolling papers and infusions of hashes or extracts also differentiate products in this category.
Extracts	Trichomes (resins) separated from plant material.	Smoked, vaporized.	Extracts vary in potency, color, texture, and how they burn or vaporize. Plant varieties and source material (flowers) quality, price, and process are also differentiators.
Vaporizer Cartridges	Extracts sold in disposable cartridges for vaporizer "pens."	Vaporized.	Quality and varieties in the source material (flowers), price, potency, and process are differentiators.
Solventless Hash	Trichomes (resins) separated from plant material using non-chemical processes such as heat, pressing, or rubbing.	Smoked, vaporized, and added to food.	Solventless hashes vary in potency, color, texture, and how they burn or vaporize. Quality and varieties of the source material (flowers), price, and process are also differentiators.
Tinctures	Plant compounds infused into glycerin, alcohol, or other edible oil sold in dropper bottles.	Taken orally under the tongue or added to food and drinks.	Quality and varieties of the source material (flowers), price, potency, and other added ingredients are differentiators.

Category	Description	Method of Ingestion	Product Differentiation
Edibles/ Ingestables	Cannabis trichomes (resins) infused into fat or extracted and added to foods and beverages.	Consumed in foods or beverages.	Types of foods or beverages, quality of other ingredients, potency and ease of dosing, price, and source material are differentiators.
Topicals	Cannabis trichomes (resins) infused into oils or extracted and added to creams, lotions, or transdermal patches.	Applied to skin.	Types of products, quality of other ingredients, potency, price, and source material are differentiators.
Clones & Seeds	Rooted starter plants (clones) and seeds.	Planted and grown at home.	Plant variety, breeder information, chemotype, and prices are differentiators. For seeds, autoflowering and feminized are also differentiators.
Hemp	Any cannabis product on this chart that tests less than 0.3% THC.	See product category.	Dispensaries may or may not carry low-THC products designated as hemp. Defer to the product category for differentiators.

From Farm to Product

Generally, all cannabis flowers leaving the farm will be trimmed, dried, and cured. There is a growing market for products that use fresh cannabis that has not been dried or cured, such as **live resin** hashes and juiced cannabis or hemp. The vast majority, however, is dried before extraction or infusion.

The two main categories of harvested cannabis are flowers and shake. **Shake** is the little buds, trim, and sometimes sugar leaf that are small enough to "shake" down to the bottom of a bag, compared with the larger, denser "flowers." Shake is often sold as "**smalls**" (little flowers), and shake may be sold directly to consumers who smoke, vaporize, or infuse them into butter at home.

Flowers and shake are extracted or infused to become other product categories. Common extraction methods include short-path distillation, hydrocarbon extraction (which uses chemical solvents), and solventless methods like sifting, pressing, and water extraction.

There is a clear distinction between extracts that are considered **solvent-free** and **solventless**. A solventless extract is produced without using any chemical solvents. The truly solventless extracts are cold water, bubble, full melt, and rosin hashes. In contrast, a solvent-free extract is produced with a hydrocarbon solvent or other chemical, such as butane or carbon dioxide (CO_2), that is later purged. **Butane hash oil (BHO)**, CO_2 oil, live resin, **shatter**, **budder**, and **wax** are examples of extracts that use a chemical solvent and are further refined through short-path distillation to become solvent-free.

Traditional Extraction Methods

Many of the earliest methods of cannabis extraction are still used to this day, with only slight refinements, because no matter what method is used, the goal of extraction is always the same: separate trichomes from plant material.

Rubbing

One of the earliest known methods of isolating active compounds from the cannabis plant that is still practiced today is rubbing to produce charas. The process involves vigorously rubbing live flowers between the hands and then scraping off the adhering resin. The slower the rubbing, the higher the quality of the charas. Some still prize charas for its unique flavor and potency, but the method for creating it is not particularly efficient and cannot be scaled up mechanically.

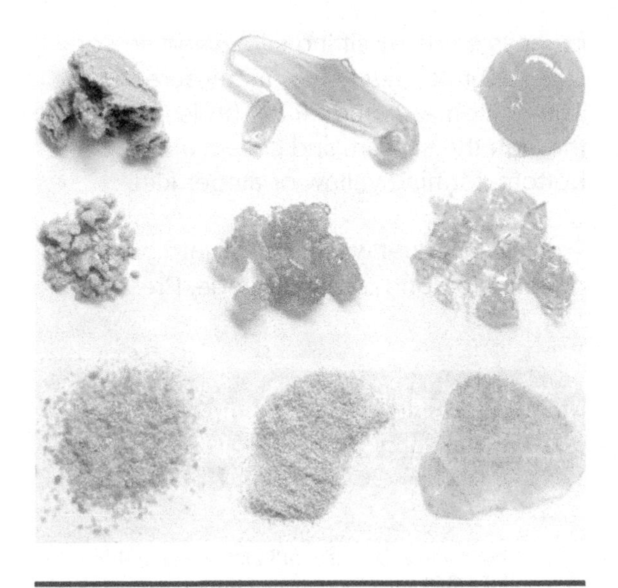

Various forms of hash. Photo Oaksterdam University Archives.

Dry Sifting

Dry sifting is an ancient extraction method that scales easily and influences the process of many contemporary extractors. The traditional approach is to stretch sheets of fabric over a bowl or basket and shake it to collect the trichomes (**kief**) that fall through the fabric. Kief is sold as is and can be added to foods, sprinkled over flower in a pipe or pre-rolled joint, and used to make further byproducts.

Today, kief is extracted using similar methods, both with handheld home devices and large-scale commercial equipment. Trichomes are usually between 70–120 microns wide, so the

What is a "live" hash?

Most hashes and extracts are produced from dried cannabis flowers. "Live" resins or rosins are made with flowers that were immediately frozen after harvesting so they can be processed in their raw state. "Fresh-frozen" cannabis extracts are prized for preserving more of the terpene profile and are thought to be more pungent.

process starts by sifting shake and flower over 120-micron mesh or metal screens. The trichomes come off the buds, pass through the screen, and collect at the bottom, forming yellow or amber kief.

Traditionally, kief was pressed into bricks or coins for longer-term storage. Pressed kief is referred to as "**hashish.**" Hashish is still the most common finished product in traditional cannabis-producing regions and is popular among connoisseurs. It is available in licensed dispensaries in some Western markets.

What is Full Extract Cannabis Oil (FECO), aka Rick Simpson Oil (RSO)?

When made correctly, **full extract cannabis oil (FECO)** is a highly-concentrated extract that includes as much of the full spectrum of phytocompounds as possible. It is thick, black, tar-like, and highly concentrated. It was popularized for use in cancer and other chronic or fatal illnesses by Canadian cancer patient Rick Simpson. Simpson popularized original methods for home production and referred to the end product as **Rick Simpson Oil (RSO)**. West Coast growers created a method to prepare the oil using food-grade alcohol solvents and referred to the resulting product as FECO.

Cannabis contains phytochemicals with anti-cancer properties, but budtenders must be aware that no formal research supports or guides its use in patients with cancer or other chronic illnesses. Nonetheless, customers tend to read about it online and seek it out in dispensaries. Budtenders should inform themselves about how the oils are produced and the source material used to help customers differentiate and discern products.

Photo by CBD Info via Unsplash.com.

Cold Water

The addition of cold temperatures makes trichome heads brittle, allowing them to snap off more easily. Because cannabinoids are not water-soluble, ice water can be used as an extraction medium while utilizing the same mechanical screening approach as dry sifting. Instead of sifting the cannabis over a screen, it is submerged in cold water and agitated. The water is drained out and filtered through a series of screens ranging in micron size. The leftover trichomes are then collected off the screens and set aside to dry. The final product is referred to as **bubble hash**. The purest bubble hashes are referred to as "**full melt**" because they do not leave behind any residues when smoked or vaporized.

For those seeking a faster, more modern approach to cold-aided sifting, dry ice can quickly separate a refined kief with little to no vegetative matter.

Alcohol Extraction & Infusion

Ethanol (alcohol) extraction was one of the earliest chemical extraction methods applied to cannabis. The process involves putting cannabis in pure grain alcohol and heating it at a relatively low temperature to emulsify the oils as the alcohol evaporates. This process leaves behind a dark viscous oil that can be smoked (though not recommended), taken orally under the tongue or in capsules, or used in cooking. This method has little to no commercial application where products intended for dabbing are concerned, but it can be useful for creating tinctures and edibles.

Cannabis can also be infused into alcohol to create a tincture. The basic process is to steep flowers and shake in enclosed bottles of alcohol in a cool, dry place for a couple of weeks or more. The plant material is strained away, and the infused alcohol is stored and dosed from dropper bottles.

Oil Infusion

One of the most popular home methods for making edibles is to infuse cannabis into butter or oil that can be added to almost any recipe. Cannabis compounds bind to fats, so they can be infused into dairy butter, ghee, coconut oil, olive oil, peanut oil, or any other edible fat through steeping, boiling, or cooking. Cannabis can be infused in liquid oil tinctures that are stored and dosed from dropper bottles or added to any recipe that calls for fat.

Contemporary Extraction Methods

Most modern commercial extraction relies on chemical solvents to separate cannabis compounds from plant matter. Solvent extraction dissolves the resin glands and carries the resulting mixture of solvent and resin away from the plant material. This process generally produces products with a purity of 75 percent or greater, and with additional refinements like distillation, potency can reach upwards of 99 percent.

Hydrocarbon Extraction

"Hydrocarbon extract" refers to extracts produced using hydrocarbon solvents such as butane, hexane, propane, or ethanol. Hydrocarbon extraction[407] is a chemical process used by other industries for decades to make products like decaffeinated coffee, vanilla extract, and other foods and cosmetics. These processes can be performed safely with proper equipment and protocols. When properly purged, the end product is free of the hydrocarbon solvent. Home or DIY production of hydrocarbon extracts is dangerous. These products should only be produced in a legal, licensed setting with well-trained staff and professional industrial equipment.

Products produced through hydrocarbon extraction include **butane hash oil** (BHO)**, ethanol hash oil** (EHO)**, and propane hash oil** (PHO). Hydrocarbon extracts are sold by the gram, half gram, or in vaporizer cartridges under various names, usually in reference to variations in processing that result in different textures, shades, and consistencies of the finished products. These names include but are not limited to wax, live resin, shatter, taffy, pull and snap, sugar, budder, and batter/badder.

Once resins have been separated from plant material, the solvent is purged off in specialized vacuum ovens. Vacuum purging involves the combination of pressure and heat to lower the temperature required to evaporate and off-gas residual solvents. This process can easily remove

Full-Spectrum vs. Isolated Extractions

There are two main classifications for extracts: full spectrum and isolates. A full spectrum product, such as full extract cannabis oil (FECO, also known as Rick Simpson Oil), contains THC and CBD and all (or most of) the cannabinoids and constituents in the plant matter. As the name implies, an isolate is just one cannabinoid isolated to effectively 100% potency, usually THC or CBD.

100 percent of all residual solvents when performed correctly. The problem is that terpenes are also technically chemical solvents, so the purging process that targets hydrocarbons can destroy the desirable aromatic profile of the extract being purged if applied too aggressively.

Hash extractors balance removing enough residual solvent to produce a safe product that meets regulatory standards while leaving enough terpenes. This balancing act between heat and pressure is always part of the purge process, but generally speaking, a higher terpene content going into the purge means a higher one in the final product. For that reason, extractors put a premium on securing "loud" material, or particularly pungent flowers, valuing the terpene profile above all else.

Live Resin

Live resin is unique because it is a type of hydrocarbon extraction that uses fresh, instead of dried, flowers. Fresh flowers yield a much higher percentage of terpenes and a more pungent smell and flavor profile. While a live resin can be turned into a distillate, the process removes the natural terpenes, which would completely waste the intense flavor profile of fresh flowers.

After harvesting, the material is immediately frozen and extracted using a system focused on maintaining cold temperatures. The relatively low temperatures help to preserve terpenes. Additional steps before the final purge, like partial purging and natural recrystallization, can create "diamonds" and other popular styles of BHO. Recrystallization can also be triggered with the addition of a secondary solvent.

Carbon Dioxide (CO_2) Extraction

CO_2 systems are generally large industrial units that use pressure to change CO_2 from a gas to a liquid state. CO_2 evaporates at room temperature and is completely non-toxic, which means products created with a CO_2 system will not require a purging process. This liquid CO_2 provides a large-scale industrial alternative to hydrocarbon solvents. CO_2 extraction is used to produce shatters, waxes, and vaporizer cartridges.

DO NOT ATTEMPT THIS AT HOME

Traditional extraction methods like sifting and pressing are safe to perform at home – hydrocarbon extraction is not. During the early 2010s, home production of hydrocarbon extracts made headlines as houses "blew up" in residential neighborhoods in the Western US. Unlike water steam, which rises into the air as it evaporates, invisible butane vapor is roughly 1.5 times heavier than air and will pool on the floor. It only takes a small spark from a nearby pilot light or electrostatic to cause an explosion. **Hydrocarbon extraction should only be performed by trained professionals using safe industrial equipment in well-ventilated legal and commercially-licensed facilities.**

Photo by Jen Theodore via Unsplash.com.

Distillation

Distillate is the most potent extract because it is nearly 100 percent pure cannabinoids. Short-path distillation strips out natural terpenes and other plant compounds and leaves a flavorless oil ideal for producing edibles without a "weed flavor." Distillate is generally easier to homogenize in a product than a cold water hash, which has a higher percentage of leftover plant matter. Manufacturers may add synthetic or naturally-occurring terpenes to the final product, particularly in vaporizer cartridges.

In terms of applications in the cannabis industry, distillation is the primary way the oil in vape pens gets produced. The primary benefit of distillation is that there is no need to secure high-quality material as long as it is cannabinoid-rich and clean. Though distillation will destroy terpenes, a process called fractional distillation removes and preserves them, to later be readded to the final product.

Rosin

The physical principle of pressing cannabis into rosin is simple: apply heat and pressure. The process begins with folding a piece of parchment paper over a flower and pressing it between a metal plate and a flat heated iron (at about 180°F/82°C) for roughly 30 to 40 seconds. The combination of pressure and heat melts the crystals off the flower and onto the paper. Once the extraction is complete, the paper is opened, and the plant material is removed and discarded. The small amount of crystals remaining is scraped off the parchment as the final product. Rosins are usually produced with dried flowers but are referred to as "live rosins" when produced with freshly-harvested flowers.

While this creates a very pure extract, provided the starting material is clean, the low yield makes it costly. Pressing rosin at higher temperatures will produce higher yields, but too high can destroy terpenes. Lowering the temperature means lower yields but will preserve more terpenes.

Rosins produced with a top-shelf flower that preserve terpene profiles are full-spectrum and are often one of the most expensive products in a dispensary. Connoisseurs will seek them out and may have more questions about how the cannabis was grown rather than how it was pressed into rosin.

End Products

These basic extraction processes form the base of all other cannabis byproducts, including foods, beverages, balms, cosmetics, transdermal patches, suppositories, and more. The following chapter breaks down how these products are consumed and how that contributes to the effects the consumer experiences.

Fresh rosin after pressing. Photo courtesy of Glass House Brands.

Methods of Ingestion

How cannabis is ingested is a significant factor in the effects it can produce. Photo by Elsa Olofsson via Unsplash.com.

Cannabis flowers produce trichomes (resinous glands) that contain the compounds that cause their effects. These compounds vary based on the plant's genetics, growing techniques, and environment. Harvested cannabis flowers are extracted or infused into various end products.

These products are consumed through various methods of ingestion: inhalation, oral ingestion (eating or drinking), under the tongue, through the skin, through suppositories inserted in the vagina or rectum, and more. These methods of ingestion play a significant role in how humans experience the effects of cannabis. (*See Part III: The Effects of Cannabis*).

While the method of ingestion is how a person consumes cannabis, the route of administration is the path the substance takes into the bloodstream. The **route of administration** influences the onset, duration, and degree of effects experienced. Not all cannabis consumed makes it into the bloodstream, and the amounts vary by ingestion method. The term "**bioavailability**" refers to the proportion of a substance that enters the bloodstream and is actively usable by the body, which affects the intensity of the effects felt.

The following chart shows how long it takes to experience the effects of different ingestion methods, how long they last, and the estimated bioavailability. The bioavailabilities are based on limited studies that found different rates, so some routes of administration show a range. Inhalation has the largest range because joints, bongs, vaporization, and other inhalation methods have different efficiencies.

Method of Ingestion	Time to Onset of Effects	Duration of Effects	Bioavailability
Inhalation	Immediate	Up to 2–3 hours	2–56%
Sublingual	10–15 minutes	Up to 2–3 hours	15–25%
Oral Ingestion	30 minutes–2 hours	4–8 hours or more	4–20%
Topical/ Transdermal	Immediate	Up to 2 hours	Unknown
Suppository	10–15 minutes	Up to 4 hours	13.50%

Each method of ingestion has advantages or disadvantages, depending on the consumer's goals. Determining the suitable method of ingestion is key to making good product decisions, especially for new consumers.

Inhalation

Photo by Grav via Unsplash.com.

The most common form of consumption is inhalation through smoking (**combustion**) or vaporization. The effects of inhaled cannabis are experienced quickly, sometimes immediately, allowing the consumer to "**titrate**" a dose better. Titration is a method of determining the ideal dose by consuming a tiny amount and waiting to experience the effects. The rapid onset of effects from inhalation makes consuming too much at once more difficult. For connoisseurs, inhalation is also the best way to experience the unique flavors of different cannabis varieties.

The distinction that separates smoke from vapor is the presence of combustion. For there to be smoke, there must be fire or at least enough heat to cause something to burn. Vaporization devices create heat to convert cannabinoids and terpenes into inhalable vapors without burning. Vaporization is associated with peak cannabinoid plasma levels, which refers to the concentration of cannabinoids in the blood.

Current Product Category Trends & Statistics

New Frontier Data provides insights on cannabis consumers and dispensary customers in yearly reports. The key takeaway from their 2022 report[408] is that customers seek specific effects when they shop for cannabis— and often both medical and adult use customers seek the same ones. New Frontier concludes, "While some crowdsourced platforms have collected input from thousands of consumers about the effects produced by different strains and products, the scientific jury remains out about how accurate effect-based outcomes are, and how much they may differ between consumers. That highlights another area where much more research is needed to effectively guide consumers to the types of experiences that they are seeking, and the opportunity for more consumer education regarding the effects typically created by different types of cannabinoids."

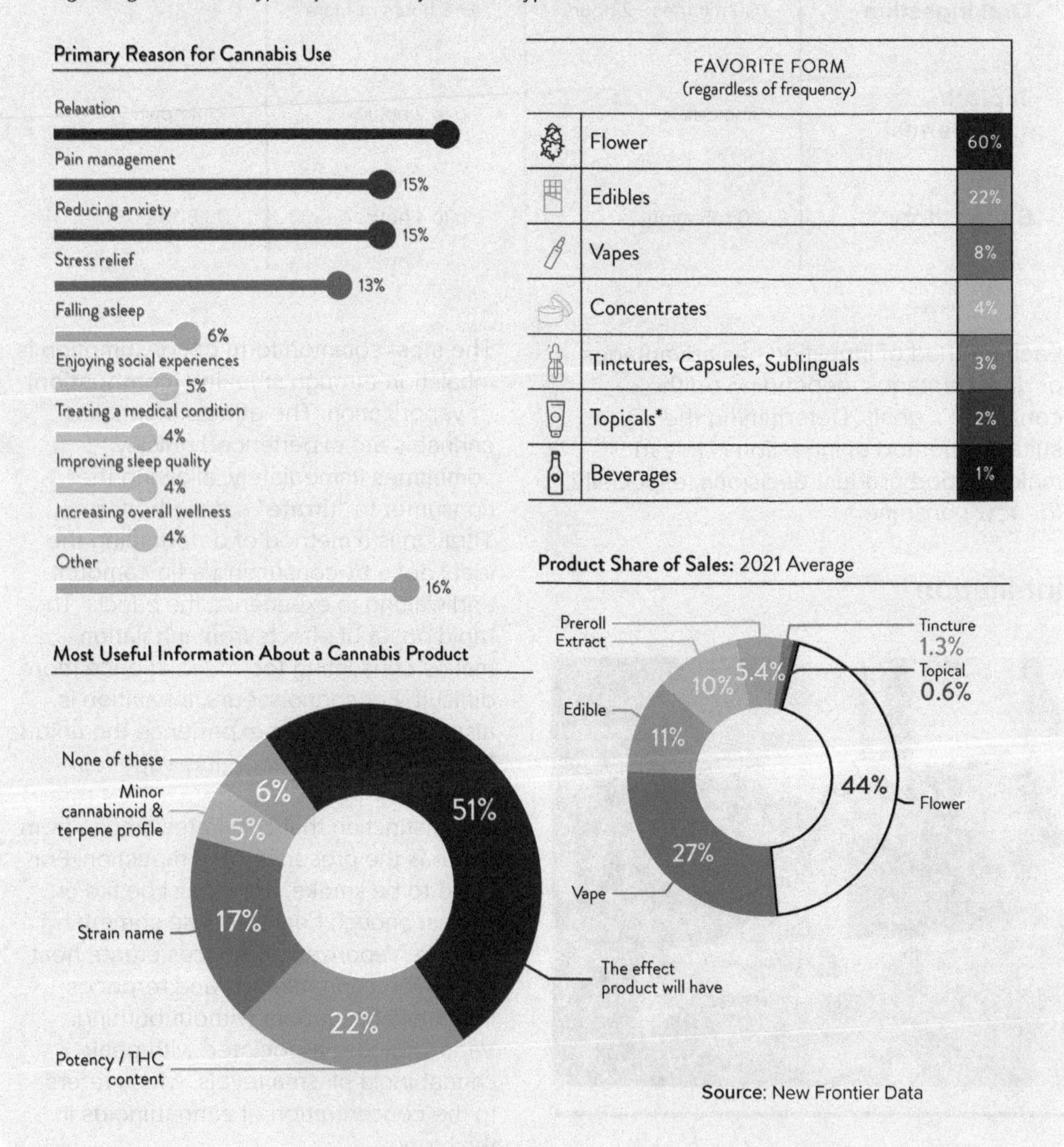

Source: New Frontier Data

Some cannabis consumers do not want to inhale anything. In particular, new consumers may be averse to smoking or vaporization, which presents a dosing challenge. The budtender's job is not to convince new consumers to inhale but to provide helpful guidance with clear information about ingestion methods and dosage to help them avoid a negative experience.

A pipe with a carburetor. Photo by Grav via Unsplash.com.

Smoking (Combustion)

Dried flowers and extracts can be smoked. Various devices are used for smoking, including joints, blunts, pipes, and bongs. Both smoking and vaporization result in a relatively short duration of drug effect, approximately two to three hours, with acute effects lasting no more than 20 to 40 minutes.

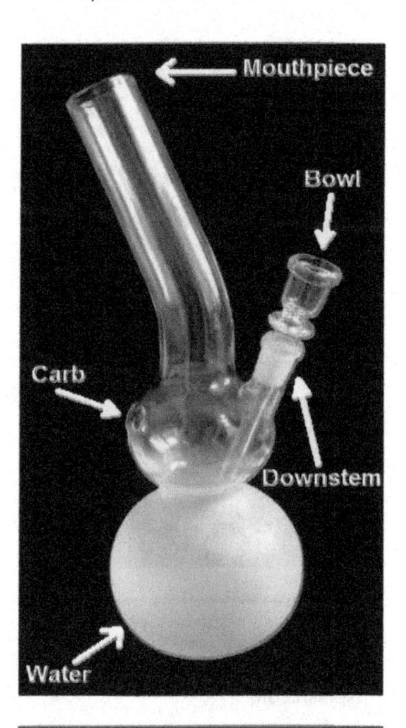

A bong. Photo Oaksterdam Archives.

A joint, or pre-roll (as they are referred to in most dispensaries), is ground cannabis flower rolled in cigarette paper (which can be made from hemp, rice paper, or numerous other materials). A blunt is more like a cigar and is traditionally rolled using a cigar/cigarillo, tobacco-based wrap, but numerous tobacco-free options exist. Blunts tend to be larger than pre-rolls because of the wraps used. Tobacco is federally regulated in the US, so tobacco-based blunts are not sold in dispensaries. However, consumers may buy cannabis flowers and roll them in tobacco papers when they leave the dispensary.

A pipe is made of three primary parts:

- the bowl (where cannabis is packed)
- the stem (the hollowed portion which contains the smoke path)
- the mouthpiece (where the consumer places their mouth and inhales smoke)

Pre-rolled joints. Photo by Elsa Olofsson via Unsplash.com.

Pipes generally do not contain any features to cool the smoke and heated air, but they can contain chambers filled with water to cool down and filter the smoke. If they do, they are called water pipes. A free-standing, larger water pipe is usually called a bong.

Though water cools down and filters the smoke inhalation, it does not mitigate exposure to unwanted carcinogens.

A vaporizer "pen," or cartridge and battery. Photo by Elsa Olofsson via Unsplash.com.

Temperature-controlled electric "dab" rig. Photo by Patrick Slade via Unsplash.com.

A dab rig. Photo by Cannabox via Unsplash.com.

For that reason, some pipes and bongs feature what is known as a carburetor (or "carb"), which allows air to be mixed into the smoke, cooling it further as it is inhaled. A carb on a pipe is usually just a hole on the side covered with a finger. On bongs, carbs also can be a hole on the side of the device, but more commonly, the down stem (where the bowl is) can be removed to act as a carb.

Combustive smoke may cause temporary cough and throat irritation. Long-term inhalation (of anything) has been associated with higher odds of adverse respiratory effects, such as bronchitis.[409] By contrast, even long-term cannabis smoke exposure has not been conclusively associated[410] with many of the significant adverse effects associated with tobacco smoking, such as lung cancer, emphysema, or reduced pulmonary function.

Vaporization

In contrast with combustion, vaporizing flower limits the intake of respiratory toxins. The flower material is heated to a temperature where vapors form but remain below the point of combustion. Clinical trials assessing the safety and efficacy of vaporization as a cannabinoid delivery device have determined[411] it to be "safe and effective."

Like the inhalation of smoke, vaporization results in the rapid onset of drug effects, the key difference is that vaporized cannabis becomes more bioavailable,[412] likely because combustion results in the loss of cannabinoids via the production of side-stream smoke.

Vaporization is increasingly popular due to technological innovations such as tabletop or portable vaporizers, dab rigs, and vaporizer "pens." Dried flowers and extracts can be vaporized.

While cannabis vaporizers and cartridge devices are popularly referred to as "vape pens," evidence shows[413] that in many cases, combustion still occurs around the heating element in the cartridge. Overall, research shows[414] vaporization as a much healthier alternative to smoking cannabis. It is crucial to ensure the device is vaporizing the cannabis rather than overheating and combusting it. In addition to being healthier than smoking, vaping cannabis appears to be more efficient,[415] which means that consumers will need to ingest less than they would if they were smoking the same product.

Does "holding it in" result in more bioavailability?

A common myth in the cannabis culture is that holding in smoke or vapor as long as possible will make the effects more potent. This is not true and is unsafe. Research suggests that more puffs will make the consumer "higher" but that "holding it in" will not.[416,417,418] Other techniques can be used to take deeper breaths that allow more compounds to be absorbed through inhalation.

Topical & Transdermal

Topical cannabis products (lotions, balms, oils, tinctures) are applied or rubbed into the skin's surface. These products generally do not pass into the blood, meaning that THC-based topicals should not cause a psychotropic effect or appear on drug tests. However, some products are actually "transdermal," meaning they pass through the skin into the bloodstream, are psychotropic, and will appear on a drug test.

Topicals are the safest method to use at higher doses because they have difficulty passing through the skin[419] into the blood. The bioavailability of topicals is unknown, and there is minimal risk of a psychotropic effect. Anecdotal research shows that even if products include THC, they should not have any psychotropic effects nor be detectable on drug tests. Anecdotes are not science. If someone faces a drug test, they are best advised not to ingest or apply any cannabis or hemp products beforehand, as a minor amount of THC can cause them to fail.

Although most products applied to the skin will be "topicals," there are "transdermal" products that pass through the skin and cause psychotropic effects. Transdermal products use various technologies,[420] usually a chemical "carrier," to pass through the skin into the bloodstream. The most common transdermal products in dispensaries are skin patches. Transdermal

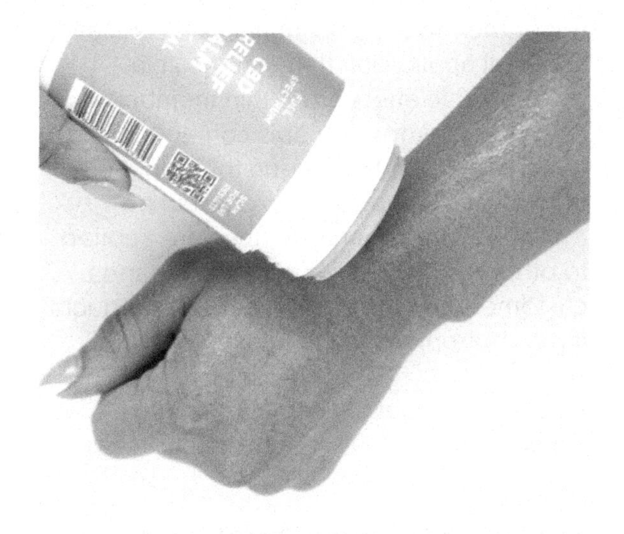

Topical cannabis balm. Photo by Elsa Olofsson via Unsplash.com.

patches release small amounts of cannabinoids into the bloodstream over an extended period and may be a good option for customers looking for constant and consistent low doses. They can easily be cut in half or quarters for smaller doses.

Two growing uses of topical products are improving sexual health[421] and heightening erogenous sensitivity. Though research is limited, anecdotal reports and preliminary studies[422] indicate that cannabis use can increase sexual pleasure. It is important to note that virtually every cannabis lube on the market is unsafe to use with latex condoms. Cannabinoids are lipophilic and hydrophobic, meaning they bind to fat but not water. Almost all cannabis lubes are oil-based, and it is well-known that oil, even natural oils like coconut oil, will dissolve latex condoms.[423] Using oil-based lubes causes condoms to break, increasing the risk of pregnancy and the transmission of STIs and STDs. A final consideration is whether the product may cross through the skin and become transdermal. For instance, taking a tincture under the tongue (sublingual) is technically a topical application that can result in psychotropic effects. The thin membranes make it easier for cannabis compounds to absorb under the tongue through the bloodstream, and the same should be assumed when cannabis lubes are applied to other similarly thin mucus membranes. A customer may wish to avoid these products if psychotropicity is a concern.

Before rubbing a topical product into a sensitive area, like a mucus membrane or open wound, always check the ingredients to ensure they are free of alcohol and other ingredients that could cause irritation.

Sublingual

When consumed sublingually (under the tongue), cannabinoids are absorbed into the mouth's mucous membranes and enter the bloodstream more quickly than when consumed orally (eaten). Even when the product is not swallowed, a small amount will still be ingested, although it is usually not enough to have an impact.

Tinctures and other sublingual products may be a good option for consumers who do not want to inhale but also want better control over dosing. Potency should be labeled on the product so that dosage can be measured by the drop, and tiny amounts can be consumed before raising the dose.

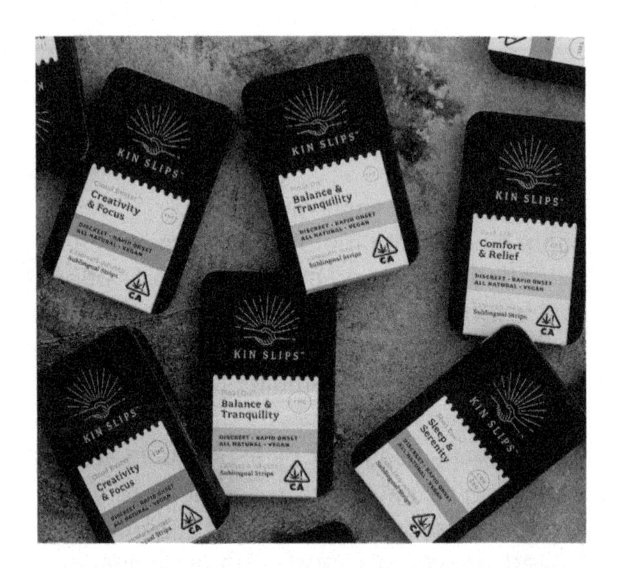

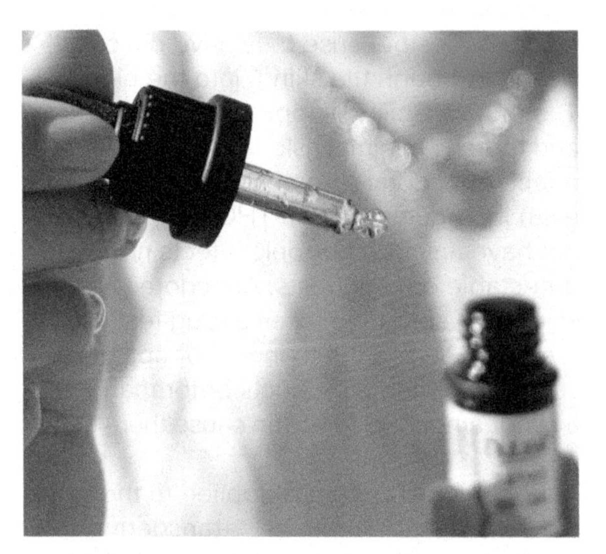

(Left) Sublingual strips. Photo courtesy of Kin Slips. (Right) Cannabis tincture. Photo by Elsa Olofsson via Unsplash.com.

Oral Ingestion

Edibles produce more intense effects than any other ingestion method. Similar edibles of similar potencies may yield varying effects from person to person, based on the individual's unique metabolism. When Δ^9-THC is orally consumed, it passes through the liver and converts to 11-hydroxy-THC, which is far more potent. It is crucial to start with low doses when eating edibles to avoid negative experiences.

The cannabis products ingested most frequently are edibles, closely followed by the growing market for cannabis-infused beverages. Tinctures also may be ingested as an addition to meals or drinks or swallowed (as opposed to sublingual absorption). It is also possible, although uncommon, to eat a cannabis extract[424] that has not been infused into a food or drink and feel some effects. However, psychotropic effects will not be experienced unless the extract is decarboxylated.

Determining the ideal dosage with edibles is more difficult because metabolism varies from one person to the next and even one day to the next. Different sources say that edibles can have a stronger or weaker effect depending on how much reaches the stomach. However, the scientific literature is limited[425] and unclear to what degree it matters. A good starting dose is between five and ten milligrams for most people. People with more body mass generally need more THC to feel the same effects. Older individuals and those with smaller frames tend to be more sensitive to THC, even with doses as small as 2.5 mg of THC, and should start with smaller doses. For more notification about starting with small doses, see the following chapter, *Dosing Guidelines*.

Edibles. Photo by Jeff W via Unsplash.com

Recommended Reading

Aunt Sandy's Medical Marijuana Cookbook by Sandy Moriarty

"Aunt Sandy" Moriarty was Oaksterdam University's original edibles instructor. This book includes her famed 10x cannabutter recipe, known for its strength and lack of grassy flavor. In the early days of Oaksterdam, around 2007 to 2010, Sandy's delicious lemon bars were one of the most popular edibles in downtown Oakland dispensaries.
That delicious recipe and 40 more are included.

THC Bioavailability of Edible Cannabis

This chart shows that oral ingestion produces a much different THC blood profile than smoking. Instead of peaking rapidly in the first few minutes and then quickly declining, it has a gradual rise, and a milder plateau reached hours later. In chronic consumers, detectable amounts of THC in the blood can persist for days.

Not shown in the chart is 11-hydroxy-THC. While not detectable at appreciable levels in smoked marijuana, 11-hydroxy-THC shows a similar blood profile to THC after oral consumption. The presence of 11-hydroxy-THC may therefore be used as an indicator of recent oral use in drug testing, although most blood tests do not bother to check for it. (*See Part III: The Effects of Cannabis*).

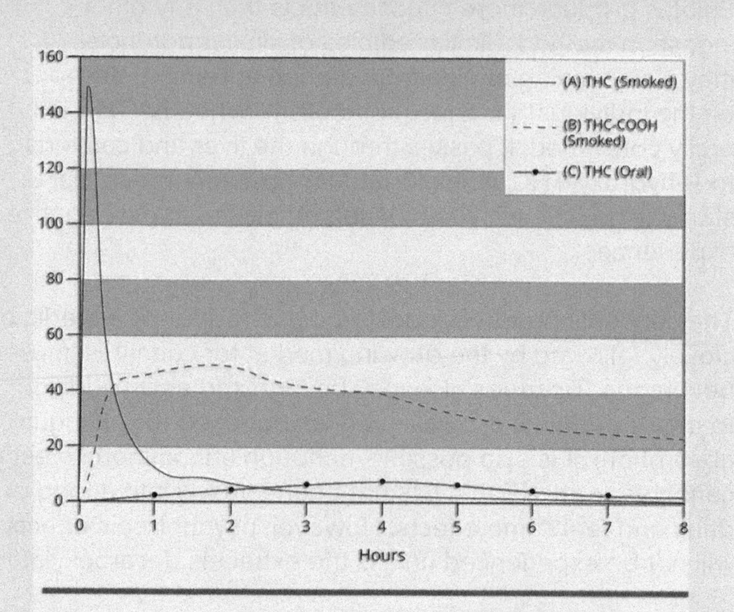

(A-B) Smoked dose based on data from M. Huestis, J. Henningfield, and E. Cone. (C) Oral dose based on data from B. Law et al.

Suppositories (Rectal & Vaginal)

Suppositories are cannabis-infused solidified oils molded for easy insertion in the rectum or vagina. There is very little research on cannabis suppositories, but many people swear by them for various reasons. The primary reason a person would choose to use a suppository is to apply cannabis directly to the area of concern. Another reason may be the perception that the psychotropic effects are milder. Always follow the manufacturer's recommendations when using suppository products.

Dosing Guidelines

Before exiting a pharmacy with prescription medicine, a pharmacist will provide detailed information on the drug, its effects, side effects, dosing regimen, and what to do if too much is ingested or specific side effects are experienced.

Unfortunately, because cannabis is a Schedule I controlled substance, it cannot be prescribed, and proper research and trials have not been conducted to guide doctors in dosage regimens to treat specific conditions or illnesses.

Fortunately, cannabis does not cause lethal overdose in humans, regardless of dose or potency. As the US Drug Enforcement Administration acknowledged,[426] "No deaths from overdose of marijuana have [ever] been reported."

Moreover, cannabis and cannabinoids generally lack the acute toxicity associated with many other medications. As a result, many experts, including a former DEA administrative law judge,[427] have said that cannabis possesses an exceptionally unique safety profile relative to many conventional medications. However, consuming too much cannabis can result in paranoia and anxiety, among other side effects. Dosing guidelines for flower and infused products are still valuable and necessary. Like conventional medications, cannabis possesses a therapeutic window — too small of a dose will fail to produce the desired effect, and too large a dose could produce undesired effects. Like other psychotropic agents, cannabinoids can potentially trigger certain adverse events — particularly in higher-risk populations. Therefore, budtenders should understand the general principles of dosing and best practices for providing guidance.

For more information about cannabis overdose, side effects, and higher-risk populations, *See Part III: Safety & Research.*

Titration

Because of the diversity of products available and the range of reactions different people have to cannabis products, the best guideline for dosing is to **titrate.** Titrating the dose means starting with minimal amounts of THC

INFORMATION FOR HEALTH CARE PROFESSIONALS

Canada

Health Canada's Information for Health Care Professionals: Cannabis and Cannabinoids – Dosing (2018)[428]

Cannabis has been legal for medical purposes in Canada since 2001. Health Canada provides formalized dosing guidelines to health care professionals.

Research: Dosing Medical Marijuana – Rational Guidelines from Washington State (2007)[429]

Drs. Sunil Aggarwal, Muraco Kyashna-Tocha and Gregory Carter examine dosing considerations for medical cannabis.

and waiting to gauge the effects before adjusting the dose up or down. This approach requires a cannabis consumer to take control of the experience rather than relying on a dosage regimen.

Titration is typical in herbalism and accounts for variations in herbal plant formulations and the inconsistency of effects experienced by different people or even the same person at different times. One of the most common forms of titration is salting food to taste. More salt can be added but not removed, so people generally sprinkle a small amount on their food and taste it before adding more.

How to Dose THC: Start Low and Go Slow

- Dosing THC can be challenging, especially with oral ingestion and edibles.
- Begin with a low dose and slowly raise it until desired effects are reached.
- Trial and error is required, with errors possibly resulting in feelings of dysphoria

THC Dose	Inexperienced	Casual	Experienced
Starter	2.5—5 mg	5—7.5 mg	7.5—10 mg
Regular	5—7.5 mg	7.5—10 mg	10—15 mg
Strong	7.5—10 mg	10—15 mg	15—20 mg

Starting dosage is based on experience and desired effects.

Titration Waiting Periods by Product

Product	Dosage	Waiting Period
Inhaled flowers	One short puff	5—10 minutes
Extracts	A dab the size of half a grain of rice or smaller	5—10 minutes
Edibles	2.5—10 mg of THC, depending on experience, tolerance, and desired effects	90 minutes

Product	Dosage	Waiting Period
Sublingual	1 drop	45 minutes
Topical/ Transdermal	Patch-test the product on a small area of skin before applying further	Follow the manufacturers instructions

How to Talk About Dosage

A prescription is a document written by a medical doctor that includes formal instructions for the use of a drug. Cannabis is a Schedule I drug and cannot be prescribed for medical treatment, even in states where cannabis is available for medical use. Instead, a doctor can "recommend" it. Unlike a prescription, a recommendation does not prescribe how to use or dose cannabis.

Doctors can give their patients dosing guidance for disease treatment or management, but budtenders should not. Budtenders are not "stand-ins" for medical professionals. They cannot act as physicians or pharmacists. The budtender should never suggest that cannabis "treats" anything or purport to have a regimen or dosing guideline to treat conditions with cannabis products. However, a budtender should be well informed about how dosing affects customers' experiences and provide detailed titration information to help them avoid adverse effects.

> *Budtenders cannot provide medical advice and should clearly and politely state this when asked.*

In some regions,[430] a medical professional such as a pharmacist must be on a dispensary's staff. In those jurisdictions, dosage questions concerning disease treatment or management should be deferred to them. In other regions, regulations may limit the communications budtenders may or may not engage in with a customer.

Even if customers seek it, budtenders cannot provide medical advice and should clearly and politely state this when asked. The budtender's role is to provide customers with education and a basic understanding of the products they sell. The goal is to help customers find what meets their needs, including providing information about the potency of products and how to titrate them to produce desired effects and avoid negative experiences. When it comes to botanical products and herbs that are not FDA-approved and have not been through clinical trials, customers must be provided with as much verifiable information as possible to make informed decisions. They usually cannot be provided with the specific dosing regimens they may seek.

Customers often turn to budtenders with medical questions because they cannot find answers elsewhere. They have heard or read about cannabis use for the conditions they are dealing with and seek as much guidance as possible before trying it and are unlikely to get help from their primary care providers.

Most medical institutions fail to provide any formal instruction on the topic. For example, a 2015 survey[431] of pharmacy students found that most had received no cannabis-specific education during their training, and the majority "lacked accurate knowledge about the approved therapeutic indications and adverse effects of medical marijuana."

A 2019 survey[432] of medical students reported that only 2% of respondents believed they had received "a sufficient amount" of formal education on medical cannabis during their undergraduate classes. As a result, most surveyed said that they were "not at all prepared" to discuss issues regarding the potential benefits and risks with patients.

Although medical cannabis has been legal nationwide in Canada since 2001, a survey[433] of Canadian nurse practitioners published in 2018 reported that most possessed "a low level of knowledge" about its use for therapeutic purposes. Only one-quarter of respondents acknowledged having initiated a conversation with their patients. Nurses self-reported having the least knowledge about issues specific to dosing and creating effective treatment plans.

A 2020 survey[434] of Canadian physicians-in-training similarly reported that "the average amount of training received was less than 25% of the amount desired, and more than three-quarters of trainees reported that further training would be required in order for them to engage comfortably with CTP [cannabis for therapeutic purposes]." Respondents said that their most significant knowledge gaps were specific to issues surrounding cannabis dosing and its risk-benefit profile.

In the US, few medical schools include cannabis-specific curricula, even in states that allow medicinal use. Although regulations in some states require physicians to receive some formal training in cannabis before they are licensed to make recommendations, these trainings are typically very short in duration — just two to four hours.

Most regions do not require physicians to receive cannabis training. Even doctors who specialize in providing recommendations may still be reluctant to engage in more comprehensive conversations with their patients, particularly regarding the creation of treatment plans.

Primary care physicians may be actively discouraged from speaking to their patients about cannabis use. Often this occurs within a large health maintenance organization (HMO). The failure in communication results from administrators' political decisions rather than individual doctors' personal choices.

Absent sound advice from professionals, many customers, especially those with serious and chronic illnesses, turn to the internet for answers. While credible sources such as PubMed[435] provide objective, peer-reviewed research, the internet also is home to numerous sites and social networks peddling false, misleading, or unsubstantiated information.

Some sites may be purposely biased against cannabis, including certain government-sponsored websites like DEA.gov. Others may be administered by those with little expertise in the field. Still others, such as many websites touting the therapeutic prowess of commercially available CBD products, may be fronts for commercial enterprises seeking to influence visitors to purchase their line of products. As a result, customers often read inaccurate or contradictory information about cannabis. It can be challenging to discern what is and is not legitimate.

Of course, there are some reliable sources of information. In addition to PubMed, some websites worth reviewing include NORML.org, the International Association of Cannabinoid Medicines,[436] and the University of California Center for Medicinal Cannabis Research.[437]

Even if the customer has stumbled upon a reputable online source, their visit to the dispensary may be their first face-to-face communication about their cannabis use or desire to consume. Even in legal jurisdictions, longstanding cultural stigmas surrounding cannabis continue to exist, making many people reluctant to talk about it, even with trusted friends and family.

The Therapeutic Window

Like other therapeutic agents, cannabis has a "therapeutic window," meaning its effects are consistent with specific doses. Doses above this therapeutic window may be more likely to trigger adverse side effects, thus offsetting their efficacy and utility. Doses below this therapeutic threshold are described as "sub-therapeutic" and may provide little to no substantial relief. An exception to this rule is the concurrent administration of sub-therapeutic doses of cannabinoids and opioids, which are documented to have synergistic therapeutic effects — even at low doses (*See Part III: Safety & Research*).

Although there are no clinical trials on whole-plant cannabis that can guide the dosage of therapeutic uses, THC and CBD are FDA-approved and have been clinically tested. Dronabinol is a pure synthetic THC suspended in sesame oil and is a Schedule III drug approved to treat anorexia, cachexia, and cancer-associated nausea. It is dosed in capsules measured in milligrams (e.g., 2.5 mg, 5 mg, and 10 mg) and has set dosing guidelines[438] in accordance with its therapeutic window. Epidolex is an FDA-approved CBD formulation consisting primarily of whole-plant CBD extracts and comes with manufacturers' dosing guidelines.[439] The FDA has approved both of these drugs to treat specific conditions. For patients seeking oral or edible cannabis products for these specific conditions, the drug manufacturers' dosing guidelines may provide some initial guidance the budtender cannot.

There is very little explicit guidance on the therapeutic window of inhaled cannabis. As a result, patients will likely need to initially experiment with self-titration — utilizing the "start low and go slow" principle — until settling on an ideal dose. If a patient eventually becomes tolerant to this dose, it can be titrated up, or new ingestion methods or varieties could be tested.

When patients have ceased using cannabis for some time, they may need to re-initiate their exposure with a lower dose.

Self-titration is not a practice unique to cannabis. Asthma patients engage in a similar practice of self-titrating their medicine either following or just prior to the onset of an attack. In such cases, a patient does not necessarily consume a one-size-fits-all dose. Instead, they ingest whatever quantity they deem necessary based on the circumstances. This same principle generally applies to patients who

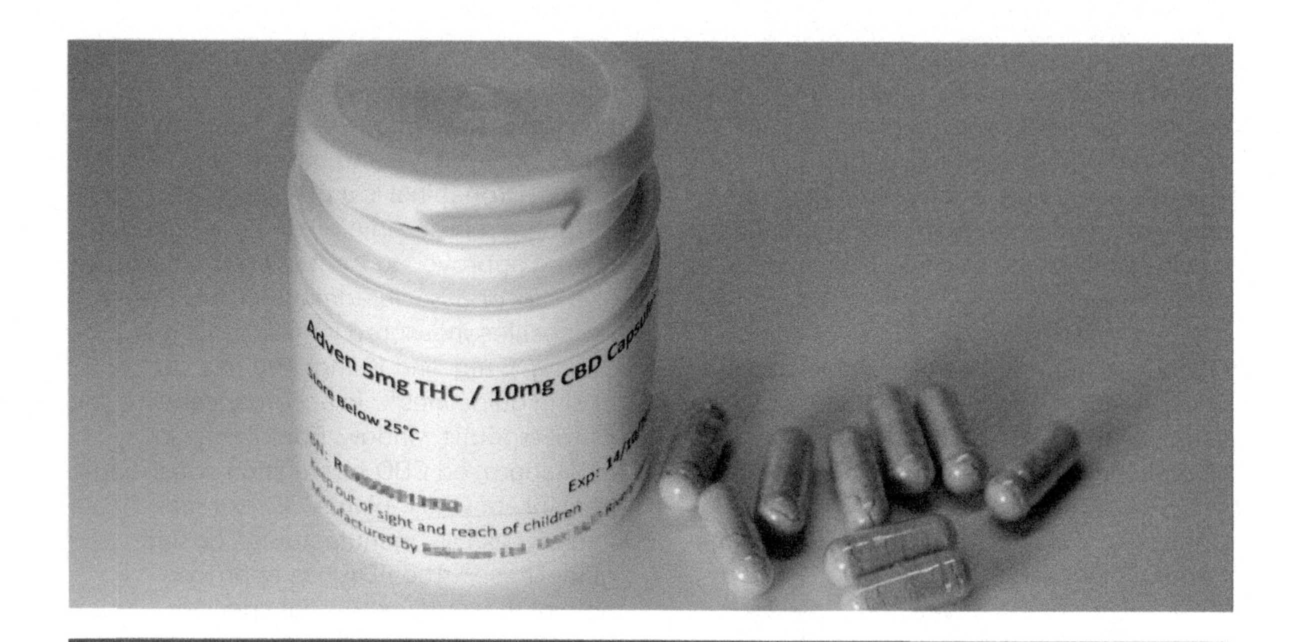

Products are labeled to show their potency, which budtenders can use to help guide guide titration. Photo by Stephen Cobb via Unsplash.com

inhale cannabis to obtain the rapid onset of symptom relief, such as those suffering from episodic migraines or spasms.

Some experts espouse[440] the potential benefits of "microdosing," the practice of ingesting small doses of cannabinoids to experience beneficial health effects but not cause mood alteration. However, the efficacy of this specific practice is not substantiated in the clinical literature.

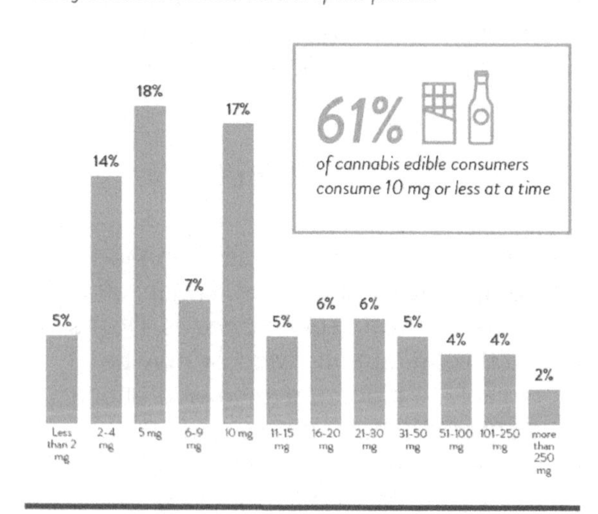

Source: New Frontier Data, "Rethinking Cannabis Potency: Are Low Dose Products the Appropriate Choice for Most Consumers? - 2023

Part V Review

- Although dried cannabis flowers are still the most popular product in dispensaries, cannabis and its compounds can be extracted and added to a wide variety of byproducts, including hashes, tinctures, foods, topical balms, cosmetics, suppositories, and more.
- How cannabis is consumed — whether inhaled, consumed orally, or rubbed into the skin — plays a significant role in how people experience its effects.
- Dosing herbal products is not an exact science. Consumers must "titrate" dosage, meaning they start by consuming minimal amounts and wait to feel the effects before deciding whether to take more.

Part VI

Customer Service

Lessons in Customer Service

Learning Outcomes:

- Recognize the spectrum of customers' knowledge and experience and identify ways to adjust service to accommodate needs
- Recognize the budtender's importance in the customer's experience and the limitations of their ability to provide information and guidance

Photo Courtesy of Green House, Walled Lake Michigan.

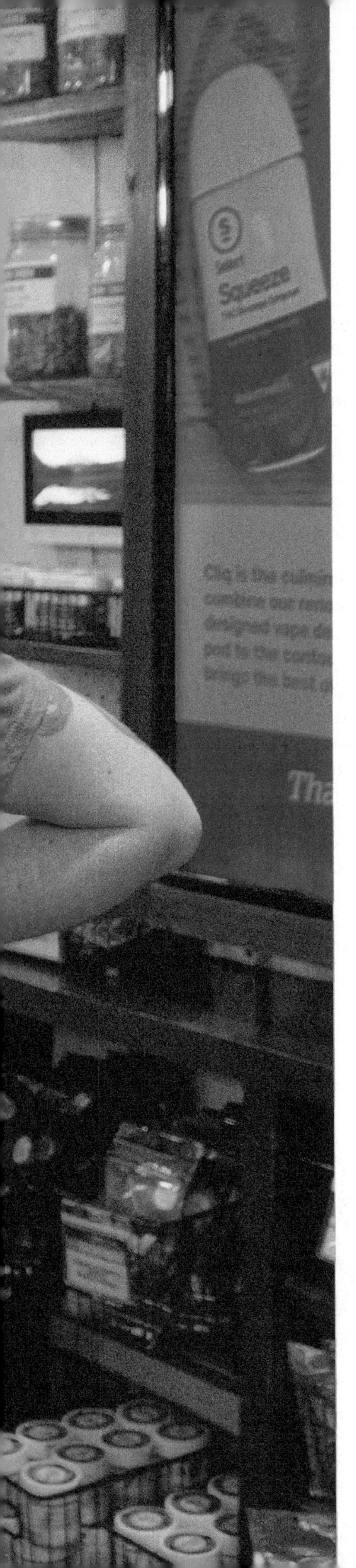

Part VI Overview

This section outlines techniques a budtender can use to gauge customers' experience level and presents strategies for engaging with the diverse mix of customers; those who know what they want, those who need lots of help, and those who are downright difficult.

Finally, all of the information from previous sections of this book — the history, policy, science, horticulture, and product manufacturing practices — comes together to inform personalized interactions with customers that lead to positive experiences. Budtenders are the face and voice of the dispensary and the cannabis industry. There is not one correct way to meet everyone's needs, and intuition and the ability to adapt to the service the customer wants and needs are vital skills.

Customer Service

Budtenders should act as if they are on stage when customers are present. This means staying focused on customers' needs and not distracted by texting or personal conversations. Customers remember when staff does not prioritize them, negatively impacting the reputation of the budtender and the dispensary. Positive, personalized interactions translate into happy repeat customers more likely to recommend the dispensary. Some customers become fiercely loyal to budtenders who provide personalized service and make good recommendations.

One of the key differences between budtending and bartending is the paramount importance of customer anonymity. Budtenders are exposed to more personal information than many other customer service jobs. Although federal US HIPAA healthcare privacy regulations do not technically bind a budtender, budtenders should know the basics and follow them. Many customers may still be hiding their cannabis use at work or home, and budtenders must be careful not to expose them as this may be detrimental to their employment, child custody, or living situation. For some customers, being outed as a cannabis consumer could get them fired or kicked out of their homes, particularly if they work for the government or live in federally-subsidized housing.

Budtenders should try to smile and be as pleasant and welcoming as possible, especially when dealing with demanding customers. They also must take the initiative to ask the right questions and have the intuition to quickly assess what level of interaction the customer wants. The budtender must meet customers where they are, meaning they can identify the customer's needs and expectations and provide the proper depth of information to help them make their own informed decisions. They should be helpful and informative when the customer indicates they need it and avoid speaking over customers' heads or coming off as pretentious.

Identifying Customer Needs & Expectations

Customers are likely to have plenty of questions about what types of cannabis products are most appropriate for them. In order to best gain a sense of their needs and expectations, the budtender should have several key questions for them too. No two customers are alike, so conversations about effects and dosing should not be "one size fits all."

A visit to the dispensary may be many customers' first exposure to products

Photo Courtesy of Glass House Brands.

beyond dried cannabis flowers, and they may feel intimidated or overwhelmed. As a result, they may be reluctant to ask basic questions and make rash or uninformed choices because they presume their inexperience will be looked upon unfavorably by either the staff or others waiting in line. The budtender's demeanor should put customers at ease and allay this concern.

Use an open-ended question to quickly gather information about the customer and customize an approach to helping them. Open-ended questions require a longer or more detailed response than "yes" or "no." The most important thing to determine is the customer's experience level. Asking a neutral open-ended question like "what are you looking for today?" may be enough for the customer to volunteer their level of comfort and experience with cannabis.

Budtenders should be most proactive and helpful with people who have never used cannabis or had very few experiences with it, perhaps only negative ones. Once it is determined that the customer is new, novice, or needs extra guidance, it helps to follow up with closed-ended questions to get a clearer picture.

Some of these follow-up questions may include the following:

- *"Is this your first time visiting a cannabis dispensary?"*
- *"When was the last time you consumed a cannabis product?"*
- *"How familiar are you with products, and how their effects differ from flower?"*

If the customer has not been to a dispensary before, or has not consumed cannabis in many years, he or she may be under the false assumption that all of the different varieties of flower are alike or that all cannabis is smoked in joints. If so, then it is the budtender's responsibility to explain how different forms of cannabis and methods of ingestion yield distinctively different effects.

Adult vs. Medical Use

In most regions, an "adult use" customer can be anyone over the age of 21. Customers who shop in adult use (aka "recreational") dispensaries are incredibly diverse, and some may actually seek the therapeutic effects of cannabis. Budtenders should never make assumptions about customers and let them say what they are looking for and why they are using cannabis. Many adult use dispensaries also serve customers with medical recommendations.

Budtender Interview

"A lot of activists have been saying for years that all use is medicinal. Even if someone is just coming into an adult use dispensary because they want to smoke weed to 'get high.' Guess what? It will still work as an anti-inflammatory, an antidepressant, and a stress reliever. There is no detaching those medical effects from it just because they are there to 'get high.' And if you think about it, what is 'getting high?' The implication is that you are feeling low. You are not feeling high. So maybe that is another way of saying they are a little bit depressed, a little bit stressed, they are under the weather in some way mentally, and need this to level out. That is medicinal use right there."

— **Mitchell Colbert**, former budtender and Oaksterdam University instructor, Oakland, California

Their experience level and understanding of products and effects may be more relevant to the interaction than the "medical" distinction. Experienced cannabis consumers will have more questions about how plants were grown, how products were processed, and the companies that produced them. Some customers may have no questions and already know exactly what they want. Some may not even know where to start asking questions, and budtenders need to be prepared to take the most initiative in helping these customers.

How Reymon Brown Makes New Customers Feel Comfortable

Reymon Brown has always loved cannabis and wanted to parlay it into a career. He decided to pursue a budtending job to get a crash course in the business as he explores the possibility of getting into the ownership side through a social equity program.

As a budtender, he strives to develop relationships with customers. His style has earned him the Oaksterdam Community Advocacy Award, which "recognizes the budtender who is educated on the history of prohibition and works to ensure that everyone has the right to safe, legal access to medicinal and adult use cannabis. This budtender goes over and above, in words and actions, to educate and advocate for patients, consumers, and the community." Due to Reymon's style, customers often wait longer to be helped by him, and he has developed a following.

"I can ease people over that hump of anxiety when they walk through the door. One of the first things I do when someone is visibly nervous is say, 'First things first. Take a deep breath. Breathe in, breathe out. You are about to buy some weed.' This always makes them laugh and start to relax."

From there, he starts with an easy, open-ended question, "What are you looking for?" If the customer is still unsure, he asks what sort of ingestion method they are interested in, followed by whether or not they plan to consume during the day or at night. At this point, they open up and provide more insight into how they feel and would like to feel.

He is cautious not to try to push products but instead find what works for the customer's goals. He believes that if a customer has a positive outcome, they will be loyal repeat customers, which is more valuable than a one-time sale.

Reymon Brown, budtender in Amesbury, Massachusetts

Community and education are significant parts of his approach to the industry in general. Coming from the US East Coast, he says there is not as deep of an understanding of the budtending world as there is in the West. Independent of his work as a budtender, he founded a pop-up membership social club designed to provide a safe space for cannabis enthusiasts, budtenders, or anybody in the industry and culture to get educated about cannabis, even non-consumers. This community education approach has helped make him an exceptional budtender.

"I basically take that education, slow it down, and put it into terms customized for my customer. That's how I advocate for everyone," he says. "When it comes to this plant, I just like helping people. I didn't have that kind of help when I started and had to learn a lot of new things. I want to feed that out. I shouldn't be the only one 'in the know.'"

Approaches for Common Customer Types

After asking open-ended questions, the budtender should know what type of customer they are helping. The following is a rough categorization of the most common customer types:

- Cannabis novice
- Well-versed connoisseur
- Someone who wants the highest THC products possible
- Someone who wants therapeutic benefits without a "high"
- Special needs
- A "difficult" customer who is impossible to satisfy

A good budtender can adjust their customer service approach and the level of detail they provide to meet the varying needs of these common customer types.

The Cannabis Novice

People new to cannabis will likely come in with many questions. They could be older patients who may have used cannabis once or twice when they were younger or perhaps never used cannabis for its therapeutic properties.

Most Useful Information About a Cannabis Product

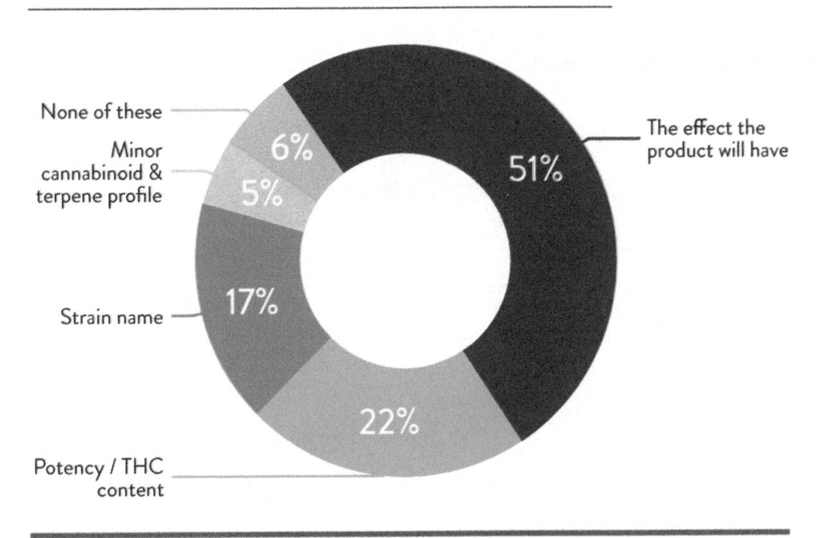

Source: New Frontier Data,[441] Cannabis Consumers in America, Part 1, 2022.

Budtender Interview

"It's very overwhelming when you walk into the shop. It's such a busy place, customers are scared of wasting our time. I tell everybody, even with a line out the door, don't ever feel rushed. Take your time. Ask me anything. There's no such thing as a dumb or stupid question."

— **Alyssa Ginella**, budtender in Walled Lake, Michigan

Budtender Interview

"I think a lot of people who are new to cannabis or have had bad experiences with it were either given something too strong or were around people who have higher tolerances and just expect them to be able to handle it. There is always time to experiment, so it's important not to overwhelm yourself with something high in THC to start."

— **Binx Taylor**, former budtender in Oakland, California

What is the Difference Between Medical and Adult Use?

Although medical and adult use cannabis commercial markets are legally distinct from one another and regulated separately, self-reported reasons for use from all types of consumers show that the lines are unclear. These charts break down research conducted by New Frontier Data in 2022 and show how people seek therapeutic effects regardless of this designation.

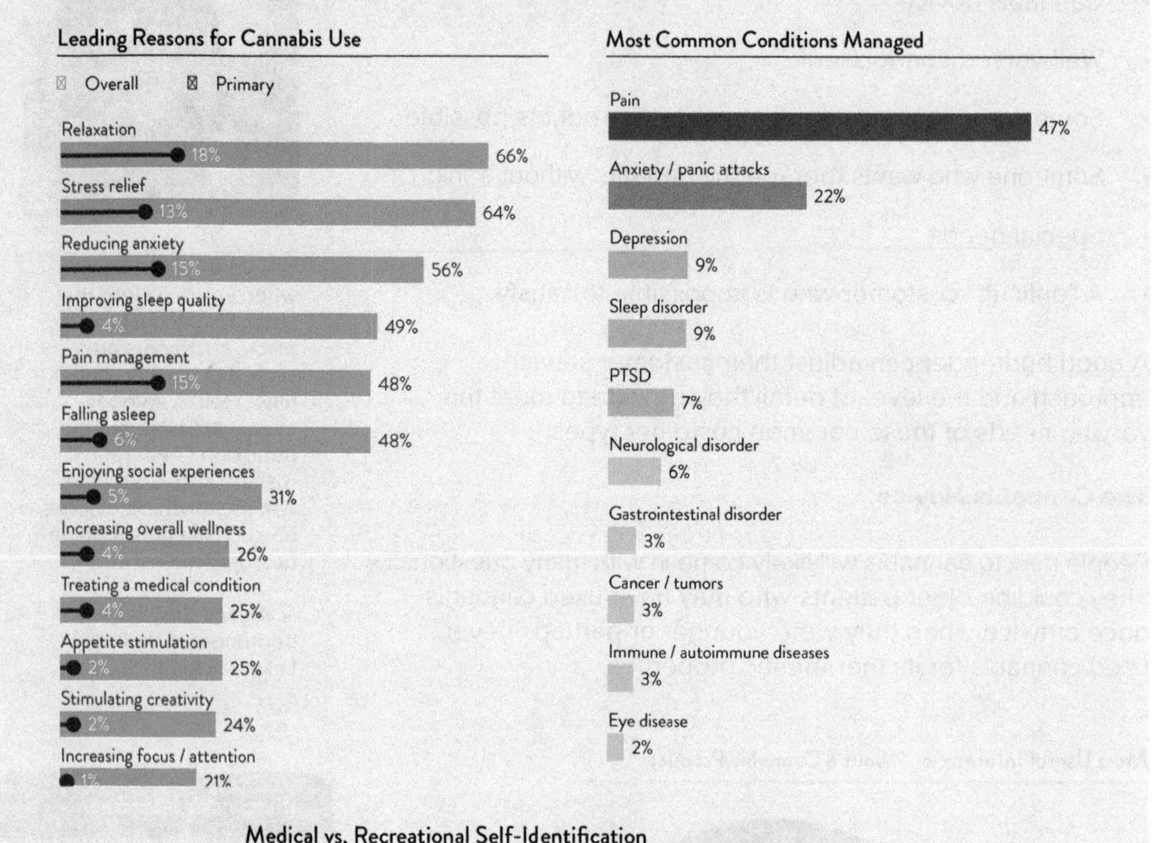

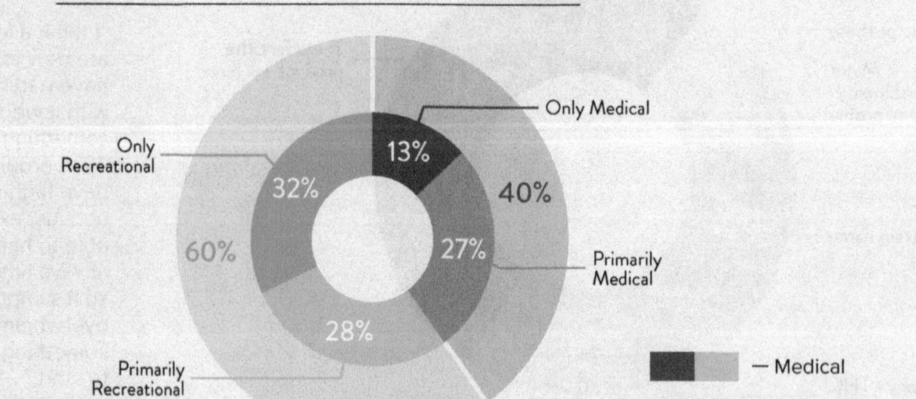

Source: New Frontier Data,[442] Cannabis Consumers in America, Part 1, 2022.

While some in this age group may have decades-long experience, many others also grew up in an environment where drug use was socially unacceptable, leaving them with reservations about getting "high" and using drugs. These customers require more education and guidance. However, they also tend to be very loyal to dispensaries and budtenders once they have seen the light, as they prefer to stick with what and who they know.

The Connoisseur

Cannabis connoisseurs are the most discerning customers with the highest expectations of product quality. They seek craft products and often come into the dispensary looking for their preferred brands and products.

Connoisseurs learn about new products faster than the average consumer. Some follow their favorite extraction artists on social media and come in to get the new, hottest extracts as soon as they drop. While some may be budget-conscious, many may be ready to spend hundreds of dollars. These visitors are big money-makers for the dispensary and should be given the utmost attention to ensure they keep coming back.

This type of customer tends to have fewer questions than new customers, but they may ask more challenging and detailed questions. For example, they may want to know whether the cannabis was grown organically or whether an extract was produced with solvents. These interactions tend to go very quickly because many customers come in the door knowing what they want.

Nevertheless, these individuals may be open to trying new things if they meet their high standards. One exception might be if someone comes in buying hundreds of dollars worth of one particular type of product, like dabs. They may not be open to other methods of ingestion, like smoking flower or edibles. However, the only way to know is to ask. When trying to interest a connoisseur in a new product, be as sure as possible to make suggestions that interest them. A string of bad suggestions could diminish their faith in the budtender.

High THC Customers

According to New Frontier Data,[443] nearly 1 out of 5 (22%) customers purchase cannabis based on THC potency. However, the THC level on flowers or extracts provides little qualifying information about the experiences consumers will have.[444,445,446] These consumers may be regular, albeit uneducated, and equate higher THC with more potency and value. A good comparison would be purchasing wine based on the alcohol content rather than the variety, flavors, company, quality, and social occasion.

Some people may still seek THC with this understanding, and it is okay to simply guide them to the highest-THC products when they indicate they have experience and tolerance.

Tracking information and phytochemical content appear on all labels. Photo by Mitchell Colbert.

Customers who purchase flowers will self-titrate their intake via inhalation and are less likely to experience dysphoria. However, exposure to high-THC flower can occasionally result in adverse short-term effects, including dizziness, sleepiness, distorted time perception, tachycardia (rapid heartbeat), paranoia, and panic attacks. In subjects with a family history of psychosis or other psychiatric conditions, high-THC products may exacerbate psychotic symptoms. These effects, though unpleasant, are not life-threatening and typically will dissipate within a couple of hours. Such adverse events are potentially more likely to last longer following the ingestion of high-potency edible products or concentrates. Customers should be aware of these potential side effects to regulate their dose accordingly.

No-High Customers

While it may be convenient to consider this group as "CBD-only" customers, a broader range of options is available to meet their needs. Products rich in CBDa, THCa, CBG, and other non-psychotropic cannabinoids may be appropriate. The main thing to remember with these customers is that they do not want to "get high," so THC, potentially THCV and CBN, are mostly off the table.

It is worth investigating why the customer opposes psychotropic effects, as many people misunderstand THC's effects relative to pharmaceutical drugs they may already be taking. Their aversion may be rooted in guilt, negative stigmas, and embedded cultural norms. They may not realize that several conventional pharmaceuticals also make people feel "high" since many are known to produce a euphoric effect just as or more potent than cannabis. They may have had a bad experience with cannabis in the past. Their hesitancy might not

There are a variety of products or methods of ingestion that do not make consumers feel "high." Photo courtesy of Ed Breslin.

have anything to do with their personal experience but based on information they read online or even something they heard second-hand long ago.

Often a customer's preference has nothing to do with fear or anxiety. Whatever their reasons, it is the budtender's job to accommodate their needs. Hopefully, the dispensary offers a wide range of products with cannabinoid profiles that feature different ratios of CBD to THC. Even patients who do not want to feel high may be able to tolerate a small amount of THC, which could enhance the effects they seek. Some ratios of CBD to THC, such as 8:1, may not produce a psychotropic effect.

Special Needs Customers

"Special needs" is a broad category that includes people who are physically disabled, neurodiverse, have severe allergies or dietary restrictions, speak other languages, or are parents or caregivers of children with serious illnesses. While dispensary owners and managers should have plans to accommodate special needs customers, budtenders may be called to adjust their approach to ensure the customer has a good experience in the dispensary.

Physical Disabilities

Local laws and regulations usually require dispensaries and other businesses to be accessible to people in wheelchairs. However, the budtender may need to take extra measures to accommodate some disabilities. For instance, it is unlikely a dispensary will have menus in braille as the offerings can change, so the budtender may need to read aloud from the menu or use it to customize verbal guidance for the customer. With deaf or hearing-impaired customers, budtenders who are not fluent in sign language will have to improvise by using printed menus and hand gestures. It is important to ensure the customer feels respected and not rushed. The University of California at San Francisco offers tips[447] for communicating with people with hearing impairments.

> *It is important to ensure the customer feels respected and not rushed.*

Budtender Interview

"When the markets were medical-only, Harborside Health Center made a point of always referring to customers as "patients." Although this is no longer the case, it did remind us that some people who came into our dispensary had psychological conditions we couldn't see. We were reminded of this in our training and instructed to always treat customers with compassion because someone in need may come off as challenging or difficult. It just boils down to the training and making sure that people have empathy and consideration for the suffering that people with mental health conditions have."

— **Goose Duarte**, former budtender and current director of operations at Oaksterdam University

Neurodiversity

The terms "neurodivergent" and "neurodiversity" usually refer to people with autism spectrum disorder (ASD). The budtender is unlikely to know right away or at all if their customer is neurodivergent. Healthline[448] and Inclusive Communication[449] offer tips for communicating with people with ASD. However, because the budtender may not be able to identify a customer with ASD, it is essential to employ these strategies with all customers who may come off as "difficult." For instance, budtenders should speak clearly and literally, be kind and patient, listen carefully to the customer, and try never to take anything a customer says personally.

Dietary Restrictions

If a customer mentions a dietary restriction, such as being gluten intolerant or vegan, be vigilant to ensure the products recommended conform to those needs. If they mention an allergy, particularly a nut allergy, be careful when recommending edibles, tinctures, and topicals, which could contain nuts or nut oils, and advise the patient of the potential risk of cross-contamination in products that may seem somewhat unlikely to pose a risk. Refer customers with allergies to the companies that manufacture the products to determine if they were produced using methods that avoid cross-contamination.

Budtender Interview

"I come from a Mexican family, and one of the things I am working on is breaking down the taboo of cannabis in Hispanic culture. I am one of the only Spanish speakers in our store, so I take about 95% of the Spanish-speaking customers. I noticed that for many Spanish speakers, it is often their first time, and they are shy, or it makes them feel scared. It is so important to make them feel comfortable so you can begin breaking down the stigmas."

— **Arturo Cano**, budtender, Las Vegas, Nevada

Language Barriers

If the dispensary is located in a region or neighborhood where a second language is common, the owners and managers should seek bilingual budtenders and consider offering menus or other materials written in the second language. Budtenders who are both bilingual and bicultural, meaning they understand and can communicate across cultural divides beyond simple translation, are invaluable to a dispensary in a region where more than one language is spoken.

However, in larger cities or tourist regions, the budtender may encounter customers who speak languages that nobody in the dispensary speaks. While the technology is not always perfect, accessing Google or another translation service on a cell phone may be the best way to bridge the divide. Google Translate allows the user to type in words or phrases in their language, show the written translation, and play an audio reading. The customer should also be encouraged to put their questions in the translation service so the budtender is clear about what they are asking. Always use simple phrases and direct sentences, avoiding slang and idioms. Remember to be kind, patient, and respectful, even if communicating becomes frustrating.

Children

Although a child may be the legal patient under a medical cannabis law, it will be the parent or caregiver purchasing cannabis in the dispensary for them. Always defer medical questions to the child's medical team, but assess what they are looking for by asking what the doctor has suggested or what the child has already tried. The parent will have guidelines for the types of products they are looking for, and the budtender should work from these and encourage the parents to take lots of notes when using products and share them with the doctor to help guide purchases.

Difficult Customers

The first rule in assisting difficult customers is NEVER to match their intensity. Always try to diffuse and de-escalate the situation, even if they are verbally abusive. If a customer does get verbally abusive, or worse, physically violent, get a manager or member of the security staff to intervene. Most difficult customers will be very demanding and not thankful for the help provided, so keeping calm is essential. Frequently, those difficult customers will come back days later and apologize for how they acted. Everyone has bad days sometimes, but not everyone handles them well.

A great way to appease difficult customers, if laws allow it, is with free products or a discount on their purchase. However, use good judgment so as not to reward bad behavior. Rewarding bad behavior may encourage more in the future, or the dispensary might gather a reputation for being easy to get a freebie or discount.

Dealing with Difficult Customers

"My skill is reading people. When you are older, you tend to be a little less shy about making suggestions. I am confident about my area of expertise here. As far as knowing what people need, I am comfortable enough to get to the point with them quickly and politely.

When we come upon difficult customers, management will tell you to step away. That is my advice, step away, take a breather. You will occasionally deal with someone very difficult. Go to the back of the house to complain, get it out with co-workers, and take a breather. It is hard to remember if people are in a bad mood that they probably waited a day or two longer than they should have to come in.

Marc Carter

A difficult customer, you can just kinda tell right from the beginning based on their tone. It is usually people trying to take advantage of a sale or overbuy when there is a limit on the number of items. Some people honestly bring their bullshit in with them too. If I feel like I can step away, I will, but if we are busy, I cannot go anywhere. It has sometimes taken me an hour to cool down. I let younger people leave to cool off.

It is miserable people coming in. They are all over the place, not just in dispensaries. When they share their misery, you have to take a few minutes."

— **Marc Carter,** budtender in Walled Lake, Michigan

Recommending Products

In some dispensaries, budtenders are referred to as "consultants," which is defined[450] as someone who "provides professional advice or services." A budtender's role is to perform a consultation that consists of asking open-ended questions that engage the customer. The budtender takes what they learn from this interaction to provide the right level of guidance and information the customer needs to make their own decisions.

The first rule of recommending products is to ensure they are in stock. It may seem obvious, but it is easy to overlook or lose track during a busy dispensary shift. Nevertheless, budtenders must always know what products are available. It is a customer service failure to guide a customer to a product not there to sell. Be familiar with how to keep track of product inventory in the point of sale (POS) system, but do not rely on the POS alone. At the start of the shift, check to see if there are new products to be aware of and what is currently in stock. Double-check the stock midway through a longer or busier shift to see whether anything has sold out.

The other rule is to respect customers' limitations and restrictions. If they mention they are on a budget, refrain from trying to upsell them or recommending top-shelf flowers and other expensive products.

Ask the Right Questions

Some customers will come into the dispensary and know what they want without guidance, but others will need help before purchasing. Regardless of

Great budtenders ask questions to identify customer goals. Photo courtesy of Glass House Brands.

their reason for use, customers seek different and specific effects, such as relieving nausea, helping sleep, relaxing, socializing, or creative inspiration. Asking the customer about their desired outcomes helps budtenders guide informed purchasing decisions. Inexperienced consumers need guidance on dosage and ingestion methods.

Gauge Past Cannabis Experience

Many point-of-sale (POS) systems flag new customers after check-in, and the budtender may get a notification at their terminal. Although it may be the first time that customer has entered the dispensary, it does not mean they are new to cannabis. An open-ended question such as "what are you looking for today?" may reveal the customer's experience level. However, it is crucial to confirm when a customer has never used cannabis before or has limited experience.

Ask about the specific ingestion methods, "Did you try smoking, edibles, or some kind of topical cream?" If the customer is primarily familiar with smoking flower, try to probe for their experience with other products by asking, "How familiar are you with [this method] and how its effects differ from smoking flower?"

Another critical question is, "Did you enjoy past experiences with cannabis, and why or why not?" This question identifies barriers to enjoying consumption and experiencing therapeutic effects. For example, a customer may want to access therapeutic benefits without smoking. In that case, the budtender can recommend alternatives like edibles or topicals. If they had bad experiences with edible products in the past, budtenders could steer them toward lower-dose edible products or topicals.

Identify Consumption Goals

Some consumers, particularly at adult use dispensaries, may just want to get "high" without recognizing or identifying their reason for use as medicinal or therapeutic. In any dispensary, a customer may seek specific therapeutic effects. A good question to gauge their goals is, "What sort of experiences are you looking for?"

As the budtender gauges the customer's experience and evaluates their goals, they may learn of a diagnosed medical condition. Follow-up questions should identify

Budtender Interview

"I like to ask, 'how do you want to feel?' It's a really great question to see what kind of day they are trying to have. A lot of customers say something like, 'I just want to try this before going to see a movie, do you have a recommendation that would be really good for that?' The more situational it is, the easier it is for me to recommend a product."

— **Binx Taylor**, former budtender in Oakland, California

the effects they seek without pressuring them to provide sensitive information. Appropriate questions are, “Do you need help falling asleep or help to stay asleep?” Due to their long-lasting effects, edibles can be recommended for staying asleep because they have delayed onset and last longer. Tinctures can be recommended as a faster way of falling asleep. These recommendations do not cross the line into unqualified medical advice because they are non-specific to treating disease or illness, and no dosing or product regimen is prescribed or recommended.

Aside from the ingestion method, specific cultivars of cannabis have become known for the effects and experiences they generate. It is crucial to remember that not everyone will have a uniform response to the same plant varieties, products, dosage, and ingestion methods. Additionally, varieties are not standardized, so they are not always a good predictor of effects. (*See Part IV: Cannabis Varieties*).

Many returning customers in the adult use market will not need the budtender to ask them questions. Instead, they will have their own, such as, “What is your strongest/best [concentrate, flower, preroll, edible, etc.] today?” or “What is your favorite?” or “Tell me more about how this product was made and how the cannabis was grown.” Some will simply want the highest THC content. Another common question will be, “What is your cheapest [concentrate, flower, pre-roll, edible, etc.] today?”

Most novice and experienced consumers will not be looking for the same products. It can be helpful to ask novice consumers about trying new product categories. A budtender may try to upsell an experienced consumer within the same category. Remember to ask questions to gauge their openness to trying new things.

Determine Desired Ingestion Method

After identifying the customer’s consumption goals, the budtender guides them to the product or ingestion method that best meets them. If they have previous experience with a particular method and enjoyed it, it may be best to stick with recommending similar products. The budtender may recommend something new if it meets the consumer’s goals. For example, if they have issues with smoking but still want to inhale, they can be guided towards vaporization or a product that is not inhaled but is also fast-acting.

Assess Preference for Sustainable Products

If organic or sustainably-produced products are available, ask customers if they prefer them. Some customers are particular about how their cannabis is grown and make choices based on cultivation and processing practices.

More consumers are seeking sustainable packaging or wish to reduce industrial waste. Their concern has led many companies to develop packaging options made from plastic alternatives or recycled materials. Learn which companies offer sustainable products and exert effort to boost sustainability in the cannabis supply chain.

Provide the Right Answers

Customers may have a lot of questions, and there may not always be easy answers. Some people will feel different effects from the same product. Dried cannabis flowers and extracts are highly variable, so the same product may not be consistent from batch to batch. This diversity and variability are expected and part of why people love cannabis.

Budtenders do not have to have all the right answers, but they should have all the correct information and the "people skills" to help customers find their own answers. Not only is it okay to admit to not having the "right answer," but it is the right thing to do. There may be no "right answer," but lots of good information about the options available and how they may or may not help customers reach their goals.

It may be tempting to provide answers where there are none. It is important not to fill in the blanks simply because the customer wants an easy answer. As cannabis laws change, more medical professionals will take an active role in guiding their patients' use and providing answers to medical questions. More research will better define cannabis varieties and the variable effects they produce. Over time, customers will become more familiar with the variability of herbal products like cannabis.

The budtender is the most critical employee in the supply chain because they are usually the only ones interacting directly with customers. It is rewarding to learn that a good recommendation helped someone or gave them a positive experience. Cannabis can be confusing because it is unfamiliar to many, and there is endless variability. A great budtender is respectful, not pretentious, knowledgeable but aware of what is not or cannot be known, and makes connections with people that lead to positive experiences with cannabis.

Budtenders provide information so that customers can make informed choices. Photo Oaksterdam Archives.

Part VI Review

- How budtenders provide customer service is both a matter of personal style and the regional market. Factors such as medical and adult use laws define the interaction between customers and budtenders.
- Budtenders should customize their interactions to properly serve common customer types.
- Budtenders should start by asking customers open-ended questions to identify their consumption goals and then present them with options and the information they need to make their own choices.

Appendix A: Advocacy

Cannabis Prohibition continues to stymy necessary research. Cannabis is still illegal in most places. People around the world are still in prison for cannabis crimes, even where it is legal. Those who choose to work in the industry express an implicit bias: they believe cannabis should be legal and regulated. Laws and regulations are still being shaped, and people who work in the industry have a right and an obligation to advocate in any way they can.

Overwhelmingly, most people in the US and many other countries support legalization. The details that shape legalization will be written with or without the input of cannabis consumers and advocates. Budtenders, business owners, and consumers can influence the future.

How to Legalize

One of the critical questions in the debate over legalization in the US is whether cannabis should be moved to a lower schedule (rescheduled) or removed entirely from the Controlled Substances Act (descheduled). The primary difference between these two options is how the federal government would regulate the production and sale of cannabis.

Based on the science, history, safety profile, and therapeutic benefits, cannabis must be descheduled. Cannabis is a plant, not a drug, and thus should be regulated like other botanical products, such as herbal supplements, plant-derived cosmetic formulations, and food products.

So, how can descheduling be accomplished? There are several ways this could occur. Congress could pass a law to amend the Controlled Substances Act to remove cannabis. In recent years, several members of Congress have introduced legislation that would do just that.

However, an act of Congress is not required to deschedule cannabis — the Drug Enforcement Administration (DEA) has always had the authority to change the classification of a scheduled substance. Over the years, advocates have petitioned the DEA to remove cannabis from Schedule I, arguing that the plant has clear, proven therapeutic benefits that warrant a re- or descheduling. The DEA has rejected these petitions.

The president has little direct authority over descheduling. However, the attorney general, as the head of the Department of Justice (DOJ), has broad authority over the actions of the DEA and could easily make the change.

The president does have the power to issue an executive order,[451] a document

Oaksterdam University Executive Chancellor Dale Sky Jones. Photo Oaksterdam Archives.

that directs the actions of federal agencies. The president could, for instance, issue an executive order directing the DOJ to halt all enforcement of federal cannabis laws. Such a move would signal Congress that the White House would support reform legislation if they passed it. However, a new president could rescind a previous president's executive order when they take power.

The judicial branch also has the power to advance legalization. The Supreme Court could overturn Prohibition with a single ruling.

It is impossible to say which route might ultimately bring about the end of cannabis Prohibition. A holding pattern of federal inaction and deference to state cannabis laws could continue for decades. Such an arrangement, in which states can pass and enforce cannabis policies without federal interference, could be formalized into federal law. Some proposals in Congress would grant legal protections to states with medical or adult use cannabis. This type of "state's rights" legislation would fall short of full descheduling.

Even with federal legalization, there will always be a patchwork of pro- and anti-cannabis laws at the state and local levels. After alcohol Prohibition, a similar regulatory patchwork emerged and still exists today. Different regions have very different regulations and restrictions. The same patchwork is already developing on the international level. Regardless of an end to domestic policy in the US or international policy through the UN, each region will still have the power to prohibit the production and consumption of cannabis, and local government approval would still be required to launch a commercial enterprise.

Forms of legalization at all levels are happening now. It is essential to stay involved in the federal, state, and local cannabis policy reform movement and keep pressing on all fronts. Stay active and keep the work of previous advocates from stalling.

The National Organization for the Reform of Marijuana Laws (NORML) has an online Action Center[452] where they provide information about recent legislation and a tool that allows people to send emails to their elected members of Congress. NORML also has an email list that delivers the latest policy news and action alerts. The Marijuana Policy Project[453] has a similar communication tool for contacting elected officials on their website and provides policy alerts via email; so does Americans for Safe Access (ASA).[454]

Cannabis Must Be Descheduled

"Cannabis is still a federal crime in the US, even though over 90% of Americans live where some form of cannabis is permitted. Cannabis must be removed from the Controlled Substances Act completely. At the international level, the United Nations must amend the Single Convention on Narcotic Drugs regarding cannabis to allow for descheduling worldwide. Descheduling will allow for healthy competition and opportunities for innovation and small businesses for women, people of color, and veterans to survive and thrive."

— Dale Sky Jones, Chancellor of Oaksterdam University

Strategies & Techniques for Effective Advocacy

Policymakers hear a broad range of opinions from various "stakeholders," a term that refers to groups that a proposed policy change would impact. Stakeholders in cannabis policy include consumers, industry employees, businesses, and regulators.

Policymakers have many interests to consider, so messaging must cut through the noise. ASA offers helpful guidance in their ABCs of Citizen Advocacy,[455] which suggests being accurate, brief, concise, and doing follow-up.

It is crucial to begin with accurate information to maintain credibility with the audience. Be brief because policymakers have limited bandwidth to allocate, and they must consider the competing viewpoints of all stakeholders. It is also essential to be concise. A concise argument gets to the point in as few words as possible. Finally, do a follow-up. It helps the message stand out among the many others policymakers receive every day and can help build relationships with potential allies.

Know the Political Landscape

Effective advocates identify decision-makers, understand the political landscape (i.e., allies and opponents), and then leverage that understanding to tailor the message to their target audience.

Below is a list of questions that can help assess the political landscape, identify the target audience, and tailor messaging with a compelling call to action:

Who makes the decisions?

Find out who has the power and authority to make the desired policy change.

Who are the allies and opposition?

Identify the proponents and opponents in previous debates on the policy. Also, try to identify stakeholders who may be on the fence. They do not necessarily oppose cannabis but are not active supporters. A well-developed message could inspire them to change their minds.

What motivates the opposition?

Take the time to learn why opponents are resistant to reform. A compromise may alleviate some concerns and sway their opinion into neutral territory rather than active opposition. There may also be some stakeholders who want the same policy outcome but for different reasons. Understanding those motivations is essential to develop common ground with potential allies.

What resources already exist?

Find out whether any other stakeholders have already launched an advocacy campaign. They may have more financial and volunteer resources or have already made valuable connections with key decision-makers. It could be more effective to shift focus to supporting their effort, or there may be ways to collaborate. At a minimum, ensure efforts are consistent with others with the same policy goal.

Where are the bridges?

Think about how to gain support from decision-makers. Are there ways to attract the support of stakeholders whom the decision-makers value highly? Are there any issues important to them that align to provide support?

Are there any existing solutions that would achieve the same outcome?

Think creatively about whether there may be existing solutions that can help achieve the desired outcome. For instance, regulators have broad authority to interpret laws passed by the legislature when drafting and enforcing rules. Convincing them to think differently about an existing law might be more effective than finding support in the legislature to pass a new one.

What is the desired policy outcome?

A focused advocacy message asks: what is the specific desired policy change? Consider whether it is realistic, given the political landscape, and whether the targeted audience can make it happen.

Likely, one or several advocacy organizations have already done this analysis to identify key decision-makers, allies, and opponents and have a plan to approach them. These groups can then guide their supporters in engaging in the policy process and crafting a compelling message. Whether planning to engage in solo advocacy or join an organized effort, it is beneficial to turn to the experience of others when learning how to evaluate and navigate the political landscape.

Choose the Right Language

Communication is a two-way street. A message is not enough; there must also be a person receiving, hearing, and understanding it. Tailoring the messaging for target audiences increases the chance of being heard and effective.

Below are some questions to guide the development of a targeted message:

- What is the desired outcome? How is it similar or different from the audience's desired outcome?
- What is the point of connection with the audience? Are there shared goals? How can a connection be made through these shared goals?
- What is the audience ready to hear? How much knowledge do they have of the issue, and how much education is needed?

Semantics Matter

Framing the message[456] is critical to political success. The cannabis industry and social justice movement should avoid using words that evoke associated stigmas. From left to right below are words that have a negative connotation and their more neutral alternatives:

- Use → Consume, Take
- User → Consumer
- Pot, Weed, Marijuana → Cannabis
- Recreational → Retail, Adult Use, Commercial

The Oaksterdam Cannabis Terminology Style Guide[457] includes helpful information about using terminology and communicating consistently about cannabis.

Find the Right Messenger

Think about the best person or group to deliver the message. Consider finding a representative who can speak to specific concerns from a first-hand perspective. For example, a parent who relies on cannabis for their child's treatment is an ideal candidate to speak to policies regarding cannabis use during school hours.

Consider Timing

The message is more likely to be heard if delivered to the right target audience at the right time. Below are a couple of things to consider about timing:

- Does the audience have a lot of competing priorities right now? If there are a lot of other issues on their plate, it may be best to wait until they have more time to consider the message.
- Can the audience take action right now? If the message is delivered too far in advance of when a decision-maker will have an opportunity to act, they may forget it by the time action is needed.

Follow Up & Develop Relationships

After taking the time to identify the audience and tailor the message, remember to follow up and be available as a resource for additional information and support. Make the time to follow through with pledges if any specific promises were made. Always thank those who were supportive, even if their efforts did not achieve the desired outcome. The goal is to develop and preserve relationships with allies whose support may be crucial in the future. In addition, establishing relationships with key decision-makers creates more opportunities to be influential.

Do's & Don'ts for Effective Advocacy

✓	X
• Relay accurate information. • Make arguments brief. • Stick to two or three main talking points. • Be courteous, punctual, and patient. • Be a resource. • Listen and share information. • Ask for a specific action. • Use time wisely. • Follow up by writing a "thank you" message.	• Lie or exaggerate. • Waste time. • Be a "know-it-all" or make others feel inferior. • Make promises that cannot be delivered. • Be argumentative. • Burn bridges. • Attack others within the movement.

Understanding the Opposition's Point of View

List anti-cannabis groups. What are some of their main arguments? More importantly, what are the counter arguments to their specific opposition points?

Opportunities for Engagement

There are multiple avenues and forums to engage in advocacy, from direct participation to financial support. Here is a list of specific actions to start getting involved:

Stay Informed & Network

The first and most crucial step in engagement is to stay informed. Sign up for newsletters offered by advocacy groups and trade associations. Many groups provide valuable email updates on proposed policy and regulatory changes and offer instructions on how to get involved. Daily updates from cannabis trade publications and news alerts for cannabis topics are also good options. Keep an eye on local news outlets, as many news aggregators miss stories from smaller sources. Find out where the local governing body posts agendas for public meetings and check for cannabis topics. Keep in touch with peers in the business community and share information.

Support an Advocacy Group

A wide range of advocacy groups focus on cannabis-related issues, and most rely heavily on support from their members for funding. Many of these groups lobby on behalf of their members and raise awareness of the benefits of cannabis through educational programs, advertising campaigns, and community events. Some also send out "action alerts" via email and social media, which offer specific instructions on contacting elected officials regarding current legislation. They have made it easy to engage directly in the policy process because they have already tracked the legislation.

Many of them also rely heavily on help from volunteers. Consider donating time and providing financial support through membership fees. Another option is to launch a local chapter of a national organization if there is yet to be one.

Contact Elected Officials & Regulators

Sending an email or making a phone call to an elected official is a simple way to influence decision-makers. Alternatively, meet with elected officials in person for greater impact. Anyone can request a meeting with an elected representative at any level of government.

Understandably though, most officials only have time to meet with some of their constituents. Organize a group of constituents with a shared interest to improve the odds of securing an in-person meeting. Many advocacy organizations already organize "lobby days" to do just that. The organization schedules meetings on behalf of members, who then can meet as a group with their representatives.

Many elected officials also host "town hall" or "open house" events to meet constituents and answer their questions. Members of Congress often hold these events during August, when Congress is in recess. However, many hold similar events throughout the year. Contact their offices to determine when they will appear in public.

Remember to contact and lobby local officials, even if the issue is being debated in the state legislature. Cities and counties are influential stakeholders in the state legislature. Citizens can call or email their mayors, county administrators, city or county council members, and regulators. Always use their official government phone number and email, and follow the advocacy tips in this appendix.

Regulators must solicit and review public feedback on proposed changes to rules and regulations. Sign up for email alerts from regulatory agencies and advocacy groups to monitor proposed regulatory changes. Submit public comments during the rulemaking process. Many regulatory agencies organize citizen advisory committees or working groups to gather feedback on potential rule changes and learn more about how existing rules affect stakeholders.

Attend Local Government Meetings & Candidate Forums

Local policies have a significant impact. The best way to learn more and have an influence is to attend local government meetings. Most cities and towns have a board of elected officials responsible for passing local ordinances, such as a city council, city commission, town council, or board of aldermen. Most counties also have an elected governing board.

Find out when they meet, and come prepared by locating and obtaining a copy of the agenda ahead of the meeting. Elected boards must release their agenda to the public within a specified time frame. Most fulfill that requirement by posting the agenda to their official websites or publishing it in the local paper. Contact the city government's administrative office for assistance if an agenda is difficult to locate.

There are debates and public forums where candidates discuss policy issues that impact the community. Come prepared with thoughtful questions about their stance. A well-crafted question can get candidates to state their position publicly.

Attending local government meetings also provides an opportunity to voice an opinion on any issue and support proposals that benefit the entire community.

Attend or Host a Cannabis Event or Rally

Events or rallies increase awareness and the public profile of cannabis policy reform. These events may draw members of the community who may not be fully aware of the benefits of cannabis or may be on the fence about legalization.

Events hosted by established advocacy organizations may draw local or regional media coverage, allowing the message to reach an even wider audience. These events are an opportunity to gain new supporters and portray the industry and its contributions to the community positively.

Support Voter Drives

Increasing voter participation among cannabis supporters is key to electing supportive officials. Consider contributing money or time to efforts to register new voters and increase voter turnout.

Want to learn more about effective advocacy?

Oaksterdam University's free, self-paced Advocacy course[458] defines advocacy as a form of marketing, reviews the role of advocates and organizations in normalizing cannabis use by achieving meaningful policy reform, and then provides strategies and techniques for engaging effectively as an advocate.

Appendix B: Know Your Rights

Photo Wikimedia Commons.

Cannabis is still illegal at the federal level. It is crucial for consumers and anyone working in the industry to know their rights and exercise them when faced with a law enforcement encounter. Below is a brief overview of constitutional rights in the United States.[459]

First Amendment: Freedom of Speech

"Congress shall make no law . . . prohibiting the free exercise thereof; or abridging the freedom of speech."

The First Amendment protects the right to freedom of speech. However, it does not protect you from the consequences of your speech. Making unqualified medical statements or expressing controversial or problematic opinions can result in loss of employment or other social consequences.

Second Amendment: The Right to Bear Arms

"... the right of the people to keep and bear Arms shall not be infringed."

The second amendment does not extend to medical patients or adults using cannabis legally under their state's laws. Due to federal drug laws, cannabis consumers often lose their second amendment rights and can not legally possess firearms.

Fourth Amendment: Search & Seizure

"The right of the people to be secure in their persons, houses, papers, and effects, against unreasonable searches and seizures, shall not be violated."

The Fourth Amendment protects citizens from illegal searches.[460] Never consent to a search and state clearly, "I do not consent to a search." Although declining consent may not prevent the search, it is illegal for a law enforcement officer to search without probable cause, consent, or a warrant, and doing so makes any evidence inadmissible in court.

Fifth Amendment: Right to Remain Silent

"No person ... shall be compelled in any criminal case to be a witness against himself."

You always have the right to remain silent. Exercising this right is arguably the most important thing you can do to avoid trouble during a law enforcement encounter. Law enforcement officers are trained to get you to give up incriminating evidence about yourself and the people you know. They are also trained to catch you in a lie — lying to an officer is a crime in and of itself, and if you do it, prosecutors will use it to build their case against you.

Many people believe you do not have the right to remain silent until you have been arrested and read your Miranda rights, which is not true; you always have the right to remain silent and decline to answer questions from law enforcement. If an officer approaches you and tries to engage, try to excuse yourself politely — say, "Sorry, I cannot talk right now," and walk away. An officer has no right to detain and question you unless they have probable cause. If the officer stops you from walking away, you are already being detained, even if you are not physically restrained with handcuffs.

Officers can be very persistent in questioning, but they know you have the right to remain silent. The best thing to do if an officer stops you is to say:

"Am I free to go? I want to remain silent. I want a lawyer. I do not consent to a search."

Sixth Amendment: Right to Legal Representation

"In all criminal prosecutions, the accused shall enjoy the right to ... have the Assistance of Counsel for his defence."

When you tell the police you want to remain silent but then choose to speak, anything you say can be used against you. However, once you demand a lawyer, anything you say after that cannot be used against you. Say, "I want a lawyer." You do not need to have a lawyer on retainer or even know a lawyer. Once you say you want a lawyer, the police are supposed to stop all questioning and allow you to find one. If you cannot afford an attorney, you may be eligible for a public defender who will represent you for no cost or a reduced cost. The Constitution guarantees your right to legal representation regardless of your ability to pay. However, you still need to ensure you invoke this right as soon as possible after you have been detained. All you need to do to invoke this right is say:

"I want to remain silent. I want a lawyer. I do not consent to a search."

Practice saying this phrase aloud so the words come out automatically when needed. A police stop can be very stressful, and it can be challenging to remember what to do in the moment. Police officers can be persuasive and will try to pressure you to cooperate. You need to be prepared to respond. The best way to be prepared is to practice.

For a quick overview of how to interact with the police, check out The Margolin Guide[461] from legendary cannabis attorney and Oaksterdam Faculty Emeritus Bruce Margolin.

Rights Outside the US

Every government has its own interpretation of fundamental human rights, and each country has its specific cannabis policy. Always be aware of the laws and rights guaranteed to citizens in your country. The following information applies only to readers in the United States. For more information about your rights outside the US, this interactive map[462] of human rights treaties ratified in each country maintained by The United Nations High Commissioner of Human Rights is a good resource.

Glossary

Adult Use
The term "adult use" distinguishes cannabis use by any person over the age of 21 from those who have a recommendation from a doctor for medicinal use. "Adult use" is used in place of "recreational" because that term is most often associated with activities for children and therefore is inappropriate.
See also Legalization, Medical/ Medicinal, Recreational

Autoflower
Autoflowering plants are genetically triggered to produce flowers based on time instead of the ratio of darkness to light (photoperiod). They finish faster than traditional varieties, allowing cultivators in mild climates to produce two to three (or more) crops per year outdoors.

Butane Hash Oil (BHO)
Also referred to as wax, shatter, budder, and live resin, among many other terms.
Butane hash oil (BHO) is a form of hydrocarbon extraction of cannabis compounds using butane as a solvent. It is not legal to produce BHO at home and is only safe to produce in a licensed facility with professional equipment and trained operators.

BHO is sold in vaporizer cartridges or by the gram for home vaporization or combustion (smoking). It is sold under various names, usually in reference to variations in processing that result in different textures, shades, and consistencies of the finished products. These names include but are not limited to wax, shatter, budder, and live resin.
See also Dabs, Extracts, Hydrocarbon Extraction

Budder ("butter")
See Butane Hash Oil (BHO), Hydrocarbon Extraction

Bud(s)
Also referred to as "flower" or "flowers."
The term "buds" refers to the dried resinous flowers of the cannabis plant, which contain the highest concentrations of THC, CBD, and other desirable phytochemical compounds.
See also Cannabis, Flower(s), Marijuana

Cannabis
Also known as marijuana and hemp
The term "cannabis" refers to any plant in the cannabis genus, including plants grown for either their resinous medicinal flowers or their industrial uses such as paper, fabric, food, lotions, plastics, and building materials. Cannabis taxonomy is not settled.[464] While the genus, *Cannabis* L., is generally agreed upon in scientific communities, species and subspecies are not as clearly defined. (*See Indica/Sativa/Ruderalis for more clarification on the taxonomy debate.*)

Sometimes "hemp" is referred to as a "cousin" to cannabis or "marijuana." This is inaccurate. Hemp is cannabis but has separate legal and traditional botanical definitions.

The entire cannabis plant — flowers, leaves, seeds, and stalks — is harvestable and usable. Traditionally, plants referred to as "hemp" or "industrial hemp" were bred to harvest their seeds and stalks, which can be manufactured into a long list of byproducts. Plants bred primarily for their resinous flowers, specifically the density of therapeutic compounds they contain, have traditionally been referred to as "marijuana." Legally, it is the overall content of the psychotropic cannabinoid Δ^9-tetrahydrocannabinol (THC) that distinguishes "hemp" from "marijuana." Although the distinction is arbitrary and confuses traditional understandings of cannabis varieties, in the United States, plants that contain less than 0.3% THC are legally considered "hemp," and those that contain greater than 0.3% THC are considered "marijuana" or "cannabis." This arbitrary threshold to distinguish "hemp" from "marijuana/cannabis" ranges from 0.3% to 1% worldwide.

Due to arbitrary THC thresholds, the majority of the global and domestic hemp producers focus on low-THC cannabis flowers that contain more significant amounts of cannabidiol (CBD) and other therapeutic compounds, as opposed to growing the plant for its industrial uses.

Cannabis Oil
The term "cannabis oil" can refer to any extract or concentrate of cannabis that is an oily consistency but most often refers to full extract cannabis oil (FECO), also known as Rick Simpson Oil (RSO). This term may have different meanings depending on the context of how it is used:

- Hemp seed oil
- Carrier oils such as olive or coconut infused with cannabis flowers
- FECO/RSO, which is a dense, thick, tar-like extraction popularized for its therapeutic use by cancer patients
- Distillate oil

See also Cannabis, Concentrates, Distillate, Extracts, Full Extract Cannabis Oil (FECO), Hemp, Hydrocarbon Extraction

Cannabinoids
Cannabinoids are compounds that bind to receptors in the endocannabinoid system, which is found in almost all animal life, including humans. There are two main types of cannabinoids, endogenous (originating within the body) and exogenous (originating outside the body).

Endogenous Cannabinoids:
- Endogenous cannabinoids or "endocannabinoids" are produced within the body. Well-known endocannabinoids include anandamide (AEA) and 2-arachidonoylglycerol (2-AG), and others yet to be identified.

Exogenous Cannabinoids:
- Plants produce phytocannabinoids that also interact with the endocannabinoid systems of animals. Cannabis is not the only plant that produces cannabinoids.[465] THC and CBD are (currently) the most commonly sought-after plant-sourced cannabinoids found in the resin of cannabis flowers.

- There are two different substances referred to as "synthetic cannabinoids." The first is FDA-approved pharmaceuticals produced in laboratory settings, such as dronabinol (Marinol®, synthetic THC). The second refers to various unregulated "designer" mixtures, like "Spice/K2," which are sold in convenience stores and smoke shops, are dubiously legal, and sometimes dangerous. These do not contain classic cannabinoids, nor do they have the same safety profile.

- Synthesized cannabinoids use chemical processes to convert hemp-sourced cannabinoids such as CBD and THC into THCO, Δ^8-tetrahydrocannabinol (Δ^8-THC), and other cannabinoids that naturally occur in the plant in minimal quantities. Cannabis researchers have raised concerns[466] about their use and safety in new products sold on the hemp market.

Chemotype/Chemovar
The term "chemotype" classifies cannabis varieties by the spectrum of phytochemicals they produce. The term "chemovar" is a portmanteau for "chemical variety." It classifies plant varieties based on their chemotype or phytochemical profile.
See also Genotype, Phenotype

Clone
Cannabis plants are commonly grown from seeds and clones. A clone, or "cutting," is a branch cut from another plant and rooted to grow a new full-sized plant. It has identical genetics to the plant it was cut from, referred to as "the mother."

Closed-Loop Extraction
Closed-loop extraction refers to making cannabis extracts using volatile solvents (like butane) with industrial equipment. Producing cannabis extractions using volatile solvents is dangerous and should never be done at home. In professional, licensed, and commercial settings, closed-loop extraction machines recycle the solvent rather than disperse it in the air, making the process safer and more sustainable.
See also Hydrocarbon Extraction, Butane Hash Oil (BHO)

Cola
The term "cola" refers to the densest stalk of cannabis flowers at the top of the plant. It is a Spanish word that translates to "tail," referring to the shape resembling a cat's tail. The term came into widespread use in the United States during the 1970s, when most cannabis consumed domestically was grown in Mexico. Today the term is commonly used internationally in the industry.

Combustion
Also referred to as "smoking."
Combustion is a chemical process that creates tar and ash and is the basis for health concerns like bronchitis. The term "combustion" has come into common use in the cannabis industry to differentiate cannabis smoking from cannabis vaporization.

Cultivar
The word "strain" is often used to describe varieties of cannabis but is usually used incorrectly. The word "cultivar" is often the more suitable replacement. It is a portmanteau derived from "cultivated variety." It refers to a genetic line of cannabis specifically bred and selected for the unique and replicable combination of physical traits it will express when grown under specific environmental conditions. Flowers available for sale on dispensary shelves should be referred to as "cultivars." Cultivar can be used instead of "strain" or "variety" where appropriate.
See also Chemotype, Strain, Variety

Dab
The term "dab" refers to the process of combusting or vaporizing small amounts ("dabs") of extracted cannabis resin. It may also refer to the extracted resins themselves.
See also Butane Hash Oil (BHO), Combustion, Concentrates, Extracts, Hydrocarbon Extraction

Distillate/Distillation
Cannabis distillate is produced using an extraction method that pulls chemicals out of cannabis resin, concentrates, or other extracts, which results in a refined oil that is almost 100% pure cannabinoids. The process removes terpenes, and while they can be captured and reintroduced, most distillate manufacturers substitute other botanically-derived terpenes. The

end product is a subcategory of "extracts" and is referred to as "distillate."
See Cannabis Oil, Extracts, Hash, Hydrocarbon Extraction

Edibles
The term "edible" refers to any food infused with cannabis. Often, cannabis beverages are legally considered edibles.

Endocannabinoid System (ECS)
The endocannabinoid system (ECS) is a group of receptors that make up a complex regulatory system throughout the human brain, body, and central and peripheral nervous systems. Some experts think the endocannabinoid system is the "mother" of all internal systems because it maintains homeostasis by regulating the processes of the body's various systems.

Both naturally occurring (endogenous or endocannabinoids) and plant-sourced (phytocannabinoids) interact with the ECS to regulate mood, insomnia, pain, digestion, and more. CB1 and CB2 receptors are the most studied and understood. They are found throughout animal bodies regardless of cannabis use. CB1 receptors are primarily found in the central nervous system, and CB2 receptors are found primarily in immune cells.
See also Cannabinoid

Entourage Effect/Ensemble Effect
The "entourage effect" is a theory postulated in 1999 by Raphael Mechoulam, Ph.D., that the effects of cannabis are a result of a synergy of all the naturally-occurring plant compounds in cannabis (or other herbs) as opposed to any isolated ingredient within it. Many experts and Oaksterdam University now prefer the term "ensemble effect," which implies harmony among all phytocompounds, as the term "entourage" can imply that one cannabinoid is more important than the others. The entourage/ensemble effect is a "theory, "not settled science.
See also Cannabinoid, Flavonoid, Terpene

Extract
The term "extract" refers to the final product of the resinous glands that have been separated from cannabis flowers and concentrated into kief or various forms of hash. Extracts are produced either with the aid of a chemical solvent or through sifting, pressing, rolling, or a combination of agitation and cool temperatures, often ice water. The resulting product is a concentration of the separated resin that can be further subcategorized by the process used to produce it. Examples of hashes produced without solvents are kief, bubble hash, pressed hash, and rosin. Examples of solvent-extracted hashes are BHO, live resin, and most oils prepared for personal vaporizer "pens."
See Butane Hash Oil (BHO), Concentrates, Distillate, Hash, Hydrocarbon Extraction

Fan Leaves
The term "fan leaves" refers to the larger leaves that grow from the cannabis stem and branches to collect sunlight to fuel the process of photosynthesis. The five-fingered fan leaf is also the symbol most commonly associated with the cannabis plant.

Feminized
A feminized seed is chemically treated to only produce female plants.

Flavonoid
Flavonoids are color pigments found in cannabis and other plants with known medicinal properties. They are part of what is referred to as the "full spectrum" of cannabis compounds found in "whole plant" cannabis products. Cannabis contains common flavonoids with known therapeutic properties found in other plants, such as quercetin, luteolin, and cannflavins,

which are unique to the cannabis plant.
See Full Spectrum, Whole Plant

Flower(s)
Also referred to as "bud" or "buds."
The term "flowers" refers to the resinous reproductive floral structures of the cannabis plant. These flowers have the highest concentration of resin, which contains THC, CBD, and other desirable chemical compounds.
See also Bud(s), Cannabis, Marijuana

Full Extract Cannabis Oil (FECO)/Rick Simpson Oil (RSO)/Cannabis Oil
When made properly, full extract cannabis oil (FECO) is a highly-concentrated extract that includes as much of the full spectrum of phytocompounds as possible. It is thick, black, tar-like, and highly concentrated. It was popularized for use in cancer and other chronic or fatal illnesses by Canadian cancer patient Rick Simpson. Simpson popularized original methods for home production, and the resulting oil was referred to as Rick Simpson Oil (RSO). West Coast growers prepare the oil using food-grade alcohol solvents and refer to the resulting product as FECO.
See also Cannabis Oil, Extracts

Full Spectrum
Full spectrum refers to the entirety of the phytochemical compounds found in cannabis.
See also Whole Plant.

Genotype
Genotype is a term used to classify cannabis varieties strictly by genetics.
See also Chemotype, Phenotype

Hash/Hashish
"Hash" is a catch-all term for all extractions or concentrations of the resins produced by cannabis flowers. "Hashish" is an Arabic term that refers to pressed cannabis resin produced using traditional methods, such as sifting.
See Butane Hash Oil (BHO), Concentrates, Extracts, Hydrocarbon Extraction

Hemp
Although "cannabis" and "hemp" are regulated separately, hemp is, in fact, also cannabis. Traditionally, plants referred to as "hemp" or "industrial hemp" were bred to harvest their seeds and stalks, which can be manufactured into a long list of byproducts. Plants bred for their leaves and resinous flowers, specifically the density of therapeutic compounds they contain, have traditionally been referred to as "marijuana." Legally, it is the overall content of the psychotropic cannabinoid Δ^9-tetrahydrocannabinol (THC) that distinguishes "hemp" from "marijuana." Although the distinction is arbitrary and confuses traditional understandings of cannabis varieties, plants that contain less than 0.3% THC are legally considered "hemp" in the United States, and those that contain greater than 0.3% THC are considered "marijuana" or "cannabis."

With the legalization of hemp, the 0.3-1% THC threshold has shifted the majority of the global and domestic "hemp" markets toward producing low-THC cannabis flowers rather than growing the plant for its industrial uses.

Common misconceptions include referring to hemp as "the male plants" or as a "cousin" to cannabis or "marijuana." Neither assertion is accurate. Hemp is cannabis.
See also Cannabis, Marijuana

Hydrocarbon Extraction
"Hydrocarbon extract" refers to hashes extracted with hydrocarbon solvents such as butane, ethanol, or propane. The end products are referred to as butane hash oil (BHO), ethanol hash oil (EHO), or propane

hash oil (PHO), respectively. The techniques used to produce each subcategory of hydrocarbon-extracted hash varies. Home or DIY production of hydrocarbon extracts is dangerous. They are only safe to produce in a legal, licensed setting with well-trained staff and professional industrial equipment.

Hydrocarbon extracts are sold by the gram, half gram, or in vaporizer cartridges under various names, usually in reference to variations in processing that result in different textures, shades, and consistencies of the finished products. These names include but are not limited to wax, live resin, shatter, taffy, pull and snap, sugar, budder, and batter/badder. *See also Butane Hash Oil (BHO), Concentrates, Dabs, Extracts*

Indica/Sativa/Ruderalis
The terms "indica," "sativa," and "ruderalis" refer to different varieties of cannabis based on their geographic origins and common traits. While the terms "indica" and "sativa" are commonly used to describe the effects of varieties – such as indicas produce sedative effects, and sativas produce stimulating effects – this is inaccurate. Although the term "ruderalis" has not taken on the same meanings as "indica" and "sativa," it is yet another variety of cannabis defined by geographic origin and common traits:

- Indicas evolved in the Hindu Kush mountain range and tend to be smaller, denser, darker green, have thicker leaf blades, and begin flowering earlier than sativa plants.
- Sativas evolved in equatorial regions and tend to be taller, looser, lighter green, have thinner leaf blades, and begin flowering later than indica plants.
- Ruderalis plants evolved in Northern Russia are smaller, and contain the "autoflowering" trait, meaning they begin flowering at germination and mature quickly, regardless of the season.

Most plants cultivated on modern markets are hybrid varieties bred from a mix of these varieties.

A Note on the Taxonomy Debate

There will be more nuance to using these classifications for those writing for scientific audiences or audiences familiar with the taxonomy debate. Over the years, various other taxonomies have been proposed. The majority are divided into two camps, the "lumpers" (who lump cannabis into as few categories as possible) and the "splitters," who feel there are more species or other species than are currently recognized. Karl Hillig and Robert Clarke view hemp plants as "sativas" and lump all other plants into sub-species of indica. In 2015, Robert McPartland proposed a new taxonomy based on geographic origin, where "sativa" would now be indica (because they evolved in India), and "indica" would become afghanica (because these plants evolved in Afghanistan), and "ruderalis" would be "sativa." Most people adhere to the old indica, sativa, and ruderalis framework, but it is subject to change as new research comes in.

See also Cannabis, Hemp

Kief
Kief is the sifted trichomes (resin) of dried cannabis flowers. It is either smoked, added to foods, or further processed into hashes.
See also Hash, Trichomes

Legalization, Decriminalization & Descheduling

- Legalization is when a jurisdiction authorizes, regulates, or otherwise permits cannabis use, possession, and commercial activities.
- Decriminalization is not legalization but removal or significant reduction of criminal or legal penalties associated with personal cannabis use and possession. Under most state-level decriminalization schemes, civil penalties/fines remain in place.
- Descheduling means the complete removal of cannabis from the Controlled Substances Act of 1970. Drug scheduling happens at the state and federal levels, so true "descheduling" would have to happen federally and state-by-state. The President, Congress, and the DEA have the power to change this federal designation.

Live Resin
Live resin is a hydrocarbon extraction of fresh, usually frozen cannabis flowers that were not cured or dried. Live resins generally have more terpenes (scent molecules).
See Butane Hash Oil (BHO), Extracts, Hydrocarbon Extraction

Looping
"Looping" is when a budtender knowingly allows customers to exceed purchase limits by conducting multiple transactions on the same day.

Marijuana (also Marihuana)
The term "marijuana" refers to the dried resinous flowers of the cannabis plant. The modern use of the term originated in Northern Mexico and was popularized in American culture through racist anti-Mexican propaganda. "Marijuana" is a controversial term today because of its use to create this negative association leading up to Prohibition.

There are several theories of the word's original etymology, as the plant did not appear to exist in the pre-Columbian Americas.

Although it is the term written into many federal and state laws, it is not scientifically accurate. It is believed this negative association was used to obscure that "marijuana" is cannabis and garner support for the prohibition of a "scary new drug" coming across the US-Mexico border.
See also Cannabis, Flower(s)

Measurements
From the 1940s to the 1970s, most of the cannabis consumed in the United States was purchased from other countries that use the metric system, and it was therefore sold in metric units; kilograms and grams. There are 1,000 grams in a kilogram, and a gram was a popular unit of measurement for small purchases. With the rise of domestic cultivation, cannabis in the United States is now sold in a blend of metric and imperial units; pounds, ounces, and grams. In the United States, units of cannabis flowers are sold under the following terms:

- Pound (16 ounces)
- Ounce (approximately 28 grams)
- "Quarter" (one-quarter of an ounce, approximately 7 grams)
- "Eighth" (one-eighth of an ounce, approximately 3.5 grams)
- "Tenth"* (one-tenth of an ounce, approximately 2.8 grams)

- Gram

**The "tenth" is only a measurement under state law in Ohio, where "eighths" are not sold in licensed dispensaries.*

Medical/Medicinal
Although they have distinct meanings, "medical" and "medicinal" are often used interchangeably. Most state laws refer to "medical" marijuana or cannabis, so this term must be used when referring to legislation or the category of the commercial market. The term "medical" refers specifically to the practice of medicine by licensed physicians, and "medicines" are FDA-approved pharmaceuticals and over-the-counter drugs.

The term "medicinal" is an adjective used to describe substances with properties of therapeutic value. Cannabis in its natural form does not fit the definition of a "medicine," but often, the purpose of consumption is therapeutic. Therefore, the term "medicinal" is more appropriate to describe the therapeutic use of cannabis.
See adult use

Phenotype
Cannabis is mostly dioecious, meaning there are separate male and female plants. As a result, breeding cannabis is relatively simpler than many other plants and can be done by amateurs and dedicated breeders alike. When two plants are bred, the resulting seeds inherit genes from the parent plants but, like human siblings, are unique from one another.

The term "phenotype" refers to different distinguishable traits between plants. These traits include plant height, yield, leaf size, the spectrum of phytochemicals, and more. A "pheno hunt" is a term used by cultivators to describe the process of germinating multiple seeds of one variety to select specific plants that express the desired traits.
See also Chemotype, Genotype

Photoperiod
Cannabis plants are summer annuals, meaning they evolved to germinate in the spring, begin growing flowers after the summer solstice, and ripen in the fall. Annual plants respond to the ratio of darkness to light, as well as other seasonal shifts in temperature and moisture. They measure when the nights become progressively longer to initiate and complete the process of flower production. The term "photoperiod" refers to this ratio of darkness to light. Different varieties of cannabis have slightly different photoperiod requirements to trigger flowering. Indoors, the grower controls the photoperiod to mimic this environmental trigger.
See Autoflower

Prescription/Recommendation
Cannabis is a Schedule I drug, so it cannot be prescribed in the United States and most of the world. The term "prescription" is often incorrectly used in reference to suggested use by a doctor. Doctors write letters of recommendation where the medicinal use of cannabis is legal. FDA-approved pharmaceutical synthetic cannabinoid medicines (like Marinol®) and botanically-derived cannabinoid medicines (like Epidiolex®) are prescribed rather than recommended.

Psychotropic/Psychoactive
Although the term "psychoactive" has come to be understood as feeling "high," the term "psychotropic" is the correct term to use in this context. While the words have similar meanings, "psychotropic" is defined as "affecting mental activity, behavior, or perception," or the feeling of "being high."

"Psychoactive" is defined as a substance

that affects mental processes. CBD affects neurological conditions such as epilepsy and is, therefore, "psychoactive." It is non-psychotropic. Do not use the term "non-psychoactive" to refer to phytochemicals from cannabis that do not produce the "high" associated with THC. Instead, use "non-psychotropic." Using a strict definition of psychoactivity, chocolate, coffee, tobacco, and many other substances are also considered psychoactive.

Recreational
Although "recreational" is commonly used to refer to the use of cannabis by adults who do not have a doctor's recommendation, the more appropriate term is "adult use." "Adult use" can and should be used in place of "recreational" because the term is most often associated with activities for children.
See Adult use, Legalization, Medical/Medicinal

Rick Simpson Oil (RSO)
See Full Extract Cannabis Oil (FECO)

Ruderalis
See Indica/Sativa/Ruderalis

Sativa
See Indica/Sativa/Ruderalis

Shatter
See BHO

Shake (Smalls)
Shake is the little buds, trim, and sometimes sugar leaf that is small enough to "shake" down to the bottom of a bag, compared with the larger, denser "flowers." Shake is often sold as "smalls" (little flowers) and may be sold directly to consumers who smoke, vaporize, or infuse them into butter at home.

Sinsemilla
The term "sinsemilla" means "without seed" in Spanish. It refers to unfertilized cannabis that results in larger, more resinous flowers rather than seeds. Its use was popularized through cultivation in Mexico in the 1970s and is not currently a common use term.

Smalls
See Shake

Solvent
The term "solvent" refers to substances that separate cannabinoids, terpenes, and flavonoids from the leaves to produce cannabis extracts. Common solvents include alcohol, butane, and carbon dioxide.
See also Butane Hash Oil (BHO), Extracts, Hash, Hydrocarbon Extraction

Strain/Cultivar/Chemovar/Variety
The word "strain" is often used to describe varieties of cannabis but is incorrectly used to refer to plants. The term "strain" is appropriate to classify viruses, fungi, and bacteria. The term "variety" is a blanket term that can refer to any different type of cannabis plant and is an acceptable alternative to "strain," as is "cultivar" when used appropriately. "Cultivar" is a portmanteau derived from "cultivated variety." It refers to the dried resinous flowers of the cannabis plant as a unique product of both the plant's genetics and the conditions provided by a cultivator. The term "chemovar" is a portmanteau for "chemical variety." It classifies plant varieties based on their chemotype or phytochemical profile.
See Chemotype, Cultivar, Variety

Terpene
Terpenes are aroma molecules found in cannabis and other plants. Terpenes have known medicinal properties. They are part of what is referred to as the "full spectrum" of cannabis compounds found in "whole plant" cannabis products. Terpenes deter pests in the living plant, are found in many other plants, and have a wide range of known therapeutic utility. The terms "terpenes" and "terpenoids"

are often used interchangeably, but this is incorrect. The term "terpenes" refers to the molecules produced by the living plant, and terpenoid refers to the molecules on the dried and cured flowers. It has become common in places where cultivation is legal for the media to report on odor complaints near cannabis cultivation sites and repeat commentary, through quotations or otherwise, that inhaling cannabis terpenes is potentially dangerous for the communities where it is cultivated. While the smell may be bothersome to some, the terpenes found in cannabis are no different from those found in all other cultivated crops and plants found in nature.
See Flavonoids, Full Spectrum, Whole Plant

THC
Δ^9-Tetrahydrocannabinol (THC) is the most abundantly found phytocannabinoid in cannabis.
See Cannabis, Cannabinoids, Hemp

Tincture
A tincture is a liquid extraction or infusion of cannabis sold in dropper bottles for easy dosing. It is often made with alcohol, glycerin, olive, or coconut oil. Tinctures are usually administered sublingually (under the tongue) for quick absorption, but they can also be used topically or in cooking.

Titrate
Titration is a method of dosing herbal products that relies on "starting low and going slow" or taking a very small amount and waiting to feel the effects before raising the dose.

Topicals
"Topicals" refers to products infused with cannabis applied to the skin for various therapeutic or cosmetic uses.

Trichome
Trichomes are glands that grow on cannabis plants, mainly the flowers, containing high concentrations of cannabinoids, terpenes, flavonoids, and other phytochemicals with therapeutic properties. They are referred to as the "resin." They are either stripped from the plant to create concentrates or removed using a solvent to produce extractions.
See Concentrate, Cannabinoid, Extract, Flavonoid, Hash, Terpene

Variety/Varietal
The word "strain" is often used to describe varieties of cannabis but is incorrectly used in reference to plants. The term "strain" is appropriately used to classify viruses, fungi, and bacteria. The term "variety" or "varietal" is a blanket term that can refer to any different type of cannabis plant.
See also Cultivar, Chemotype, Indica/Sativa/Ruderalis, Strain

Wax
See BHO

Whole Plant
Whole plant technically means using all parts of the plant, but in the cannabis industry it is often synonymous with "full spectrum."
See also Full Spectrum.

Endnotes

Clickable links for all of these references are available at **www.OaksterdamUniversity.com/TBGextras**

1. McPartland, John M., and Geoffrey W. Guy. "Models of Cannabis Taxonomy, Cultural Bias, and Conflicts between Scientific and Vernacular Names - the Botanical Review." SpringerLink. Springer US, June 22, 2017. https://link.springer.com/article/10.1007/s12229-017-9187-0.

2. Lawler, Andrew. "Oldest Evidence of Marijuana Use Discovered in 2500-Year-Old Cemetery .." Science, June 12, 2019. https://www.science.org/content/article/oldest-evidence-marijuana-use-discovered-2500-year-old-cemetery-peaks-western-china.

3. McPartland, John M., William Hegman, and Tengwen Long. "Cannabis in Asia: Its Center of Origin and Early Cultivation, Based on a Synthesis of Subfossil Pollen and Archaeobotanical Studies - Vegetation History and Archaeobotany." SpringerLink. Springer Berlin Heidelberg, May 14, 2019. https://link.springer.com/article/10.1007/s00334-019-00731-8.

4. *Ibid.*

5. Bian, Z., Sining Ling, Qi Yao, Shu, N. Shu, and Lvchao Qiu. "[PDF] Ethnobotanical Research on Origin , Cultivation , Distribution and Utilization of Hemp (Cannabis Sativa L .) in China: Semantic Scholar." [PDF] Ethnobotanical research on origin , cultivation , distribution and utilization of hemp (Cannabis sativa L .) in China I Semantic Scholar, January 1, 1970. https://www.semanticscholar.org/paper/Ethnobotanical-research-on-origin-%2C-cultivation-%2C-(-Bian-Ling/42b04d14f2cf386f289794481b58a11d513223d3.

6. Journal, The Asia Pacific. "The Secret History of Cannabis in Japan." The Asia-Pacific Journal: Japan Focus, December 5, 2014. https://apjjf.org/2014/12/49/Jon-Mitchell/4231.html.

7. Lawler, Andrew. "Oldest Evidence of Marijuana Use Discovered in 2500-Year-Old Cemetery .." Science, June 12, 2019. https://www.science.org/content/article/oldest-evidence-marijuana-use-discovered-2500-year-old-cemetery-peaks-western-china.

8. Ren, Meng, Zihua Tang, Xinhua Wu, Robert Spengler, Hongen Jiang, Yimin Yang, and Nicole Boivin. "The Origins of Cannabis Smoking: Chemical Residue Evidence from the First Millennium BCE in the Pamirs." ScienceAdvances, June 12, 2019. https://www.science.org/doi/10.1126/sciadv.aaw1391.

9. Liu, Fei-Hu, Hua-Ran Hu, Guang-Hui Du, Gang Deng, and Yang Yang. "Ethnobotanical Research on Origin, Cultivation, Distribution and Utilization of Hemp (Cannabis Sativa L.) in China." NOPR. NISCAIR-CSIR, India, April 1, 2017. http://nopr.niscpr.res.in/handle/123456789/40123.

10. JP, Hou. "The Development of Chinese Herbal Medicine and the Pen-Ts'ao." Comparative medicine East and West. U.S. National Library of Medicine, 1977. https://pubmed.ncbi.nlm.nih.gov/343983/.

11. Ved, Sonal. "The Surprising History of Bhang, India's Edible Cannabis Drink." Food52. Food52, March 17, 2022. https://food52.com/blog/27234-what-is-bhang.

12. Blaszczak, Agata. "Marijuana's History: How One Plant Spread through the World." LiveScience. Purch, February 10, 2022. https://www.livescience.com/48337-marijuana-history-how-cannabis-travelled-world.html.

13. Stoa, Ryan. "A Brief Global History of the War on Cannabis." The MIT Press Reader, April 20, 2021. https://thereader.mitpress.mit.edu/a-brief-global-history-of-the-war-on-cannabis/.

14. Bennet, Chris. "Cannabis in the Ancient World ." NaturalMood. Accessed January 19, 2023. http://naturalmood.com/pdfs/pot-book/bennett.pdf.

15. Bennett, Chris. "The Herb of the Magi: Zoroaster's Good Narcotic." Cannabis Culture, October 1, 2019. https://www.cannabisculture.com/content/2019/10/01/the-herb-of-the-magi-zoroasters-good-narcotic/.

16. Blaszczak, Agata. "Marijuana's History: How One Plant Spread through the World." LiveScience. Purch, February 10, 2022. https://www.livescience.com/48337-marijuana-history-how-cannabis-travelled-world.html.

17. Stoa, Ryan. "A Brief Global History of the War on Cannabis." The MIT Press Reader, April 20, 2021. https://thereader.mitpress.mit.edu/a-brief-global-history-of-the-war-on-cannabis/.

18. *Ibid.*

19. Duvall, Chris S. "Cannabis and Tobacco in Precolonial and Colonial Africa." Oxford Research Encyclopedia of African History. Oxford, March 29, 2017. https://oxfordre.com/africanhistory/display/10.1093/acrefore/9780190277734.001.0001/acrefore-9780190277734-e-44;jsessionid=5E22EA892F174258FE5B7BCA6AAC1048#:~:text=Cannabis%2C%20the%20source%20of%20marijuana,it%20had%20been%20consumed%20orally.

20. Duvall, Chris S. "African Roots of Marijuana." Duke University Press, 2019. https://www.dukeupress.edu/Assets/PubMaterials/978-1-4780-0394-6_601.pdf.

21. Blaszczak, Agata. "Marijuana's History: How One Plant Spread through the World." LiveScience. Purch, February 10, 2022. https://www.livescience.com/48337-marijuana-history-how-cannabis-travelled-world.html.

22. Ecohustler. "The UK's Compulsory Cannabis Law - Grow Hemp... or Else." Ecohustler, January 26, 2018. https://ecohustler.com/technology/the-uks-compulsory-cannabis-law-grow-hemp-or-else.

23. McNearney, Allison. "The Complicated History of Cannabis in the US." History.com. A&E Television Networks, April 20, 2018. https://www.history.com/news/marijuana-criminalization-reefer-madness-history-flashback#:~:text=The%20United%20States%20of%20Hemp&text=It%20was%20so%20important%2C%20in,well%20as%20Pennsylvania%20and%20Maryland.

24. Gandhi, Lakshmi. "A History of 'Snake Oil Salesmen'." NPR. NPR, August 26, 2013. https://www.npr.org/sections/codeswitch/2013/08/26/215761377/a-history-of-snake-oil-salesmen.

25. "The Pure Food and Drug Act." US House of Representatives: History, Art & Archives, June 23, 1906. https://history.house.gov/Historical-Highlights/1901-1950/Pure-Food-and-Drug-Act/.

26. Woodward, William C. "Statement of William C. Woodward, Legislative Counsel of the American Medical Association." Statement of dr. William C. Woodward, Legislative Council, American Medical Association. House of Representatives, Committee of Ways and Means, May 4, 1937. https://www.druglibrary.org/schaffer/hemp/taxact/woodward.htm.

27. "Single Convention on Narcotic Drugs." United Nations : Office on Drugs and Crime, 1961. https://www.unodc.org/unodc/en/treaties/single-convention.html?ref=menuside.

28. "The Controlled Substances Act." United States Drug Enforcement Agency, 1971. https://www.dea.gov/drug-information/csa.

29. History.com Editors. "War on Drugs." History.com. A&E Television Networks, May 31, 2017. https://www.history.com/topics/crime/the-war-on-drugs.

30. ProCon.org. "Nov. 5, 1991 - First Medical Marijuana Initiative Passed in San Francisco -." ProCon.org, September 24, 2019. https://medicalmarijuana.procon.org/timeline-events/nov-5-1991-first-medical-marijuana-initiative-passed-in-san-francisco/.

31. "California Proposition 215, Medical Marijuana Initiative (1996)." Ballotpedia. Accessed January 19, 2023. https://ballotpedia.org/California_Proposition_215,_Medical_Marijuana_Initiative_(1996).

32. Canada, Health. "Government of Canada." Understanding the Access to Cannabis for Medical Purposes Regulations - Canada.ca. / Gouvernement du Canada, September 30, 2016. https://www.canada.ca/en/health-canada/services/publications/drugs-health-products/understanding-new-access-to-cannabis-for-medical-purposes-regulations.html.

33. Ogden, David W. "Memorandum for Selected United State Attorneys on Investigations and Prosecutions in States Authorizing the Medical Use of Marijuana." The United States Department of Justice, October 19, 2009. https://www.justice.gov/archives/opa/blog/memorandum-selected-united-state-attorneys-investigations-and-prosecutions-states.

34. Coffman, Keith, and Nicole Neroulias. "Colorado, Washington First States to Legalize Recreational Pot." Reuters. Thomson Reuters, November 7, 2012. https://www.reuters.com/article/us-usa-marijuana-legalization/colorado-washington-first-states-to-legalize-recreational-pot-idUSBRE8A602D20121107.

35. Cole, James M. "Memorandum for All United States Attorneys." Justice.gov. United States Department of Justice, August 29, 2013. https://www.justice.gov/iso/opa/resources/3052013829132756857467.pdf.

36. Maybin, Simon. "Uruguay: The World's Marijuana Pioneer." BBC News. BBC, April 3, 2019. https://www.bbc.com/news/business-47785648.

37. Bulose, Sihle. "Cannabis Law and Legislation in South Africa." CMS Expert Guides. Accessed January 19, 2023. https://cms.law/en/int/expert-guides/cms-expert-guide-to-a-legal-roadmap-to-cannabis/south-africa.

38. Government of Canada, Department of Justice. "Cannabis Legalization and Regulation." Government of Canada, Department of Justice, Electronic Communications, October 17, 2018. https://www.justice.gc.ca/eng/cj-jp/cannabis/.

39. Hand, A, A Blake, Paul J Kerrigan, and P Samuel. "(PDF) History of Medical Cannabis - ." ResearchGate.net, January 2016. https://www.researchgate.net/publication/316545890_History_of_medical_cannabis.

40. Gandhi, Lakshmi. "A History of 'Snake Oil Salesmen'." NPR. NPR, August 26, 2013. https://www.npr.org/sections/codeswitch/2013/08/26/215761377/a-history-of-snake-oil-salesmen.

41. "The Pure Food and Drug Act." The Pure Food and Drug Act | U.S. Capitol - Visitor Center. Accessed January 19, 2023. https://www.visitthecapitol.gov/exhibitions/congress-and-progressive-era/pure-food-and-drug-act.

42. Commissioner, Office of the. "FDA History." U.S. Food and Drug Administration. FDA, June 29, 2018. https://www.fda.gov/about-fda/fda-history.

43. "A History of the Drug War." Drug Policy Alliance. Accessed January 19, 2023. https://drugpolicy.org/issues/brief-history-drug-war.

44. "The Marihuana Tax Act If 1937." DrugLibrary.org, May 4, 1937. https://www.druglibrary.org/schaffer/hemp/taxact/taxact.htm.

45. Gierginger, Dale H. "The Origins of California's 1913 Cannabis Law." CaNorml.org. California NORML, November 1999. https://www.canorml.org/the-origins-of-californias-1913-cannabis-law/.

46. Hoeffel, John. "Jack Herer Dies at 70; Author and Advocate for Marijuana Legalization." LATimes.com. Los Angeles Times, April 24, 2010. https://www.latimes.com/local/obituaries/la-me-jack-herer-20100424-story.html.

47. Solomon, Robert. "Racism and Its Effect on Cannabis Research." Cannabis and cannabinoid research. U.S. National Library of Medicine, February 27, 2020. https://www.ncbi.nlm.nih.gov/pmc/articles/PMC7173675/.

48. "Hemp for Victory." Hash Marihuana & Hemp Museum, August 12, 2021. https://hashmuseum.com/en/collection/growing-hemp/hemp-for-victory/.

49. Wishnia, Steven. "Debunking the Hemp Conspiracy Theory." Alternet.org, February 21, 2008. https://www.alternet.org/2008/02/debunking_the_hemp_conspiracy_theory.

50. Galliher, John F., and Allynn Walker. "The Puzzle of the Social Origins of the Marihuana Tax Act of 1937." JSTOR. Oxford University Press, February 1977. https://www.jstor.org/stable/800089.

51. Woodward, William C. "Statement of William C. Woodward, Legislative Counsel of the American Medical Association." Statement of dr. William C. Woodward, Legislative Council, American Medical Association. House of Representatives, Committee of Ways and Means, May 4, 1937. https://www.druglibrary.org/schaffer/hemp/taxact/woodward.htm.

52. "Leary v. United States, 395 U.S. 6 (1969)." Justia Law. Accessed January 20, 2023. https://supreme.justia.com/cases/federal/us/395/6/.

53. Däumichen, Marvin. "The Great Cannabis Scare - Harry J. Anslinger in the 1930s - Researchgate." Research Gate, September 2016. https://www.researchgate.net/publication/326780539_The_Great_Cannabis_Scare_-_Harry_J_Anslinger_in_the_1930s_-_Marvin_Daumichen.

54. "UN, United Nations, UN Treaties, Treaties." United Nations. Accessed January 20, 2023. https://treaties.un.org/Pages/ViewDetails.aspx?src=TREATY&mtdsg_no=VI-18&chapter=6&clang=_en.

55. Roosevelt, Franklin D. "United States National Archives Catalog." Archives.gov. National Archives and Records Administration, December 5, 1933. https://catalog.archives.gov/id/299967.

56. Smith, Laura. “How a Racist Hate-Monger Masterminded America’s War on Drugs.” Medium. Timeline, February 28, 2018. https://timeline.com/harry-anslinger-racist-war-on-drugs-prison-industrial-complex-fb5cbc281189.

57. “Single Convention on Narcotic Drugs.” United Nations : Office on Drugs and Crime, 1961. https://www.unodc.org/unodc/en/treaties/single-convention.html?ref=menuside.

58. “The Controlled Substances Act.” United States Drug Enforcement Agency, 1971. https://www.dea.gov/drug-information/csa.

59. Baum, Dan. “Legalize It All.” Harper’s Magazine , March 31, 2016. https://harpers.org/archive/2016/04/legalize-it-all/.

60. “A History of the Drug War.” Drug Policy Alliance. Accessed January 19, 2023. https://drugpolicy.org/issues/brief-history-drug-war.

61. “Single Convention on Narcotic Drugs.” United Nations : Office on Drugs and Crime, 1961. https://www.unodc.org/unodc/en/treaties/single-convention.html?ref=menuside.

62. “Uruguay Is Breaking the International Conventions on Drug Control with the Cannabis Legislation Approved by Its Congress.” United Nations Information Service Vienna International Center, December 11, 2013. https://www.incb.org/documents/Publications/PressRelease/PR2013/press_release_111213.pdf.

63. Bewley-Taylor, David, and Martin Jelsma. “Regime Change: Re-Visiting the 1961 Single Convention on Narcotic Drugs.” International Journal of Drug Policy. Department of Political and Cultural Studies, College of Arts and Humanities, Swansea University, Singleton Park, Swansea SA2 8PP, UK and Drugs & Democracy Programme at the Transnational Institute (TNI) in Amsterdam, The Netherlands, October 12, 2011. https://www.sciencedirect.com/science/article/abs/pii/S0955395911001575.

64. Bacca, Angela. “What Is Stalling the Change in Global Cannabis Policy?” Big Buds Magazine. Advanced Nutrients, May 23, 2019. https://bigbudsmag.com/what-is-stalling-the-change-in-global-cannabis-legislation/.

65. “High Compliance: Treaty Law Cannabis Legalization Report: Faaat: 2022.” FAAAT, April 1, 2022. https://faaat.net/highcompliance/.

66. Research and Markets. “The Worldwide Cannabis Industry Is Projected to Reach $90.4 Billion by 2026.” GlobeNewswire News Room. Research and Markets, February 18, 2021. https://www.globenewswire.com/news-release/2021/02/18/2177949/0/en/The-Worldwide-Cannabis-Industry-is-Projected-to-Reach-90-4-Billion-by-2026.html.

67. “The Controlled Substances Act.” United States Drug Enforcement Agency, 1971. https://www.dea.gov/drug-information/csa.

68. “The Report of the National Commission on Marihuana and Drug Abuse.” DrugLibrary.org. US National Commission on Marihuana and Drug Abuse, March 1972. https://www.druglibrary.org/schaffer/Library/studies/nc/ncmenu.htm.

69. “25 Years Ago: DEA’s Own Administrative Law Judge Ruled Cannabis Should Be Reclassified under Federal Law.” NORML.org. National Organization for the Reform of Marijuana Laws, September 5, 2013. https://norml.org/news/2013/09/05/25-years-ago-dea-s-own-administrative-law-judge-ruled-cannabis-should-be-reclassified-under-federal-law/.

70. Glass, Andrew. “Reagan Declares ‘War on Drugs,’ October 14, 1982.” POLITICO, October 14, 2010. https://www.politico.com/story/2010/10/reagan-declares-war-on-drugs-october-14-1982-043552.

71. The Editors of Encyclopaedia Britannica. “War on Drugs.” Encyclopædia Britannica. Accessed January 20, 2023. https://www.britannica.com/topic/war-on-drugs.

72. “Anti-Drug Abuse Act of 1986.” Anti-Drug Abuse Act of 1986 | Office of Justice Programs. United States Department of Justice, 1986. https://www.ojp.gov/ncjrs/virtual-library/abstracts/anti-drug-abuse-act-1986.

73. Lopez, German. “The Reagan Administration’s Unbelievable Response to the HIV/AIDS Epidemic.” Vox. Vox, December 1, 2015. https://www.vox.com/2015/12/1/9828348/ronald-reagan-hiv-aids.

74. Pietrangelo, Ann. “The Effects of HIV on the Immune System, Nervous System, and More.” Healthline. Healthline Media, March 29, 2022. https://www.healthline.com/health/hiv-aids/effects-on-body.

75. Skinner, David, Steve Moyer, Peter Tonguette, Anna Maria Gillis, and Jim Downs. "AIDS in One City: The San Francisco Story." The National Endowment for the Humanities. Accessed January 20, 2023. https://www.neh.gov/article/aids-one-city-san-francisco-story.

76. Gardner, Fred. "Dennis Peron and the Passage of Proposition 215." BeyondTHC.com. O'Shaughnessy's, 2007. https://beyondthc.com/wp-content/uploads/2019/12/Dennis-and-Prop-215-NB.pdf.

77. "California Proposition 215, Medical Marijuana Initiative (1996)." Ballotpedia. Accessed January 19, 2023. https://ballotpedia.org/California_Proposition_215,_Medical_Marijuana_Initiative_(1996).

78. "SB-420 Medical Marijuana." California Legislative Information. State of California Legilsature, October 2003. https://leginfo.legislature.ca.gov/faces/billNavClient.xhtml?bill_id=200320040SB420.

79. Ogden, David W. "Memorandum for Selected United State Attorneys on Investigations and Prosecutions in States Authorizing the Medical Use of Marijuana." The United States Department of Justice, October 19, 2009. https://www.justice.gov/archives/opa/blog/memorandum-selected-united-state-attorneys-investigations-and-prosecutions-states.

80. Cole, James M. "Memorandum for All United States Attorneys." Justice.gov. United States Department of Justice, August 29, 2013. https://www.justice.gov/iso/opa/resources/3052013829132756857467.pdf.

81. https://oaksterdamuniversity.com/a-look-back-at-brownie-mary/

82. "Recipients of Legal Medical Cannabis, Provided by the U.S. Government under the Investigational New Drug Program (Compassionate Access I.N.D.)." Patients Out of Time. Accessed January 20, 2023. https://medicalcannabis.com/patients-care-givers/federal-ind-patients/.

83. "U.S. v. Oakland Cannabis Buyers' Cooperative, 190 F.3d 1109: 9th Cir., Judgment, Law." Casemine.com. United States Court of Appeals, Ninth Circuit, September 13, 1999. https://www.casemine.com/judgement/us/59147f26add7b0493445ca94.

84. Canada, Global Affairs. "Cannabis and International Travel." Travel.gc.ca, April 1, 2021. https://travel.gc.ca/travelling/cannabis-and-international-travel.

85. Sabaghi, Dario. "You Can Risk Death Penalty for Cannabis in These Countries." Forbes. Forbes Magazine, November 8, 2022. https://www.forbes.com/sites/dariosabaghi/2022/03/30/you-can-risk-death-penalty-for-cannabis-in-these-countries/?sh=2a4f78827c8e.

86. itchell, Thomas. "Sweet Leaf Owners Get a Year in Jail for Illegal Pot Sales." Westword. Denver Westword, January 26, 2019. https://www.westword.com/marijuana/sweet-leaf-owners-accept-plea-over-looping-charges-get-one-year-in-jail-11199046.

87. "Health Insurance Portability and Accountability Act of 1996 (HIPAA)." Centers for Disease Control and Prevention. Centers for Disease Control and Prevention, June 27, 2022. https://www.cdc.gov/phlp/publications/topic/hipaa.html.

88. Leos-Toro, Cesar, Geoffrey T. Fong, Samantha B. Meyer, and David Hammond. "Cannabis Labelling and Consumer Understanding of THC Levels and Serving Sizes." ScienceDirect. School of Public Health & Health Systems, University of Waterloo, 200 University Ave. W., Waterloo, N2L 3G1, ON, Canada and Department of Psychology, University of Waterloo, 200 University Ave. W., N2L 3G1, Waterloo, ON, Canada and Ontario Institute for Cancer Research, MaRS Centre, 661 University Avenue, Suite 510, Toronto, M5G 0A3, ON, Canada, February 7, 2020. https://www.sciencedirect.com/science/article/abs/pii/S0376871620300089.

89. Dowd, Maureen. "Don't Harsh Our Mellow, Dude." The New York Times. The New York Times, June 4, 2014. https://www.nytimes.com/2014/06/04/opinion/dowd-dont-harsh-our-mellow-dude.html.

90. "Health Insurance Portability and Accountability Act of 1996 (HIPAA)." Centers for Disease Control and Prevention. Centers for Disease Control and Prevention, June 27, 2022. https://www.cdc.gov/phlp/publications/topic/hipaa.html.

91. Downs, David. "40% THC Flower?! How Lab Shopping and THC Inflation Cheat Cannabis Consumers." Leafly, January 26, 2021. https://www.leafly.com/news/strains-products/lab-shopping-thc-inflation-marijuana-2019-leafly-review.

92. Black, Lester. "America's Pot Labs Have a THC Problem." FiveThirtyEight, June 29, 2021. https://fivethirtyeight.com/features/americas-pot-labs-have-a-thc-problem/.

93. Roberts, Chris. "Science Reveals the Cannabis Industry's Greatest Lie: You're Buying Weed Wrong (and so Is Everyone Else)." Forbes. Forbes Magazine, October 12, 2022. https://www.forbes.com/sites/chrisroberts/2020/06/16/science-reveals-the-cannabis-industrys-greatest-lie-youre-buying-weed-wrong-and-so-is-everyone-else/?sh=46055c42ee35.

94. "VSB Medical Marijuana Identification Card Program - FAQS." VSB Medical Marijuana Identification Card Program - FAQs. Accessed January 20, 2023. https://www.cdph.ca.gov/Programs/CHSI/Pages/MMICP-FAQs.aspx#What%20is%20a%20Medical%20Marijuana%20Identification%20Card%20(MMIC)%20and%20how%20can%20it%20help%20me?

95. "Single Convention on Narcotic Drugs." United Nations : Office on Drugs and Crime, 1961. https://www.unodc.org/unodc/en/treaties/single-convention.html?ref=menuside.

96. Veiligheid, Ministerie van Justitie en. "Drugs." Government.nl. Government of the Netherlands, February 2, 2022. https://www.government.nl/topics/drugs#:~:text=In%20the%20Netherlands%2C%20it%20is,drinks%20are%20sold%20or%20consumed.

97. Felder, B Otis, and Ian A. Stewart. "Cannabis Consumption Lounges Present a Unique Risk Management Challenge." Wilson Elser, February 7, 2022. https://www.wilsonelser.com/news_and_insights/insights/4458-cannabis_consumption_lounges_present_a_unique_risk.

98. Jensen, Kelly. "PD: Budtender Sold Ounce of Pot to Undercover Cop 9 Times in 2 Hours." KUSA.com. KUSA, December 16, 2017. https://www.9news.com/article/news/crime/pd-budtender-sold-ounce-of-pot-to-undercover-cop-9-times-in-2-hours/73-499748902.

99. "Is It Illegal to Steal Tips?" Are Your Tips Being Stolen? EmploymentLawHelp.org. Accessed January 20, 2023. https://www.employmentlawhelp.org/wage-theft/illegal-to-steal-tips.

100. "A Practical Guide to Situational Awareness." Stratfor. Accessed January 20, 2023. https://worldview.stratfor.com/article/practical-guide-situational-awareness.

101. "Know Your Money ." SecretService.gov. United States Secret Service. Accessed January 20, 2023. https://www.secretservice.gov/sites/default/files/reports/2020-12/KnowYourMoney.pdf.

102. "How to Detect Counterfeit U.S. Money." dfa.cornell.edu. Cornell University. Accessed January 20, 2023. https://www.dfa.cornell.edu/sites/default/files/detect-counterfeit.pdf.

103. "Counterfeit Prevention." Bank of Canada/ Banque du Canada. Accessed January 20, 2023. https://www.bankofcanada.ca/banknotes/counterfeit-prevention/.

104. "European Central Bank." ecb.europa.eu. European Central Bank. Accessed January 20, 2023. https://www.ecb.europa.eu/euro/pdf/material/Quick_Guide_EN_Specimen.pdf.

105. "The Raid." Oaksterdam University, April 12, 2021. https://oaksterdamuniversity.com/the-raid/.

106. "THC - Search Results ." PubMed. U.S. National Library of Medicine. Accessed January 20, 2023. https://pubmed.ncbi.nlm.nih.gov/?term=THC.

107. Weinberg, Bill. "The Arbitrary Legal Line That Separates Hemp & Marijuana." Cannabis Now, December 20, 2018. https://cannabisnow.com/the-arbitrary-legal-line-that-separates-hemp-marijuana/.

108. Ben-Shabat, S, E Fride, T Sheskin, T Tamiri, MH Rhee, Z Vogel, T Bisogno, L De Petrocellis, V Di Marzo, and R Mechoulam. "An Entourage Effect: Inactive Endogenous Fatty Acid Glycerol Esters Enhance 2-Arachidonoyl-Glycerol Cannabinoid Activity." European journal of pharmacology. U.S. National Library of Medicine, July 17, 1998. https://pubmed.ncbi.nlm.nih.gov/9721036/.

109. Russo, Ethan B. "TAMING THC: Potential Cannabis Synergy and Phytocannabinoid-Terpenoid Entourage Effects." British journal of pharmacology. U.S. National Library of Medicine, August 2011. https://www.ncbi.nlm.nih.gov/pmc/articles/PMC3165946/.

110. "Marinol (Dronabinol) Capsules." AccessData.FDA.gov. United States Food & Drug Administration, September 2004. https://www.accessdata.fda.gov/drugsatfda_docs/label/2005/018651s021lbl.pdf.

111. "Epidiolex® (Cannabidiol)." EPIDIOLEX.com. Accessed January 20, 2023. https://www.epidiolex.com/.

112. Russo, Ethan B. "The Case for the Entourage Effect and Conventional Breeding of Clinical Cannabis: No 'Strain,' No Gain." Frontiers. Frontiers, December 19, 2018. https://www.frontiersin.org/articles/10.3389/fpls.2018.01969/full?&field=&journalName=Frontiers_in_Plant_Science&id=434025.

113. Pertwee, Roger G. "The 90th Birthday of Professor Raphael Mechoulam, a Top Cannabinoid Scientist and Pioneer." International journal of molecular sciences. U.S. National Library of Medicine, October 16, 2020. https://www.ncbi.nlm.nih.gov/pmc/articles/PMC7593926/.

114. Howlett, Allyn C, Lawrence C Blume, and George D Dalton. "CB(1) Cannabinoid Receptors and Their Associated Proteins." Current medicinal chemistry. U.S. National Library of Medicine, September 25, 2011. https://www.ncbi.nlm.nih.gov/pmc/articles/PMC3179980/.

115. Bie, Bihua, Jiang Wu, Joseph F Foss, and Mohamed Naguib. "An Overview of the Cannabinoid Type 2 Receptor System and Its Therapeutic Potential." Current opinion in anaesthesiology. U.S. National Library of Medicine, August 1, 2018. https://www.ncbi.nlm.nih.gov/pmc/articles/PMC6035094/.

116. Luchicchi, Antonio, and Marco Pistis. "Anandamide and 2-Arachidonoylglycerol: Pharmacological Properties, Functional Features, and Emerging Specificities of the Two Major Endocannabinoids." Molecular neurobiology. U.S. National Library of Medicine, October 17, 2012. https://pubmed.ncbi.nlm.nih.gov/22801993/.

117. Seltenrich, Nate. "Dolphin Study Identifies Hitherto Unknown Endocannabinoid." Project CBD, September 14, 2022. https://www.projectcbd.org/dolphin-study-identifies-hitherto-unknown-endocannabinoid.

118. Reggio, Patricia H. "Endocannabinoid Binding to the Cannabinoid Receptors: What Is Known and What Remains Unknown." PubMed Central. U.S. National Library of Medicine, August 4, 2014. https://www.ncbi.nlm.nih.gov/pmc/articles/PMC4120766/.

119. Lavelle, Judy. "New Brain Effects behind 'Runner's High.'" Scientific American. Scientific American, October 8, 2015. https://www.scientificamerican.com/article/new-brain-effects-behind-runner-s-high/.

120. "How Does Marijuana Produce Its Effects?" National Institutes of Health. U.S. Department of Health and Human Services, April 13, 2021. https://nida.nih.gov/publications/research-reports/marijuana/how-does-marijuana-produce-its-effects.

121. Lu, Hui-Chen, and Ken Mackie. "An Introduction to the Endogenous Cannabinoid System." PubMed. U.S. National Library of Medicine, April 1, 2016. https://www.ncbi.nlm.nih.gov/pmc/articles/PMC4789136/.

122. Gülck, Thies, and Birger Lindberg Møller. "Phytocannabinoids: Origins and Biosynthesis - Trends in Plant Science." Trends in Plant Science. Phytocannabinoids: Origins and Biosynthesis, July 6, 2020. https://www.cell.com/trends/plant-science/fulltext/S1360-1385(20)30187-4.

123. McPartland, John M, Geoffrey W Guy, and Vincenzo Di Marzo. "Care and Feeding of the Endocannabinoid System: A Systematic Review of Potential Clinical Interventions That Upregulate the Endocannabinoid System." PloS one. U.S. National Library of Medicine, March 12, 2014. https://www.ncbi.nlm.nih.gov/pmc/articles/PMC3951193/.

124. Walsh, Kenneth B., Amanda E. McKinney, and Andrea E. Holmes. "Minor Cannabinoids: Biosynthesis, Molecular Pharmacology and Potential Therapeutic Uses." Frontiers. Frontiers in Pharmacology, November 8, 2021. https://www.frontiersin.org/articles/10.3389/fphar.2021.777804/full.

125. Borrelli, Francesca. "Non-Psychotropic Plant Cannabinoids: New Therapeutic Opportunities from an Ancient Herb." Trends in Pharmacological Sciences. Elsevier BV, July 15, 2022. https://www.academia.edu/14021755/Non_psychotropic_plant_cannabinoids_new_therapeutic_opportunities_from_an_ancient_herb.

126. McPartland, John M, Geoffrey W Guy, and Vincenzo Di Marzo. "Care and Feeding of the Endocannabinoid System: A Systematic Review of Potential Clinical Interventions That Upregulate the Endocannabinoid System." PloS one. U.S. National Library of Medicine, March 12, 2014. https://www.ncbi.nlm.nih.gov/pmc/articles/PMC3951193/.

127. Russo, Ethan B. "Clinical Endocannabinoid Deficiency Reconsidered: Current Research Supports the Theory in Migraine, Fibromyalgia, Irritable Bowel, and Other Treatment-Resistant Syndromes." Cannabis and cannabinoid research. U.S. National Library of Medicine, July 1, 2016. https://www.ncbi.nlm.nih.gov/pmc/articles/PMC5576607/.

128. "Clinical Endocannabinoid Deficiency Issue Brief ." health.state.mn.us. Minnesota Department of Health, September 2017. https://www.health.state.mn.us/people/cannabis/docs/rulemaking/endocannabinoidbrief.pdf.

129. Russo, Ethan B. "Russo Clinical Endocannabinoid Deficiency NEL 2004." ResearchGate.net. CReDO Health, April 2015. https://www.researchgate.net/publication/274389723_Russo_Clinical_Endocannabinoid_Deficiency_NEL_2004.

130. Smith, Steele Clarke, and Mark S Wagner. "Clinical Endocannabinoid Deficiency (CECD) Revisited: Can This Concept Explain the Therapeutic Benefits of Cannabis in Migraine, Fibromyalgia, Irritable Bowel Syndrome and Other Treatment-Resistant Conditions?" PubMed. U.S. National Library of Medicine, 2014. https://pubmed.ncbi.nlm.nih.gov/24977967/.

131. Russo, Ethan B. "Clinical Endocannabinoid Deficiency Reconsidered: Current Research Supports the Theory in Migraine, Fibromyalgia, Irritable Bowel, and Other Treatment-Resistant Syndromes." Cannabis and cannabinoid research. U.S. National Library of Medicine, July 1, 2016. https://www.ncbi.nlm.nih.gov/pmc/articles/PMC5576607/.

132. Smithsonian Magazine. "Marijuana Isn't a Pain Killer-It's a Pain Distracter." Smithsonian.com. Smithsonian Institution, December 20, 2012. https://www.smithsonianmag.com/science-nature/marijuana-isnt-a-pain-killerits-a-pain-distracter-169786068/.

133. Wilsey, Barth, Thomas Marcotte, Reena Deutsch, Ben Gouaux B, Staci Sakai S, and Haylee Donaghe H; "Low-Dose Vaporized Cannabis Significantly Improves Neuropathic Pain." The journal of pain. U.S. National Library of Medicine, February 2013. https://pubmed.ncbi.nlm.nih.gov/23237736/.

134. Wallace, Mark S, Thomas D Marcotte, Anya Umlauf, Ben Gouaux, and Joseph H Atkinson. "Efficacy of Inhaled Cannabis on Painful Diabetic Neuropathy." The journal of pain. U.S. National Library of Medicine, July 2015. https://pubmed.ncbi.nlm.nih.gov/25843054/.

135. Doheny, Kathleen. "Marijuana Relieves Chronic Pain, Research Shows." Edited by Laura J Martin. WebMD.com. WebMD, August 30, 2010. https://www.webmd.com/pain-management/news/20100830/marijuana-relieves-chronic-pain-research-show#2.

136. Kinsey, Steven G, and Erica C Cole. "Acute δ(9)-Tetrahydrocannabinol Blocks Gastric Hemorrhages Induced by the Nonsteroidal Anti-Inflammatory Drug Diclofenac Sodium in Mice." European journal of pharmacology. U.S. National Library of Medicine, September 5, 2013. https://pubmed.ncbi.nlm.nih.gov/23769745/.

137. Swaminath, Arun, Eric P Berlin, Adam Chiefetz, Ed Hoffenberg, Jami Kinnucan, Laura Wingate, Sarah Buchanan, Nada Zmeter, and David T Reubin. "The Role of Cannabis in the Management of Inflammatory Bowel Disease: A Review of Clinical, Scientific, and Regulatory Information: Commissioned by the Crohn's and Colitis Foundation." Academic.oup.com. Oxford Academic - Inflammatory Bowel Diseases, October 24, 2018. https://academic.oup.com/ibdjournal/article/25/3/427/5144402.

138. "US6630507B1 - Cannabinoids as Antioxidants and Neuroprotectants." Google Patents. Google, April 21, 1999. https://patents.google.com/patent/US6630507B1/en.

139. Roberts, Chris. "What You Should Know about the Cannabis Patent." Cannabis Now, July 8, 2021. https://cannabisnow.com/what-you-should-know-about-the-cannabis-patent/.

140. Järvinen, Tomi, David W Pate, and Krista Laine. "Cannabinoids in the Treatment of Glaucoma." Pharmacology & Therapeutics. Pergamon, August 14, 2002. https://www.sciencedirect.com/science/article/abs/pii/S0163725802002590.

141. Tomida, Ileana, Augusto Azuara-Blanco, Heather House, Maggie Flint, Roger G. Pertwee, Dphil, and Philip J Robson. "Effect of Sublingual Application of Cannabinoids on Intraocular Pressure: A Pilot Study." Journal of Glaucoma, October 2006. https://journals.lww.com/glaucomajournal/Abstract/2006/10000/Effect_of_Sublingual_Application_of_Cannabinoids.1.aspx.

142. Tomida, I, R G Pertwee, and A Azuara-Blanco. "Cannabinoids and Glaucoma." The British journal of ophthalmology. U.S. National Library of Medicine, May 2004. https://www.ncbi.nlm.nih.gov/pmc/articles/PMC1772142/.

143. Walsh, Kenneth B., Amanda E. McKinney, and Andrea E. Holmes. "Minor Cannabinoids: Biosynthesis, Molecular Pharmacology and Potential Therapeutic Uses." Frontiers. Frontiers, November 8, 2021. https://www.frontiersin.org/articles/10.3389/fphar.2021.777804/full.

144. Moldzio, Rudolf, Thomas Pacher, Christopher Krewenka, Barbara Kranner, Johannes Novak, Johanna Catharina Duvigneau, and Wolf-Dieter Rausch. "Effects of Cannabinoids δ(9)-Tetrahydrocannabinol, δ(9)-Tetrahydrocannabinolic Acid and Cannabidiol in MPP+ Affected Murine Mesencephalic Cultures." Phytomedicine : international journal of phytotherapy and phytopharmacology. U.S. National Library of Medicine, June 15, 2012. https://pubmed.ncbi.nlm.nih.gov/22571976/.

145. Rock, E M, R L Kopstick, C L Limebeer, and L A Parker. “Tetrahydrocannabinolic Acid Reduces Nausea-Induced Conditioned Gaping in Rats and Vomiting in Suncus Murinus.” British journal of pharmacology. U.S. National Library of Medicine, October 2013. https://pubmed.ncbi.nlm.nih.gov/23889598/.

146. http://www.cannabisinternational.org/

147. Lee, Martin A. “Is Juicing Raw Cannabis the Miracle Health Cure That Some of Its Proponents Believe It to Be?” Alternet.org. Alternet Media Inc., April 3, 2013. https://www.alternet.org/2013/04/juicing-raw-cannabis-miracle-health-cure-some-its-proponents-believe-it-be.

148. Maheshwari, Rahul, and Rakesh K. Tekade. “Manipulation of Physiological Processes for Pharmaceutical Product Development.” First Pass Effect - an overview I ScienceDirect Topics, 2018. https://www.sciencedirect.com/topics/pharmacology-toxicology-and-pharmaceutical-science/first-pass-effect#:~:text=The%20first%2Dpass%20metabolism%20or,thus%20showing%20subtherapeutic%20action%20.

149. Huestis, Marilyn A. “Human Cannabinoid Pharmacokinetics.” Chemistry & biodiversity. U.S. National Library of Medicine, August 2007. https://www.ncbi.nlm.nih.gov/pmc/articles/PMC2689518/.

150. “Psychotropic vs. Psychoactive: See the Difference.” Dictionary.com. Dictionary.com. Accessed January 21, 2023. https://www.dictionary.com/compare-words/psychotropic-vs-psychoactive.

151. Ibid.

152. Marchini, Marie, Celine Charvoz, Laurence Dujourdy, Nicolas Baldovini, and Jean-Jacques Filippi. “Multidimensional Analysis of Cannabis Volatile Constituents: Identification of 5,5-Dimethyl-1-Vinylbicyclo[2.1.1]Hexane as a Volatile Marker of Hashish, the Resin of Cannabis Sativa L.” Journal of chromatography. U.S. National Library of Medicine, November 28, 2018. https://pubmed.ncbi.nlm.nih.gov/25454145/.

153. “Understanding Medical Cannabis (PDF).” Elemental Wellness. Elemental Wellness & Steep Hill Labs, 2015. https://elementalwellnesscenter.com/media/EWC_UMC.pdf.

154. Sharma, Priyamvada, Pratima Murthy, and M M Srinivas Bharath. “Chemistry, Metabolism, and Toxicology of Cannabis: Clinical Implications.” Iranian journal of psychiatry. U.S. National Library of Medicine, 2012. https://www.ncbi.nlm.nih.gov/pmc/articles/PMC3570572//.

155. Colbert, Mitchell. “Cannabinoid Profiles: A Crash Course in THCV.” The Leaf Online, April 5, 2018. http://theleafonline.com/c/science/2014/06/cannabinoid-profiles-a-crash-course-in-thcv/%20.

156. https://youtu.be/wkA6mcAE7Sw

157. Bolognini, Daniele, Barbara Costa, Sabatino Maione, Francesca Comelli, Pietro Marini, Vincenzo Di Marzo, Daniela Parolaro, et al. “The Plant Cannabinoid delta9-Tetrahydrocannabivarin Can Decrease Signs of Inflammation and Inflammatory Pain in Mice.” British journal of pharmacology. U.S. National Library of Medicine, June 2010. https://www.ncbi.nlm.nih.gov/pmc/articles/PMC2931567/.

158. García, C, C Palomo-Garo, M García-Arencibia, Ja Ramos, J Fernández-Ruiz, and R G Pertwee. “Symptom-Relieving and Neuroprotective Effects of the Phytocannabinoid Δ^9-THCV in Animal Models of Parkinson's Disease.” British journal of pharmacology. U.S. National Library of Medicine, August 2011. https://pubmed.ncbi.nlm.nih.gov/21323909/.

159. Rahn, Bailey. “What Is THCV and What Are the Benefits of This Cannabinoid?” Leafly, September 27, 2022. https://www.leafly.com/news/cannabis-101/what-is-thcv-and-what-are-the-benefits-of-this-cannabinoid.

160. Walsh, Kenneth B., Amanda E. McKinney, and Andrea E. Holmes. “Minor Cannabinoids: Biosynthesis, Molecular Pharmacology and Potential Therapeutic Uses.” Frontiers. Frontiers in Pharmacology, November 8, 2021. https://www.frontiersin.org/articles/10.3389/fphar.2021.777804/full.

161. Burns, Janet. “Tests of CBD Oils Reveal Three Surprise Chemicals, One Big Problem.” Leafly, July 28, 2020. https://www.leafly.com/news/industry/tests-of-cbd-oils-reveal-three-surprise-chemicals-one-big-problem.

162. Commissioner, Office of the. “FDA Regulation of Cannabis and Cannabis-Derived Products: Q&A.” U.S. Food and Drug Administration. FDA. Accessed January 21, 2023. https://www.fda.gov/news-events/public-health-focus/fda-regulation-cannabis-and-cannabis-derived-products-including-cannabidiol-cbd.

163. Colbert, Mitchell. "Cannabinoid Profile: Cannabidiolic Acid (CBDA)." The Leaf Online, October 16, 2016. http://www.theleafonline.com/c/science/2014/07/cannabinoid-profile-crash-course-cbda/.

164. Walsh, Kenneth B., Amanda E. McKinney, and Andrea E. Holmes. "Minor Cannabinoids: Biosynthesis, Molecular Pharmacology and Potential Therapeutic Uses." Frontiers. Frontiers in Pharmacology, November 8, 2021. https://www.frontiersin.org/articles/10.3389/fphar.2021.777804/full.

165. Takeda, Shuso, Shunsuke Okajima, Hiroko Miyoshi, Kazutaka Yoshida, Yoshiko Okamoto, Tomoko Okada, Toshiaki Amamoto, Kazuhito Watanabe, Curtis J Omiecinski, and Hironori Aramaki. "Cannabidiolic Acid, a Major Cannabinoid in Fiber-Type Cannabis, Is an Inhibitor of MDA-MB-231 Breast Cancer Cell Migration." Toxicology letters. U.S. National Library of Medicine, November 15, 2012. https://pubmed.ncbi.nlm.nih.gov/22963825/.

166. Rock, Erin M, Cheryl L Limebeer, Roshan Navaratnam, Martin A Sticht, Natasha Bonner, Kristin Engeland, Rachel Downey, Heather Morris, Meagan Jackson, and Linda A Parker. "A Comparison of Cannabidiolic Acid with Other Treatments for Anticipatory Nausea Using a Rat Model of Contextually Elicited Conditioned Gaping." Psychopharmacology. U.S. National Library of Medicine, August 2014. https://pubmed.ncbi.nlm.nih.gov/24595502/.

167. Rock, EM, and LA Parker. "Effect of Low Doses of Cannabidiolic Acid and Ondansetron on LiCl-Induced Conditioned Gaping (a Model of Nausea-Induced Behaviour) in Rats." British journal of pharmacology. U.S. National Library of Medicine, June 2013. https://pubmed.ncbi.nlm.nih.gov/23488964/.

168. https://pubchem.ncbi.nlm.nih.gov/compound/Cannabigerolic-acid

169. Walsh, Kenneth B., Amanda E. McKinney, and Andrea E. Holmes. "Minor Cannabinoids: Biosynthesis, Molecular Pharmacology and Potential Therapeutic Uses." Frontiers. Frontiers, November 8, 2021. https://www.frontiersin.org/articles/10.3389/fphar.2021.777804/full.

170. Anderson, Lyndsey L, Marika Heblinski, Nathan L Absalom, Nicole A Hawkins, Michael T Bowen, Melissa J Benson, Fan Zhang, et al. "Cannabigerolic Acid, a Major Biosynthetic Precursor Molecule in Cannabis, Exhibits Divergent Effects on Seizures in Mouse Models of Epilepsy." British journal of pharmacology. U.S. National Library of Medicine, December 2021. https://pubmed.ncbi.nlm.nih.gov/34384142/.

171. Janecki, Marcin, Michal Graczyk, Agata Anna Lewandowska, and Lukasz Pawlak. "Anti-Inflammatory and Antiviral Effects of Cannabinoids in Inhibiting and Preventing SARS-COV-2 Infection." International journal of molecular sciences. U.S. National Library of Medicine, April 10, 2022. https://pubmed.ncbi.nlm.nih.gov/35456990/.

172. Dawidowicz, Andrzej L, Malgorzata Olszowy-Tomczyk, and Rafal Typek. "CBG, CBD, Δ9-THC, CBN, CBGA, CBDA and Δ9-THCA as Antioxidant Agents and Their Intervention Abilities in Antioxidant Action." Fitoterapia. U.S. National Library of Medicine, July 2021. https://pubmed.ncbi.nlm.nih.gov/33964342/.

173. Williamson, EM, and FJ Evans. "Cannabinoids in Clinical Practice." PubMed.gov. U.S. National Library of Medicine, December 2000. https://pubmed.ncbi.nlm.nih.gov/11152013/.

174. Cascio, M G, L A Gauson, L A Stevenson, R A Ross, and R G Pertwee. "Evidence That the Plant Cannabinoid Cannabigerol Is a Highly Potent alpha2-Adrenoceptor Agonist and Moderately Potent 5HT1A Receptor Antagonist." British journal of pharmacology. U.S. National Library of Medicine, January 2010. https://www.ncbi.nlm.nih.gov/pmc/articles/PMC2823359/.

175. Celada, Pau, M Puig, Mercè Amargós-Bosch, Albert Adell, and Francesc Artigas. "The Therapeutic Role of 5-HT1A and 5-HT2A Receptors in Depression." Journal of psychiatry & neuroscience : JPN. U.S. National Library of Medicine, July 2004. https://www.ncbi.nlm.nih.gov/pmc/articles/PMC446220/.

176. Williamson, EM, and FJ Evans. "Cannabinoids in Clinical Practice." PubMed.gov. U.S. National Library of Medicine, December 2000. https://pubmed.ncbi.nlm.nih.gov/11152013/.

177. Colasanti, Brenda K. "A Comparison of the Ocular and Central Effects of Δ9 ..." Journal of Ocular Pharmacology and Therapeutics. Mary Anne Libert, Inc. Publishers, March 18, 2009. https://www.liebertpub.com/doi/abs/10.1089/jop.1990.6.259.

178. Walsh, Kenneth B., Amanda E. McKinney, and Andrea E. Holmes. "Minor Cannabinoids: Biosynthesis, Molecular Pharmacology and Potential Therapeutic Uses." Frontiers. Frontiers in Pharmacology, November 8, 2021. https://www.frontiersin.org/articles/10.3389/fphar.2021.777804/full.

179. Colbert, Mitchell. "Cannabinoid Profile: Cannabichromene (CBC)." The Leaf Online, November 17, 2016. http://www.theleafonline.com/c/science/2014/07/cannabinoid-profile-crash-course-cbc/.

180. Maione, Sabatino, Fabiana Piscitelli, Luisa Gatta, Daniela Vita, Luciano De Petrocellis, Enza Palazzo, Vito de Novellis, and Vincenzo Di Marzo. "Non-Psychoactive Cannabinoids Modulate the Descending Pathway of Antinociception in Anaesthetized Rats through Several Mechanisms of Action." British journal of pharmacology. U.S. National Library of Medicine, February 2011. https://pubmed.ncbi.nlm.nih.gov/20942863/.

181. Wirth, PW, ES Watson, M ElSohly M, CE Turner, and JC Murphy JC. "Anti-Inflammatory Properties of Cannabichromene." Life sciences. U.S. National Library of Medicine, June 9, 1980. https://pubmed.ncbi.nlm.nih.gov/7401911/.

182. El-Alfy, Abir T, Kelly Ivey, Keisha Robinson, Safwat Ahmed, Mohamed Radwan, Desmond Slade, Ikhlas Khan, Mahmoud ElSohly, and Samir Ross. "Antidepressant-like Effect of delta9-Tetrahydrocannabinol and Other Cannabinoids Isolated from Cannabis Sativa L." Pharmacology, biochemistry, and behavior. U.S. National Library of Medicine, June 2010. https://pubmed.ncbi.nlm.nih.gov/20332000/.

183. Shinjyo, Noriko, and Vincenzo Di Marzo. "The Effect of Cannabichromene on Adult Neural Stem/Progenitor Cells." Neurochemistry International. Pergamon, August 10, 2013. https://www.sciencedirect.com/science/article/abs/pii/S0197018613002106.

184. Sparr-Jaswa, Andrea. "Type I, Type II, Type III: How Science Is Changing the Way the Industry Describes Cannabis Varieties." Cannabis Business Times, November 8, 2019. https://www.cannabisbusinesstimes.com/news/chemotype-classification-how-science-is-changing-the-way-the-industry-describes-cannabis-varieties/.

185. Salamone, Stefano, Lorenz Waltl, Anna Pompignan, Gianpaolo Grassi, Giuseppina Chianese, Andreas Koeberle, and Federica Pollastro. "Phytochemical Characterization of Cannabis Sativa L. Chemotype V Reveals Three New Dihydrophenanthrenoids That Favorably Reprogram Lipid Mediator Biosynthesis in Macrophages." Plants (Basel, Switzerland). U.S. National Library of Medicine, August 16, 2022. https://pubmed.ncbi.nlm.nih.gov/36015434/.

186. Colbert, Mitchell. "Cannabinoid Profile: Cannabinol (CBN)." The Leaf Online, October 16, 2016. http://www.theleafonline.com/c/science/2014/07/cannabinoid-profile-crash-course-cbn/.

187. https://greencamp.com/cannabinol/

188. Farrimond, Jonathon A, Benjamin J Whalley, and Claire M Williams. "Cannabinol and Cannabidiol Exert Opposing Effects on Rat Feeding Patterns." Psychopharmacology. U.S. National Library of Medicine, September 2012. https://pubmed.ncbi.nlm.nih.gov/22543671/.

189. "Cannabis and Cannabinoids (PDQ®)–Health Professional Version." National Cancer Institute. Accessed January 21, 2023. https://www.cancer.gov/about-cancer/treatment/cam/hp/cannabis-pdq#section/all.

190. Walters, Sam. "The Dangers of 'Spice' and Other Synthetic Cannabinoids." Discover Magazine. Discover Magazine, October 28, 2021. https://www.discovermagazine.com/health/the-dangers-of-spice-and-other-synthetic-cannabinoids.

191. Russo, Sarah. "SCC Consensus on Delta-8-THC." Society of Cannabis Clinicians. Sarah Russo https://www.cannabisclinicians.org/wp-content/uploads/2020/06/scc_logo-long-R-2-1.png, December 27, 2021. https://www.cannabisclinicians.org/2021/08/30/scc-consensus-on-delta-8-thc/.

192. "5 Things to Know about Delta-8 Tetrahydrocannabinol – Delta-8 THC." U.S. Food and Drug Administration. FDA. Accessed January 21, 2023. https://www.fda.gov/consumers/consumer-updates/5-things-know-about-delta-8-tetrahydrocannabinol-delta-8-thc.

193. SC Labs. "Learn about Terpenes." SC Labs, October 13, 2022. https://www.sclabs.com/terpenes/.

194. https://www.britannica.com/science/isomerism/Conformational-isomers

195. Meehan-Atrash, Jiries, Wentai Luo, and Robert M Strongin. "Toxicant Formation in Dabbing: The Terpene Story." ACS omega. U.S. National Library of Medicine, September 30, 2017. https://www.ncbi.nlm.nih.gov/pmc/articles/PMC5623941/.

196. "Best Dabbing Temperatures." Leafly, September 16, 2022. https://www.leafly.com/learn/consume/dabs/best-dabbing-temperatures.

197. Colbert, Mitchell. "Terpene Profile: Myrcene." The Leaf Online, October 16, 2016. http://www.theleafonline.com/c/science/2014/09/terpene-profile-myrcene/.

198. Mediavilla, Vito, and Simon Steinemann. "Essential Oil of Cannabis Sativa L. Strain." International Hemp Association. Swiss Federal Research Station for Agroecology and Agriculture. Accessed January 21, 2023. http://www.internationalhempassociation.org/jiha/jiha4208.html.

199. Hall, Patrick. "Stoner Fruit Cocktail: Mangos, Marijuana and Myrcene." CelebStoner.com, July 31, 2013. https://www.celebstoner.com/news/marijuana-news/2013/07/30/stoner-fruit-cocktail-mangos,-marijuana-and-mycene/.

200. https://www.medicaljane.com/category/cannabis-classroom/terpenes/#terpenes-in-cannabis

201. Russo, Ethan B. "Cannabinoids in the Management of Difficult to Treat Pain." Therapeutics and clinical risk management. U.S. National Library of Medicine, February 2008. https://www.ncbi.nlm.nih.gov/pmc/articles/PMC2503660/.

202. Rao, VS, AM Menezes, and GS Viana. "Effect of Myrcene on Nociception in Mice." The Journal of pharmacy and pharmacology. U.S. National Library of Medicine, December 1998. https://pubmed.ncbi.nlm.nih.gov/1983154/.

203. Lorenzetti, BB, GE Souza, SJ Sarti, D Santos Filho, and SH Ferreira. "Myrcene Mimics the Peripheral Analgesic Activity of Lemongrass Tea." Journal of ethnopharmacology. U.S. National Library of Medicine, August 1991. https://pubmed.ncbi.nlm.nih.gov/1753786/.

204. Gurgel do Vale, T, E Couto Furtado, JG Santos, and GSB Viana. "Central Effects of Citral, Myrcene and Limonene, Constituents of Essential Oil Chemotypes from Lippia Alba (Mill.) N.E. Brown." Phytomedicine : international journal of phytotherapy and phytopharmacology. U.S. National Library of Medicine, December 2002. https://pubmed.ncbi.nlm.nih.gov/12587690/.

205. Colbert, Mitchell. "Terpene Profile: Caryophyllene." The Leaf Online, March 30, 2018. http://www.theleafonline.com/c/science/2014/10/terpene-profile-caryophyllene/.

206. Gertsch, Jürg, Marco Leonti, Stefan Raduner, Ildiko Racz, Jian-Zhong Chen, Xiang-Qun Xie, Karl-Heinz Altmann, Meliha Karsak, and Andreas Zimmer. "Beta-Caryophyllene Is a Dietary Cannabinoid." Proceedings of the National Academy of Sciences of the United States of America. U.S. National Library of Medicine, July 1, 2008. https://www.ncbi.nlm.nih.gov/pmc/articles/PMC2449371/.

207. Al Mansouri, Shamma, Shreesh Ojha, Elyazia Al Maamari, Mouza Al Ameri, Syed M Nurulain, and Amine Bahi. "The Cannabinoid Receptor 2 Agonist, β-Caryophyllene, Reduced Voluntary Alcohol Intake and Attenuated Ethanol-Induced Place Preference and Sensitivity in Mice." Pharmacology, biochemistry, and behavior. U.S. National Library of Medicine, September 2014. https://pubmed.ncbi.nlm.nih.gov/24999220/.

208. Calleja, Miguel Angel, Jose Maria Vieites, Trinidad Montero-Meléndez, Maria Isabel Torres, Maria Jose Faus, Angel Gil, and Antonia Suárez. "The Antioxidant Effect of β-Caryophyllene Protects Rat Liver from Carbon Tetrachloride-Induced Fibrosis by Inhibiting Hepatic Stellate Cell Activation." The British journal of nutrition. U.S. National Library of Medicine, February 14, 2013. https://pubmed.ncbi.nlm.nih.gov/22717234/.

209. Klauke, A-L, I Racz, B Pradier, A Markert, AM Zimmer, J Gertsch, and A Zimmer. "The Cannabinoid CB_2 Receptor-Selective Phytocannabinoid Beta-Caryophyllene Exerts Analgesic Effects in Mouse Models of Inflammatory and Neuropathic Pain." European neuropsychopharmacology : the journal of the European College of Neuropsychopharmacology. U.S. National Library of Medicine, April 2014. https://pubmed.ncbi.nlm.nih.gov/24210682/.

210. Ghelardini, C, N Galeotti, L Di Cesare Mannelli, G Mazzanti, and A Bartolini. "Local Anaesthetic Activity of Beta-Caryophyllene." Farmaco (Societa chimica italiana : 1989). U.S. National Library of Medicine, May 2001. https://pubmed.ncbi.nlm.nih.gov/11482764/.

211. Bahi, Amine, Shamma Al Mansouri, Elyazia Al Memari, Mouza Al Ameri, Syed M Nurulain, and Shreesh Ojha S. "Β-Caryophyllene, a CB2 Receptor Agonist Produces Multiple Behavioral Changes Relevant to Anxiety and Depression in Mice." Physiology & behavior. U.S. National Library of Medicine, August 2014. https://pubmed.ncbi.nlm.nih.gov/24930711/.

212. Bento, Allisson Freire, Rodrigo Marcon, Rafael Cypriano Dutra, Rafaela Franco Claudino, Maíra Cola, Daniela Ferraz Pereira Leite, and João B Calixto. "Β-Caryophyllene Inhibits Dextran Sulfate Sodium-Induced Colitis in Mice through CB2 Receptor Activation and PPARΓ Pathway." The American journal of pathology. U.S. National Library of Medicine, March 2011. https://pubmed.ncbi.nlm.nih.gov/21356367/.

213. Legault, Jean, and André Pichette. "Potentiating Effect of Beta-Caryophyllene on Anticancer Activity of Alpha-Humulene, Isocaryophyllene and Paclitaxel." The Journal of pharmacy and pharmacology. U.S. National Library of Medicine, December 2007. https://pubmed.ncbi.nlm.nih.gov/18053325/.

214. Kim, Chulwon, Somi K Cho, Ki-Dong Kim, Dongwoo Nam, Won-Seok Chung, Hyeung-Jin Jang, Seok-Jeun Lee, Bum Sang Shim, Guatam Sethi, and Kwang Seok Ahn. "Β-Caryophyllene Oxide Potentiates Tnfα-Induced Apoptosis and Inhibits Invasion through down-Modulation of NF-ΚB-Regulated Gene Products." Apoptosis : an international journal on programmed cell death. U.S. National Library of Medicine, April 2014. https://pubmed.ncbi.nlm.nih.gov/24370994/.

215. Pant, Aakanksha, Vikas Mishra, Shilpi K Saikia, Virenda Shukla, Jyotsna Asthana, Bashir A Akhoon, and Rakesh Pandey R; "Beta-Caryophyllene Modulates Expression of Stress Response Genes and Mediates Longevity in Caenorhabditis Elegans." Experimental gerontology. U.S. National Library of Medicine, September 2014. https://pubmed.ncbi.nlm.nih.gov/24835194/.

216. Colbert, Mitchell. "Terpene Profile: Limonene." The Leaf Online, October 16, 2016. http://www.theleafonline.com/c/science/2014/09/terpene-profile-limonene/.

217. de Almeida, Antonia Amanda C, Jéssica Pereira Costa, Rusbene Bruno F de Carvalho, Damião Pergentino de Sousa, and Rivelilson Mendes de Freitas. "Evaluation of Acute Toxicity of a Natural Compound (+)-Limonene Epoxide and Its Anxiolytic-like Action." Brain research. U.S. National Library of Medicine, April 11, 2012. https://pubmed.ncbi.nlm.nih.gov/22364736/.

218. Hirota, Ryoji, Ngatu Nlandu Roger, Hiroyuki Nakamura, Hee-Sun Song, Masayoshi Sawamura, and Narufumi Suganuma. "Anti-Inflammatory Effects of Limonene from Yuzu (Citrus Junos Tanaka) Essential Oil on Eosinophils." Journal of food science. U.S. National Library of Medicine, April 2010. https://pubmed.ncbi.nlm.nih.gov/20492298/.

219. Chaudhary, SC, MS Siddiqui, M Athar, and M Sarwar Alam. "D-Limonene Modulates Inflammation, Oxidative Stress and Ras-Erk Pathway to Inhibit Murine Skin Tumorigenesis." Human & experimental toxicology. U.S. National Library of Medicine, August 2012. https://pubmed.ncbi.nlm.nih.gov/22318307/.

220. d'Alessio, Patrizia A, Rita Ostan, Jean-François Bisson, Joerg D Schulzke, Matilde V Ursini, and Marie C Béné. "Oral Administration of D-Limonene Controls Inflammation in Rat Colitis and Displays Anti-Inflammatory Properties as Diet Supplementation in Humans." Life sciences. U.S. National Library of Medicine, July 10, 2013. https://pubmed.ncbi.nlm.nih.gov/23665426/.

221. Crowell, PL, and MN Gould. "Chemoprevention and Therapy of Cancer by D-Limonene." Critical reviews in oncogenesis. U.S. National Library of Medicine, 1994. https://pubmed.ncbi.nlm.nih.gov/7948106/.

222. Rabi, Thangaiyan, and Anupam Bishayee. "D -Limonene Sensitizes Docetaxel-Induced Cytotoxicity in Human Prostate Cancer Cells: Generation of Reactive Oxygen Species and Induction of Apoptosis." Journal of carcinogenesis. U.S. National Library of Medicine, 2009. https://pubmed.ncbi.nlm.nih.gov/19465777/.

223. Crowell, PL, A Siar Ayoubi, and YD Burke. "Antitumorigenic Effects of Limonene and Perillyl Alcohol against Pancreatic and Breast Cancer." Advances in experimental medicine and biology. U.S. National Library of Medicine, 1996. https://pubmed.ncbi.nlm.nih.gov/8886131/.

224. Gould, M N. "Cancer Chemoprevention and Therapy by Monoterpenes." Environmental health perspectives. U.S. National Library of Medicine, June 1997. https://www.ncbi.nlm.nih.gov/pmc/articles/PMC1470060/.

225. Vigushin, DM, GK Poon, A Boddy, J English, GW Halbert, C Pagonis, M Jarman, and RC Coombes. "Phase I and Pharmacokinetic Study of D-Limonene in Patients with Advanced Cancer. Cancer Research Campaign Phase I/II Clinical Trials Committee." Cancer chemotherapy and pharmacology. U.S. National Library of Medicine, 1998. https://pubmed.ncbi.nlm.nih.gov/9654110/.

226. "Terpinolene." Terpinolene - an overview | ScienceDirect Topics. Accessed January 22, 2023. https://www.sciencedirect.com/topics/pharmacology-toxicology-and-pharmaceutical-science/terpinolene.

227. Ito, Ken, and Michiho Ito. "The Sedative Effect of Inhaled Terpinolene in Mice and Its Structure-Activity Relationships." Journal of natural medicines. U.S. National Library of Medicine, October 2013. https://pubmed.ncbi.nlm.nih.gov/23339024/.

228. Aydin, Elanur, Hasan Türkez, and Şener Taşdemir. "Anticancer and Antioxidant Properties of Terpinolene in Rat Brain Cells." Archives of Industrial Hygiene and Toxicology, September 1, 2013. https://sciendo.com/article/10.2478/10004-1254-64-2013-2365.

229. Colbert, Mitchell. "Terpene Profile: Pinene." The Leaf Online, October 5, 2017. http://www.theleafonline.com/c/science/2014/10/terpene-profile-pinene/.

230. Bae, Gi-Sang, Kyoung-Chel Park, Sun Bok Choi, Il-Joo Jo, Mee-Ok Choi, Seung-Heon Hong, Kyung Song, Ho-Joon Song, and Sung-Joo Park. "Protective Effects of Alpha-Pinene in Mice with Cerulein-Induced Acute Pancreatitis." Life Sciences. Pergamon, September 12, 2012. https://www.sciencedirect.com/science/article/abs/pii/S0024320512004870.

231. Aydin, Elanur, Hasan Türkez, and Fatime Geyikoğlu. "Antioxidative, Anticancer and Genotoxic Properties of α-Pinene on N2A Neuroblastoma Cells - Biologia." SpringerLink. Springer Vienna, August 31, 2013. https://link.springer.com/article/10.2478/s11756-013-0230-2#page-1.

232. Kusuhara, Masatoshi, Kenichi Urakami, Yoko Masuda, Vincent Zangiacomi, Hidee Ishii, Sachiko Tai, Koj Maruyama, and Ken Yamaguchi. "Fragrant Environment with α-Pinene Decreases Tumor Growth in Mice." Biomedical research (Tokyo, Japan). U.S. National Library of Medicine, February 2012. https://pubmed.ncbi.nlm.nih.gov/22361888/.

233. Chen, Wei-Qiang, Bin Xu, Jian-Wen Mao, Feng-Xiang Wei, Ming Li, Tao Liu, Xiao-Bao Jin, and Li-Rong Zhang . "Inhibitory Effects of α-Pinene on Hepatoma Carcinoma Cell Proliferation." Asian Pacific journal of cancer prevention : APJCP. U.S. National Library of Medicine, 2014. https://pubmed.ncbi.nlm.nih.gov/24815485/.

234. Russo, Ethan B. "TAMING THC: Potential Cannabis Synergy and Phytocannabinoid-Terpenoid Entourage Effects." British journal of pharmacology. U.S. National Library of Medicine, August 2011. https://www.ncbi.nlm.nih.gov/pmc/articles/PMC3165946/.

235. Rufino, Ana T, Madalena Ribeiro, Lígia Salgueiro, Maria C. Lopes, Carlos Cavaleiro, Alexandrina F Mendes, and Fernando Judas. "Anti-Inflammatory and Chondroprotective Activity of (+)-α-Pinene: Structural and Enantiomeric Selectivity." ACS Publications. The American Chemical Society and American Society of Pharmacognosy, 2014. https://pubs.acs.org/doi/10.1021/np400828x.

236. Hurt, Raymond. "Tuberculosis Sanatorium Regimen in the 1940s: A Patient's Personal Diary." Journal of the Royal Society of Medicine. U.S. National Library of Medicine, July 2004. https://www.ncbi.nlm.nih.gov/pmc/articles/PMC1079536/.

237. Rohr, Annette C, Cornelius K Wilkins, Per A Clausen, Maria Hammer, Gunnar D Nielsen, Peder Wolkoff, and John D Spengler. "Upper Airway and Pulmonary Effects of Oxidation Products of (+)-Alpha-Pinene, D-Limonene, and Isoprene in BALB/C Mice." Inhalation toxicology. U.S. National Library of Medicine, July 2002. https://pubmed.ncbi.nlm.nih.gov/12122569/.

238. Yang, Zhiwei, Nan Wu, Yuangang Zu, and Yujie Fu. "Comparative Anti-Infectious Bronchitis Virus (IBV) Activity of (-)-Pinene: Effect on Nucleocapsid (N) Protein." Molecules (Basel, Switzerland). U.S. National Library of Medicine, January 25, 2011. https://pubmed.ncbi.nlm.nih.gov/21350392/.

239. SC Labs. "Learn about Terpenes." SC Labs, October 13, 2022. https://www.sclabs.com/terpenes/.

240. Zviely, Michael. "Ocimene - a Versatile Floral Ingredient (PDF)." ResearchGate.net. Jiangnan University, January 2013. https://www.researchgate.net/publication/235659815_Ocimene_-_A_Versatile_Floral_Ingredient.

241. Russo, Ethan B, and Jahan Marcu. "Cannabis Pharmacology: The Usual Suspects and a Few Promising Leads." EthanRusso.org. Advances in Pharmacology, 2017. http://ethanrusso.org/wp-content/uploads/2020/02/Russo-Marcu-Cannabis-Pharmacology-The-Usual-Suspects-and-a-Few-Promising-Leads-Adv-Pharmacol-2017-1.pdf.

242. Kim, Min-Jin, Kyong-Wol Yang, Sang Suk Kim, Suk Man Park, Kyung Jin Park, Kwang Sik Kim, Young Hun Choi, Kwang Keun Cho, and Chang-Gu Hyun. "Chemical Composition and Anti-Inflammation Activity of Essential Oils from Citrus Unshiu Flower." Natural product communications. U.S. National Library of Medicine, May 2014. https://pubmed.ncbi.nlm.nih.gov/25026734/.

243. Colbert, Mitchell. "Terpene Profile: Linalool." The Leaf Online, October 16, 2016. http://www.theleafonline.com/c/science/2014/09/terpene-profile-linalool/.

244. Koulivand, Peir Hossein, Maryam Khaleghi Ghadiri, and Ali Gorji. "Lavender and the Nervous System." Evidence-based complementary and alternative medicine : eCAM. U.S. National Library of Medicine, 2013. https://www.ncbi.nlm.nih.gov/pmc/articles/PMC3612440/.

245. López, Víctor, Birgitte Nielsen, Maite Solas, Maria J Ramírez, and Anna K Jäger. "Exploring Pharmacological Mechanisms of Lavender (Lavandula Angustifolia) Essential Oil on Central Nervous System Targets." Frontiers in pharmacology. U.S. National Library of Medicine, May 19, 2017. https://www.ncbi.nlm.nih.gov/pmc/articles/PMC5437114/.

246. Peana, Alessandra T, Paolo S D'Aquila, M Loredana Chessa, Mario DL Moretti, Gino Serra, and Proto Pippia. "(-)-Linalool Produces Antinociception in Two Experimental Models of Pain." European journal of pharmacology. U.S. National Library of Medicine, January 26, 2003. https://pubmed.ncbi.nlm.nih.gov/12535857/.

247. de Sousa, Damião P, Franklin FF Nóbrega, Camila CMP Santos, and Reinaldo N de Almeida. "Anticonvulsant Activity of the Linalool Enantiomers and Racemate: Investigation of Chiral Influence." Natural product communications. U.S. National Library of Medicine, December 2010. https://pubmed.ncbi.nlm.nih.gov/21299105/.

248. Peana, AT, PS D'Aquila, F Panin, G Serra, P Pippia, and MDL Moretti. "Anti-Inflammatory Activity of Linalool and Linalyl Acetate Constituents of Essential Oils." Phytomedicine : international journal of phytotherapy and phytopharmacology. U.S. National Library of Medicine, December 2002. https://pubmed.ncbi.nlm.nih.gov/12587692/.

249. https://go.drugbank.com/drugs/DB03852

250. Conti, Barbara, Guido Flamini, Pier Luigi Cioni, Lucia Ceccarini, Mario Macchia, and Giovanni Benelli. "Mosquitocidal Essential Oils: Are They Safe against Non-Target Aquatic Organisms?" Parasitology research. U.S. National Library of Medicine, January 2014. https://pubmed.ncbi.nlm.nih.gov/24146210/.

251. Chehregani, Abdolkarim, Morteza Atri, Somayeh Yousefi, Fariba Mohsenzadeh, and Zahra Albooyeh. "Essential Oil Variation in the Populations of Artemisia Spicigera from Northwest of Iran: Chemical Composition and Antibacterial Activity." Pharmaceutical biology. U.S. National Library of Medicine, February 2013. https://pubmed.ncbi.nlm.nih.gov/23126238/.

252. Khan, Andleeb, Kumar Vaibhav, Hayate Javed, RIzwana Tabassum, Md Ejaz Ahmed, Mohd Moshahid Khan, M Badruzzaman Khan, et al. "1,8-Cineole (Eucalyptol) Mitigates Inflammation in Amyloid Beta Toxicated PC12 Cells: Relevance to Alzheimer's Disease." Neurochemical research. U.S. National Library of Medicine, February 2014. https://pubmed.ncbi.nlm.nih.gov/24379109/.

253. Ramos Alvarenga, René F, Baojie Wan, Taichi Inui, Scott G Franzblau, Guido F Pauli, and Birgit U Jaki. "Airborne Antituberculosis Activity of Eucalyptus Citriodora Essential Oil." Journal of natural products. U.S. National Library of Medicine, March 28, 2014. https://pubmed.ncbi.nlm.nih.gov/24641242/.

254. Worth, Heinrich, and Uwe Dethlefsen. "Patients with Asthma Benefit from Concomitant Therapy with Cineole: A Placebo-Controlled, Double-Blind Trial." The Journal of asthma : official journal of the Association for the Care of Asthma. U.S. National Library of Medicine, October 2012. https://pubmed.ncbi.nlm.nih.gov/22978309/.

255. Santos, FA, RM Silva, AR Campos, RP De Araújo, RC Lima Júnior, and VS Rao. "1,8-Cineole (Eucalyptol), a Monoterpene Oxide Attenuates the Colonic Damage in Rats on Acute TNBS-Colitis." Food and chemical toxicology : an international journal published for the British Industrial Biological Research Association. U.S. National Library of Medicine, April 2004. https://pubmed.ncbi.nlm.nih.gov/15019181/.

256. Santos, FA, and VS Rao. "Antiinflammatory and Antinociceptive Effects of 1,8-Cineole a Terpenoid Oxide Present in Many Plant Essential Oils." Phytotherapy research : PTR. U.S. National Library of Medicine, June 2000. https://pubmed.ncbi.nlm.nih.gov/10861965/.

257. Cho, Kyung-Hyun. "1,8-Cineole Protected Human Lipoproteins from Modification by Oxidation and Glycation and Exhibited Serum Lipid-Lowering and Anti-Inflammatory Activity in Zebrafish." BMB reports. U.S. National Library of Medicine, October 2012. https://pubmed.ncbi.nlm.nih.gov/23101510/.

258. Moteki, Hiroyuki, HIroshige Hibasami, Yayoi Yamada, Hirotaka Katsuzaki, Kunio Imai, and Takashi Komiya. "Specific Induction of Apoptosis by 1,8-Cineole in Two Human Leukemia Cell Lines, but Not a in Human Stomach Cancer Cell Line." Oncology reports. U.S. National Library of Medicine, 2002. https://pubmed.ncbi.nlm.nih.gov/12066204/.

259. Murata, Soichiro, Risa Shiragami, Chihiro Kosug, Tohru Tezuka, Masato Yamazaki, Atsushi Hirano, Yukino Yoshimura, et al. "Antitumor Effect of 1, 8-Cineole against Colon Cancer." Oncology reports. U.S. National Library of Medicine, December 2013. https://pubmed.ncbi.nlm.nih.gov/24085263/.

260. Colbert, Mitchell. "Terpene Profile: Humulene." The Leaf Online, October 16, 2016. http://www.theleafonline.com/c/science/2014/11/terpene-profile-humulene/.

261. https://pubchem.ncbi.nlm.nih.gov/compound/Humulene

262. Siqueira Chaves, Juliana, Paulo César Leal, Luis Pianowisky, and João B Calixto. "Pharmacokinetics and Tissue Distribution of the Sesquiterpene Alpha-Humulene in Mice." Planta medica. U.S. National Library of Medicine, November 2008. https://pubmed.ncbi.nlm.nih.gov/18951339/.

263. Legault, Jean, Wivecke Dahl, Eric Debiton, André Pichette, and Jean-Claude Madelmont. "Antitumor Activity of Balsam Fir Oil: Production of Reactive Oxygen Species Induced by Alpha-Humulene as Possible Mechanism of Action." Planta medica. U.S. National Library of Medicine, May 2003. https://pubmed.ncbi.nlm.nih.gov/12802719/.

264. Colbert, Mitchell. "Terpene Profile: Hashishene." The Leaf Online, October 16, 2016. http://www.theleafonline.com/c/science/2016/06/terpene-profile-hashishene/.

265. Marchini, Marie, Céline Charvoz, Laurence Dujourdy, Nicolas Baldovini, and Jean-Jacques Filippi. "Multidimensional Analysis of Cannabis Volatile Constituents: Identification of 5,5-Dimethyl-1-Vinylbicyclo[2.1.1]Hexane as a Volatile Marker of Hashish, the Resin of Cannabis Sativa L." Journal of chromatography. A. U.S. National Library of Medicine, November 28, 2014. https://pubmed.ncbi.nlm.nih.gov/25454145/.

266. Dias, Maria Celeste, Diana C G A Pinto, and Artur M S Silva. "Plant Flavonoids: Chemical Characteristics and Biological Activity." Molecules (Basel, Switzerland). U.S. National Library of Medicine, September 4, 2021. https://www.ncbi.nlm.nih.gov/pmc/articles/PMC8434187/.

267. Umar, Olayinka Bolaji, Lawal Amudalat Ranti, Abdulbaki Shehu Abdulbaki, Abdulra'uf Lukman Bola, Abdulkareem Khadijat Abdulhamid, Murtadha Ramat Biola, and Kayode Oluwagbenga Victor. "Stresses in Plants: Biotic and Abiotic." IntechOpen. IntechOpen, October 18, 2021. https://www.intechopen.com/chapters/79012.

268. Dias, Maria Celeste, Diana C G A Pinto, and Artur M S Silva. "Plant Flavonoids: Chemical Characteristics and Biological Activity." Molecules (Basel, Switzerland). U.S. National Library of Medicine, September 4, 2021. https://www.ncbi.nlm.nih.gov/pmc/articles/PMC8434187/.

269. Ibid.

270. "Foods That Fight Inflammation." Harvard Health, November 16, 2021. https://www.health.harvard.edu/staying-healthy/foods-that-fight-inflammation.

271. Panche, A N, A D Diwan, and S R Chandra. "Flavonoids: An Overview." Journal of nutritional science. U.S. National Library of Medicine, December 29, 2016. https://www.ncbi.nlm.nih.gov/pmc/articles/PMC5465813/.

272. Singh, B K, T K Koley, Arti Maurya, P M Singh, and B Singh. "Phytochemical and Antioxidative Potential of Orange, Red, Yellow, Rainbow and Black Coloured Tropical Carrots (Daucus Carota Subsp.. Sativus Schubl. & Martens)." Physiology and molecular biology of plants : an international journal of functional plant biology. U.S. National Library of Medicine, September 2018. https://www.ncbi.nlm.nih.gov/pmc/articles/PMC6103943/#:~:text=1c.

273. Kalt, Wilhelmina, Aedin Cassidy, Luke R Howard, Robert Krikorian, April J Stull, Francois Tremblay, and Raul Zamora-Ros. "Recent Research on the Health Benefits of Blueberries and Their Anthocyanins." Oxford Academic. Advances in Nutrition, July 22, 2019. https://academic.oup.com/advances/article/11/2/224/5536953.

274. Zhou, Dan-Dan, Min Luo, Si-Yu Huang, Adila Saimaiti, Ao Shang, Ren-You Gan, and Hua-Bin Li. "Effects and Mechanisms of Resveratrol on Aging and Age-Related Diseases." Oxidative medicine and cellular longevity. U.S. National Library of Medicine, July 11, 2021. https://www.ncbi.nlm.nih.gov/pmc/articles/PMC8289612/.

275. Fernandes, Iva, Rosa Pérez-Gregorio, Susana Soares, Nuno Mateus, and Victor de Freitas. "Wine Flavonoids in Health and Disease Prevention." Molecules (Basel, Switzerland). U.S. National Library of Medicine, February 14, 2017. https://www.ncbi.nlm.nih.gov/pmc/articles/PMC6155685/.

276. Devitt-Lee, Adrian. "Cannabis: Gateway to Herbal Medicine." Project CBD, May 14, 2019. https://www.projectcbd.org/wellness/cannabis-gateway-herbal-medicine.

277. Eker, Merve Eda, Kjersti Aaby, Irena Budic-Leto, Suzana Rimac Brnčić, Sedef Nehir El, Sibel Karakaya, Sebnem Simsek, Claudine Manach, Wieslaw Wiczkowski, and Sonia de Pascual-Teresa. "A Review of Factors Affecting Anthocyanin Bioavailability: Possible Implications for the Inter-Individual Variability." Foods (Basel, Switzerland). U.S. National Library of Medicine, December 18, 2019. https://www.ncbi.nlm.nih.gov/pmc/articles/PMC7023094/.

278. Thilakarathna, Surangi H, and H P Vasantha Rupasinghe. "Flavonoid Bioavailability and Attempts for Bioavailability Enhancement." Nutrients. U.S. National Library of Medicine, August 28, 2013. https://www.ncbi.nlm.nih.gov/pmc/articles/PMC3798909/.

279. Egert, Sarah, and Gerald Rimbach. "Which Sources of Flavonoids: Complex Diets or Dietary Supplements?" Advances in nutrition (Bethesda, Md.). U.S. National Library of Medicine, January 2011. https://www.ncbi.nlm.nih.gov/pmc/articles/PMC3042792/.

280. Bautista, Johanna L, Shu Yu, and Li Tian. "Flavonoids in Cannabis Sativa Biosynthesis, Bioactivities, and Biotechnology." ACS omega. U.S. National Library of Medicine, February 18, 2021. https://www.ncbi.nlm.nih.gov/pmc/articles/PMC7931196/.

281. Salem, Manar M, Jeffrey Capers, Shawn Rito, and Karl A Werbovetz. "Antiparasitic Activity of C-Geranyl Flavonoids from Mimulus Bigelovii." Phytotherapy research : PTR. U.S. National Library of Medicine, August 2011. https://pubmed.ncbi.nlm.nih.gov/21796699/.

282. Raman, Ryan. "What Is Quercetin? Benefits, Foods, Dosage, and Side Effects." Healthline. Healthline Media, July 1, 2020. https://www.healthline.com/nutrition/quercetin.

283. Bischoff, Stephan C. "Quercetin: Potentials in the Prevention and Therapy of Disease." Current opinion in clinical nutrition and metabolic care. U.S. National Library of Medicine, November 2008. https://pubmed.ncbi.nlm.nih.gov/18827577/.

284. Mlcek, Jiri, Tunde Jurikova, Sona Skrovankova, and Jiri Sochor. "Quercetin and Its Anti-Allergic Immune Response." Molecules (Basel, Switzerland). U.S. National Library of Medicine, May 12, 2016. https://pubmed.ncbi.nlm.nih.gov/27187333/.

285. Shaik, YB, ML Castellani, A Perrella, F Conti, V Salini, S Tete, B Madhappan, et al. "Role of Quercetin (a Natural Herbal Compound) in Allergy and Inflammation." Journal of biological regulators and homeostatic agents. U.S. National Library of Medicine, July 2006. https://pubmed.ncbi.nlm.nih.gov/18187018/.

286. Chirumbolo, Salvatore. "Quercetin as a Potential Anti-Allergic Drug: Which Perspectives?" Iranian journal of allergy, asthma, and immunology. U.S. National Library of Medicine, June 2011. https://pubmed.ncbi.nlm.nih.gov/21625024/.

287. Devitt-Lee, Adrian. "Cannabis: Gateway to Herbal Medicine." Project CBD, May 14, 2019. https://www.projectcbd.org/wellness/cannabis-gateway-herbal-medicine.

288. Lin, Yong, Ranxin Shi, Xia Wang, and Han-Ming Shen. "Luteolin, a Flavonoid with Potential for Cancer Prevention and Therapy." Current cancer drug targets. U.S. National Library of Medicine, November 2008. https://www.ncbi.nlm.nih.gov/pmc/articles/PMC2615542/.

289. Ibid.

290. Ristic, Aleksa. "Luteolin: Potential Benefits + Foods & Side Effects." SelfDecode Supplements, September 9, 2021. https://supplements.selfdecode.com/blog/luteolin-benefits/.

291. Theoharides, Theoharis Constantin PhD, Julia M RN Stewart, and Erifili MD Hatziagelaki. "Brain 'Fog,' Inflammation and Obesity: Key Aspects of Neuropsychiatric Disorders Improved by Luteolin." Frontiers. Frontiers, June 10, 2015. https://www.frontiersin.org/articles/10.3389/fnins.2015.00225/full.

292. Wang, Zhenyu, Maomao Zeng, Zhaojun Wan, Fang Qin, Jie Chen, and Zhiyong He. "Dietary Luteolin: A Narrative Review Focusing on Its Pharmacokinetic Properties and Effects on Glycolipid Metabolism." ACS Publications, 2021. https://pubs.acs.org/doi/10.1021/acs.jafc.0c08085.

293. Petre, Alina. "Anthocyanin: Foods, Benefits, Side Effects, and Supplements." Healthline. Healthline Media, February 24, 2022. https://www.healthline.com/nutrition/anthocyanin.

294. Khoo, Hock Eng, Azrina Azlan, Sou Teng Tang, and See Meng Lim. "Anthocyanidins and Anthocyanins: Colored Pigments as Food, Pharmaceutical Ingredients, and the Potential Health Benefits." Food & nutrition research. U.S. National Library of Medicine, August 13, 2017. https://pubmed.ncbi.nlm.nih.gov/28970777/.

295. Korte, Gabriele, Andrea Dreiseitel, Peter Schreier, Anett Oehme, Sanja Locher, Goeran Hajak, and Philipp G. Sand. "An Examination of Anthocyanins' and Anthocyanidins' Affinity for Cannabinoid Receptors." Mary Ann Liebert, Inc Publishers. Journal of Medicinal Food, December 30, 2009. https://www.liebertpub.com/doi/abs/10.1089/jmf.2008.0243.

296. Eker, Merve Eda, Kjersti Aaby, Irena Budic-Leto, Suzana Rimac Brnčić, Sedef Nehir El, Sibel Karakaya, Sebnem Simsek, Claudine Manach, Wieslaw Wiczkowski, and Sonia de Pascual-Teresa. "A Review of Factors Affecting Anthocyanin Bioavailability: Possible Implications for the Inter-Individual Variability." Foods (Basel, Switzerland). U.S. National Library of Medicine, December 18, 2019. https://www.ncbi.nlm.nih.gov/pmc/articles/PMC7023094/.

297. Werz, Oliver, Julia Seegers, Anja Maria Schaible, Christina Weinigel, Dagmar Barz, Andreas Koeberle, Gianna Allegrone, et al. "Cannflavins from Hemp Sprouts, a Novel Cannabinoid-Free Hemp Food Product, Target Microsomal Prostaglandin E2 Synthase-1 and 5-Lipoxygenase." Science Direct. Pharma Nutrition, July 2014. https://www.sciencedirect.com/science/article/abs/pii/S2213434414000176.

298. Eggers, Carly, Masaya Fujitani, Ryuji Kato, and Scott Smid. "Novel Cannabis Flavonoid, Cannflavin a Displays Both a Hormetic and Neuroprotective Profile against Amyloid β-Mediated Neurotoxicity in PC12 Cells: Comparison with Geranylated Flavonoids, Mimulone and Diplacone." Biochemical pharmacology. U.S. National Library of Medicine, November 2019. https://pubmed.ncbi.nlm.nih.gov/31437460/.

299. Bautista, Johanna L, Shu Yu, and Li Tian. "Flavonoids in Cannabis Sativa Biosynthesis, Bioactivities, and Biotechnology." ACS omega. U.S. National Library of Medicine, February 18, 2021. https://www.ncbi.nlm.nih.gov/pmc/articles/PMC7931196/.

300. Brunelli, Elisa, Giulia Pinton, Paolo Bellini, Alberto Minassi, Giovanni Appendino, and Laura Moro. "Flavonoid-Induced Autophagy in Hormone Sensitive Breast Cancer Cells." Fitoterapia. U.S. National Library of Medicine, September 2009. https://pubmed.ncbi.nlm.nih.gov/19371773/.

301. Moreau, Michele, Udoka Ibeh, Kaylie Decosmo, Noella Bih, Sayeda Yasmin-Karim, Ngeh Toyang, Henry Lowe, and Wilfred Ngwa. "Flavonoid Derivative of Cannabis Demonstrates Therapeutic Potential in Preclinical Models of Metastatic Pancreatic Cancer." Frontiers in oncology. U.S. National Library of Medicine, July 23, 2019. https://pubmed.ncbi.nlm.nih.gov/31396485/.

302. Brunelli, Elisa, Giulia Pinton, Paolo Bellini, Alberto Minassi, Giovanni Appendino, and Laura Moro. "Flavonoid-Induced Autophagy in Hormone Sensitive Breast Cancer Cells." Fitoterapia. U.S. National Library of Medicine, September 2009. https://pubmed.ncbi.nlm.nih.gov/19371773/.

303. Giupponi, Luca, Valeria Leoni, Radmila Pavlovic, and Annamaria Giorgi. "Influence of Altitude on Phytochemical Composition of Hemp Inflorescence: A Metabolomic Approach." Molecules (Basel, Switzerland). U.S. National Library of Medicine, March 18, 2020. https://pubmed.ncbi.nlm.nih.gov/32197420/.

304. McPartland, John M, Geoffrey W Guy, and Vincenzo Di Marzo. "Care and Feeding of the Endocannabinoid System: A Systematic Review of Potential Clinical Interventions That Upregulate the Endocannabinoid System." PloS one. U.S. National Library of Medicine, March 12, 2014. https://www.ncbi.nlm.nih.gov/pmc/articles/PMC3951193/.

305. https://pubmed.ncbi.nlm.nih.gov/

306. https://pubmed.ncbi.nlm.nih.gov/?term=ibuprofen

307. https://pubmed.ncbi.nlm.nih.gov/?term=ritalin

308. https://pubmed.ncbi.nlm.nih.gov/?term=hydrocodone

309. "25 Years Ago: DEA's Own Administrative Law Judge Ruled Cannabis Should Be Reclassified under Federal Law." NORML.org. National Organization for the Reform of Marijuana Laws, September 5, 2013. https://norml.org/news/2013/09/05/25-years-ago-dea-s-own-administrative-law-judge-ruled-cannabis-should-be-reclassified-under-federal-law/.

310. "Information on Cannabis Safety." Americans for Safe Access. Accessed January 23, 2023. https://www.safeaccessnow.org/cannabis_safety.

311. Hall, Wayne. "A Comparative Appraisal of the Health and Psychological Consequences of Alcohol, Cannabis, Nicotine and Opiate Use." Academia.edu, June 12, 2014. https://www.academia.edu/2868073/A_comparative_appraisal_of_the_health_and_psychological_consequences_of_alcohol_cannabis_nicotine_and_opiate_use.

312. Grant, Igor, J Hampton Atkinson, Ben Gouaux, and Barth Wilsey. "Medical Marijuana: Clearing Away the Smoke." The open neurology journal. U.S. National Library of Medicine, 2012. https://www.ncbi.nlm.nih.gov/pmc/articles/PMC3358713/.

313. "What Are Clinical Trials and Studies?" National Institute on Aging. U.S. Department of Health and Human Services. Accessed January 23, 2023. https://www.nia.nih.gov/health/what-are-clinical-trials-and-studies.

314. Treister-Goltzman, Yulia, Tamar Freud, Yan Press, and Roni Peleg. "Trends in Publications on Medical Cannabis from the Year 2000." Population health management. U.S. National Library of Medicine, August 2019. https://pubmed.ncbi.nlm.nih.gov/30300079/.

315. https://norml.org/marijuana/library/recent-medical-marijuana-research/

316. "Applications To Become Registered Under the Controlled Substances Act To Manufacture Marijuana To Supply Researchers in the United States." Federal Register: The Daily Journal of the United States Government. US National Archives, August 12, 2016. https://www.federalregister.gov/documents/2016/08/12/2016-17955/applications-to-become-registered-under-the-controlled-substances-act-to-manufacture-marijuana-to.

317. Rabin, Roni Caryn. "Marijuana Edibles May Pose Special Risks." The New York Times. The New York Times, March 25, 2019. https://www.nytimes.com/2019/03/25/well/eat/marijuana-edibles-may-pose-special-risks.html.

318. Armentano, Paul. "Cannabis and Driving: A Scientific and Rational Review." NORML, August 21, 2020. https://norml.org/marijuana/library/cannabis-and-driving-a-scientific-and-rational-review/.

319. Fischer, Benedikt, Victoria Jeffries, Wayne Hall, Robin Room, Elliot Goldner, and Jürgen Rehm. "Lower Risk Cannabis Use Guidelines for Canada (LRCUG): A Narrative Review of Evidence and Recommendations." Canadian journal of public health = Revue canadienne de sante publique. U.S. National Library of Medicine, 2011. https://www.ncbi.nlm.nih.gov/pmc/articles/PMC6973752/.

320. Rogeberg, Ole, and Rune Elvick. "The Effects of Cannabis Intoxication on Motor Vehicle Collision Revisited and Revised." Wiley Online Library. Society for the Study of Addiction, February 16, 2016. https://onlinelibrary.wiley.com/doi/abs/10.1111/add.13347.

321. Calabrese, Edward J., and Alberto Rubio-Casillas Rubio-Casillas. "Biphasic Effects of THC in Memory and Cognition - Wiley Online Library." Wiley Online Library. European Journal of Clinical Investigation, March 25, 2018. https://onlinelibrary.wiley.com/doi/abs/10.1111/eci.12920.

322. Havelka, Jacqueline. "Does CBD Help or Hinder Sleep?" Leafly, July 28, 2020. https://www.leafly.com/news/strains-products/how-to-use-cbd-marijuana-for-sleep.

323. Tzavara, Eleni T., Mark Wade, and George G. Nomikos. "Biphasic Effects of Cannabinoids on Acetylcholine Release in the Hippocampus: Site and Mechanism of Action." Journal of Neuroscience. Society for Neuroscience, October 15, 2003. https://www.jneurosci.org/content/23/28/9374.

324. Rey, Alejandro Aparisi, Martin Purrio, Maria-Paz Viveros, and Beat Lutz. "Biphasic Effects of Cannabinoids in Anxiety Responses: CB1 and Gaba(b) Receptors in the Balance of GABAergic and Glutamatergic Neurotransmission." Neuropsychopharmacology : official publication of the American College of Neuropsychopharmacology. U.S. National Library of Medicine, November 2012. https://www.ncbi.nlm.nih.gov/pmc/articles/PMC3473327/.

325. Havelka, Jacqueline. "Does CBD Help or Hinder Sleep?" Leafly, July 28, 2020. https://www.leafly.com/news/strains-products/how-to-use-cbd-marijuana-for-sleep.

326. Linares, Ila M, Antonio W Zuardi, Luis C Pereira, Regina H Queiroz, Raphael Mechoulam, Francisco S Guimarães, and José A Crippa. "Cannabidiol Presents an Inverted U-Shaped Dose-Response Curve in a Simulated Public Speaking Test." Revista brasileira de psiquiatria (Sao Paulo, Brazil : 1999). U.S. National Library of Medicine, 2019. https://pubmed.ncbi.nlm.nih.gov/30328956/.

327. Jackson, Nicholas J., Joshua D. Isen, Rubin Khoddam, Daniel Irons, Catherine Tuvblad, William G Iacono, Matt McGue, Adrian Raine, and Laura A. Baker. "Impact of Adolescent Marijuana Use on Intelligence: Results from Two Longitudinal Twin Studies." PNAS. Cornell University, January 19, 2016. https://www.pnas.org/doi/10.1073/pnas.1516648113.

328. Scott, J. Cobb, Samantha T. Slomiak, Jason D Jones, Adon F.G. Rosen, Tyler M Moore, and Ruben C. Gur. "Meta-Analysis of Cannabis and Cognitive Function in Adolescents and Young Adults." JAMA Psychiatry. JAMA Network, June 1, 2018. https://jamanetwork.com/journals/jamapsychiatry/article-abstract/2678214.

329. "Marijuana Exposure and Cognitive Performance." NORML, April 21, 2022. https://norml.org/marijuana/fact-sheets/marijuana-exposure-and-cognitive-performance.

330. Zongo, Arsene, Cerina Lee, Jason RB Dyck, Jihane El-Mourad, Elaine Hyshka, John G Hanlon, and Dean T Eurich. "Incidence and Predictors of Cannabis-Related Poisoning and Mental and Behavioral Disorders among Patients with Medical Cannabis Authorization: A Cohort Study." Substance use & misuse. U.S. National Library of Medicine, July 2022. https://pubmed.ncbi.nlm.nih.gov/35866679/.

331. Schoeler, Tabea, Jason Ferris, and Adam R. Winstock. "Rates and Correlates of Cannabis-Associated Psychotic Symptoms in over 230,000 People Who Use Cannabis." Nature News. Nature Publishing Group, September 6, 2022. https://www.nature.com/articles/s41398-022-02112-8.

332. Armentano, Paul. "Cannabis, Mental Health and Context: The Case for Regulation." NORML, March 26, 2022. https://norml.org/marijuana/library/cannabis-mental-health-and-context-the-case-for-regulation/.

333. "Is Marijuana Addictive?" National Institutes of Health. U.S. Department of Health and Human Services, April 13, 2021. https://nida.nih.gov/publications/research-reports/marijuana/marijuana-addictive.

334. "Data and Statistics." Centers for Disease Control and Prevention. Centers for Disease Control and Prevention, June 8, 2021. https://www.cdc.gov/marijuana/data-statistics.htm.

335. Grucza, Richard A., Arpana Agrawal, Melissa J. Krauss, Patricia A Cavazos-Rehg, and Laura J. Bierut. "Prevalence of Marijuana Use and Associated Disorders in the US." JAMA Psychiatry. JAMA Network, March 1, 2016. https://jamanetwork.com/journals/jamapsychiatry/fullarticle/2491353.

336. Santaella-Tenorio, Julian, Natalie S Levy, Luis E Segura, Pia M Mauro, and Silvia S Martins. "Cannabis Use Disorder among People Using Cannabis Daily/Almost Daily in the United States, 2002-2016." Drug and alcohol dependence. U.S. National Library of Medicine, December 1, 2019. https://pubmed.ncbi.nlm.nih.gov/31698323/.

337. "Marijuana Use Seldom Associated with Emergency Room Visits, Study Says." NORML, June 16, 2020. https://norml.org/news/2010/07/22/marijuana-use-seldom-associated-with-emergency-room-visits-study-says.

338. Cao, Dazhe, Sahaphume Srisuma, Alvin C Bronstein, and Christopher O Hoyte. "Characterization of Edible Marijuana Product Exposures Reported to United States Poison Centers." Clinical toxicology (Philadelphia, Pa.). U.S. National Library of Medicine, July 15, 2016. https://pubmed.ncbi.nlm.nih.gov/27418198/.

339. Ibid.

340. Ibid.

341. Rahn, Bailey. "Can CBD Undo the Anxious Side Effects of THC?" Leafly, August 14, 2022. https://www.leafly.com/news/cannabis-101/can-cbd-undo-the-anxious-side-effects-of-thc.

342. Moore, Melissa. "Can CBD Negate Your THC High?: Cannabis Sciences." Labroots. Labroots, April 27, 2018. https://www.labroots.com/trending/cannabis-sciences/8647/cbd-negate-thc-high.

343. Team, Edibles List. "CBD... the THC Overdose Anectdote: Edibles Magazine™." January 19, 2015. http://ediblesmagazine.com/science/cbd-the-thc-overdose-anectdote/.

344. Rahn, Bailey. "Can CBD Undo the Anxious Side Effects of THC?" Leafly, August 14, 2022. https://www.leafly.com/news/cannabis-101/can-cbd-undo-the-anxious-side-effects-of-thc.

345. Mitchell, Thomas. "Too High? A Medical Marijuana Expert Explains How to Stop THC Freakouts." Westword, October 15, 2021. https://www.westword.com/marijuana/how-to-stop-weed-freakouts-medical-marijuana-expert-12505835.

346. Greger, Jessica, Vernice Bates, Laszlo Mechtler, and Fran Gengo. "A Review of Cannabis and Interactions with Anticoagulant and Antiplatelet Agents." Journal of clinical pharmacology. U.S. National Library of Medicine, November 13, 2019. https://pubmed.ncbi.nlm.nih.gov/31724188/.

347. Damkier, Per, Dorte Lassen, Mette Marie Hougaard Christensen, Kenneth Grønkjaer Madsen, Maja Hellfritzsch, and Anton Pottegård. "Interaction between Warfarin and Cannabis." Basic & clinical pharmacology & toxicology. U.S. National Library of Medicine, November 6, 2018. https://pubmed.ncbi.nlm.nih.gov/30326170/.

348. "Marinol (Dronabinol) Capsules." AccessData.FDA.gov. United States Food & Drug Administration, September 2004. https://www.accessdata.fda.gov/drugsatfda_docs/label/2005/018651s021lbl.pdf.

349. Yamaori, Satoshi, Juri Ebisawa, Yoshimi Okushima, Ikuo Yamamoto, and Kazuhito Watanabe. "Potent Inhibition of Human Cytochrome P450 3A Isoforms by Cannabidiol: Role of Phenolic Hydroxyl Groups in the Resorcinol Moiety." Life sciences. U.S. National Library of Medicine, February 26, 2011. https://pubmed.ncbi.nlm.nih.gov/21356216/.

350. https://www.accessdata.fda.gov/drugsatfda_docs/label/2018/210365lbl.pdf

351. "Relationship between Marijuana and Opioids." NORML, December 9, 2022. https://norml.org/marijuana/fact-sheets/relationship-between-marijuana-and-opioids/.

352. Vigil, Jacob M., Sarah S. Stith, Ian M. Adams, and Anthony P. Reeve. "Associations between Medical Cannabis and Prescription Opioid Use in Chronic Pain Patients: A Preliminary Cohort Study." PLOS ONE. Public Library of Science, November 16, 2017. https://journals.plos.org/plosone/article?id=10.1371%2Fjournal.pone.0187795.

353. Schneider-Smith, Elisabeth, Kristin Salottolo, Claire Swartwood, Casey Melvin, Robert M Madayag, and David Bar-Or. "Matched Pilot Study Examining Cannabis-Based Dronabinol for Acute Pain Following Traumatic Injury." Trauma Surgery & Acute Care Open. BMJ Specialist Journals, February 1, 2020. https://tsaco.bmj.com/content/5/1/e000391.abstract.

354. Capano, Alex, Richard Weaver, and Elisa Burkman. "Evaluation of the Effects of CBD Hemp Extract on Opioid Use and Quality of Life Indicators in Chronic Pain Patients: A Prospective Cohort Study." Postgraduate medicine. U.S. National Library of Medicine, November 12, 2019. https://pubmed.ncbi.nlm.nih.gov/31711352/.

355. Abrams, DI, P Couey, SB Shade, ME Kelly, and NL Benowitz. "Cannabinoid-Opioid Interaction in Chronic Pain." Clinical pharmacology and therapeutics. U.S. National Library of Medicine, November 2, 2011. https://pubmed.ncbi.nlm.nih.gov/22048225/.

356. Cooper, Ziva D., Gillinder Bedi, Divya Ramesh, Rebecca Balter, Sandra D. Comer, and Margaret Haney. "Impact of Co-Administration of Oxycodone and Smoked Cannabis on Analgesia and Abuse Liability." Nature News. Nature Publishing Group, February 5, 2018. https://www.nature.com/articles/s41386-018-0011-2.

357. Wiese, Beth, and Adrianne R Wilson-Poe. "Emerging Evidence for Cannabis' Role in Opioid Use Disorder." Cannabis and cannabinoid research. U.S. National Library of Medicine, September 1, 2018. https://www.ncbi.nlm.nih.gov/pmc/articles/PMC6135562/.

358. Lines, Lisa M. "Why Pain Clinics Should Stop Testing for Marijuana." RTI International, September 3, 2019. https://www.rti.org/insights/why-pain-clinics-should-stop-testing-marijuana.

359. Shah, Siddharth, Siddharth Patel, Shweta Paulraj, and Debanik Chaudhuri. "Association of Marijuana Use and Cardiovascular Disease: A Behavioral Risk Factor Surveillance System Data Analysis of 133,706 US Adults." The American Journal of Medicine. Elsevier, November 8, 2020. https://www.amjmed.com/article/S0002-9343(20)30959-1/fulltext.

360. Pasha, Ahmed K, Charlene Y Clements, Charity A Reynolds, Maegan K Lopez, Ciara A Lugo, Yulisa Gonzalez, Farshad M Shirazi, and Aiden Abidov. "Cardiovascular Effects of Medical Marijuana: A Systematic Review." The American journal of medicine. U.S. National Library of Medicine, November 11, 2020. https://pubmed.ncbi.nlm.nih.gov/33186596/.

361. Jakob, Julian, Roman von Wyl, Odile Stalder, Mark J Pletcher, Eric Vittinghoff, Kali Tal, Jamal S Rana, Stephen Sidney, Jared P Reis, and Reto Auer. "Cumulative Marijuana Use and Carotid Intima-Media Thickness at Middle Age: The Cardia Study." The American journal of medicine. U.S. National Library of Medicine, December 24, 2020. https://pubmed.ncbi.nlm.nih.gov/33359272/.

362. Jivanji, Dhaval, Maverick Mangosing, Sean P. Mahoney, Grettel Castro, Juan Zevallos, and Juan Lozano. "Association between Marijuana Use and Cardiovascular Disease in US Adults." Cureus, December 3, 2020. https://www.cureus.com/articles/45502-association-between-marijuana-use-and-cardiovascular-disease-in-us-adults.

363. Watanabe, Alexandre H, Leenhapong Navaravong, Thitipong Sirilak, Ratthanon Prasitwarachot, Surakit Nathisuwan, Robert L Page, and Nathorn Chaiyakunapruk. "A Systematic Review and Meta-Analysis of Randomized Controlled Trials of Cardiovascular Toxicity of Medical Cannabinoids." Journal of the American Pharmacists Association : JAPhA. U.S. National Library of Medicine, March 26, 2021. https://pubmed.ncbi.nlm.nih.gov/33952424/.

364. "Hypertension." NORML, September 21, 2021. https://norml.org/marijuana/library/recent-medical-marijuana-research/hypertension/.

365. Abuhasira, Ran, Yosef F Haviv, Merav Leiba, Adi Leiba, Larisa Ryvo, and Victor Novack. "Cannabis Is Associated with Blood Pressure Reduction in Older Adults - a 24-Hours Ambulatory Blood Pressure Monitoring Study." European journal of internal medicine. U.S. National Library of Medicine, January 20, 2021. https://pubmed.ncbi.nlm.nih.gov/33483174/.

366. https://www.projectcbd.org/hub/heart-disease

367. Peter Grinspoon, MD. "Cannabidiol (CBD): What We Know and What We Don't." Harvard Health, September 24, 2021. https://www.health.harvard.edu/blog/cannabidiol-cbd-what-we-know-and-what-we-dont-2018082414476.

368. Sandomir, Richard. "Lester Grinspoon, Influential Marijuana Scholar, Dies at 92." The New York Times. The New York Times, July 2, 2020. https://www.nytimes.com/2020/07/02/science/lester-grinspoon-dead.html.

369. Armentano, Paul. "Will Smoking Cannabis Make You Psychotic? Not Likely." The Hill. The Hill, March 24, 2019. https://thehill.com/opinion/healthcare/435448-will-smoking-cannabis-make-you-psychotic-not-likely/.

370. Norml. "Study: CBD Effective as Adjunctive Therapy for Psychosis." NORML, June 8, 2020. https://norml.org/news/2017/12/21/study-cbd-effective-as-adjunctive-therapy-for-psychosis.

371. Beedham, William, Magda Sbai, Isabel Allison, Roisin Coary, and David Shipway. "Cannabinoids in the Older Person: A Literature Review." Geriatrics (Basel, Switzerland). U.S. National Library of Medicine, January 13, 2020. https://www.ncbi.nlm.nih.gov/pmc/articles/PMC7151062/.

372. Abuhasira, Ran, Lihi Bar-Lev Schleider, Raphael Mechoulam, and Victor Novack. "Epidemiological Characteristics, Safety and Efficacy of Medical Cannabis in the Elderly." European journal of internal medicine. U.S. National Library of Medicine, March 2018. https://pubmed.ncbi.nlm.nih.gov/29398248/.

373. Bouso, José C, Daniel Jiménez-Garrido, Genís Ona G, Damian Woźnica, Rafael G Dos Santos, Jaime EC Hallak, Beatriz APB Paranhos, et al. "Quality of Life, Mental Health, Personality and Patterns of Use in Self-Medicated Cannabis Users with Chronic Diseases: A 12-Month Longitudinal Study." Phytotherapy research : PTR. U.S. National Library of Medicine, February 21, 2020. https://pubmed.ncbi.nlm.nih.gov/32083789/.

374. Norml. "Study: Use of Cannabis Long-Term Not Associated with Cognitive Differences in Older Adults." NORML, September 24, 2020. https://norml.org/blog/2020/09/24/study-use-of-cannabis-long-term-not-associated-with-cognitive-differences-in-older-adults/.

375. Vacaflor, Blanca E, Olivier Beauchet, G Eric Jarvis, Alessandra Schavietto, and Soham Rej. "Mental Health and Cognition in Older Cannabis Users: A Review." Canadian geriatrics journal : CGJ. U.S. National Library of Medicine, September 1, 2020. https://www.ncbi.nlm.nih.gov/pmc/articles/PMC7458597/.

376. Mueller, Raeghan L., Jarrod M. Ellingson, L. Cinnamon Bidwell, Angela D. Bryan, and Kent E. Hutchison. "Are the Acute Effects of THC Different in Aging Adults?" MDPI. Multidisciplinary Digital Publishing Institute, May 1, 2021. https://www.mdpi.com/2076-3425/11/5/590.

377. Weinstein, Galit, and Sharon R Sznitman. "The Implications of Late-Life Cannabis Use on Brain Health: A Mapping Review and Implications for Future Research." Ageing research reviews. U.S. National Library of Medicine, February 25, 2020. https://pubmed.ncbi.nlm.nih.gov/32109605/.

378. Silver, Robert J. "The Endocannabinoid System of Animals." Animals : an open access journal from MDPI. U.S. National Library of Medicine, September 16, 2019. https://www.ncbi.nlm.nih.gov/pmc/articles/PMC6770351/.

379. Gollakner, Rania, and Lynn Buzhardt. "Cannabis (Marijuana) Intoxication in Cats and Dogs: VCA Animal Hospital." VCA Animal Hospitals. Accessed January 23, 2023. https://vcahospitals.com/know-your-pet/marijuana-intoxication-in-dogs-and-cats.

380. "Cannabis Use and Pets." American Veterinary Medical Association. Accessed January 23, 2023. https://www.avma.org/resources-tools/animal-health-and-welfare/cannabis-use-and-pets.

381. https://veterinarycannabissociety.org/

382. https://www.achemed.org/

383. https://newfrontierdata.com/cannabis-consumers-in-america-2022/

384. “Plant Tissue Culture.” Plant Tissue Culture - an overview | ScienceDirect Topics. Accessed January 23, 2023. https://www.sciencedirect.com/topics/biochemistry-genetics-and-molecular-biology/plant-tissue-culture.

385. https://cleangreencertified.com/

386. https://dragonflyearthmedicine.com/dem-pure-certificate.html

387. https://www.demeter-usa.org/certification/

388. https://www.cannabiscertificationcouncil.org/about-us

389. https://sunandearth.org/

390. https://www.certified-kind.com/about

391. https://www.cdfa.ca.gov/is/ocal.html

392. https://www.usda.gov/topics/organic

393. https://agriculture.ec.europa.eu/farming/organic-farming/organics-glance_en

394. https://www.canada-organic.ca/en/what-we-do/organic-101/organic-certification

395. https://www.ifoam.bio/our-work/how/standards-certification/organic-guarantee

396. Sawler, Jason, Jake M. Stout, Kyle M. Gardner, Darryl Hudson, John Vidmar, Laura Butler, Jonathan E. Page, and Sean Myles. “The Genetic Structure of Marijuana and Hemp.” PLOS ONE. Public Library of Science, August 26, 2015. https://journals.plos.org/plosone/article?id=10.1371%2Fjournal.pone.0133292.

397. McPartland, John M. “Cannabis Systematics at the Levels of Family, Genus, and Species.” Cannabis and cannabinoid research. U.S. National Library of Medicine, October 1, 2018. https://www.ncbi.nlm.nih.gov/pmc/articles/PMC6225593/#__ffn_sectitle.

398. https://newfrontierdata.com/cannabis-consumers-in-america-2022/

399. Palus, Shannon. “The Indica vs. Sativa Distinction Isn’t Real.” Slate Magazine. Slate, April 20, 2019. https://slate.com/technology/2019/04/indica-sativa-difference-cannabis-weed-science.html.

400. Erkelens, Jacob L, and Arno Hazekamp. “That Which We Call Indica, by Any Other Name Would Smell as Sweet.” Bedrocan, February 23, 2014. https://bedrocan.com/wp-content/uploads/2014-that-which-we-call-indica-by-any-other-name-hazekamp-erkelens.pdf.

401. Schwabe, Anna L., and Mitchell E. McGlaughlin. “Genetic Tools Weed out Misconceptions of Strain Reliability in Cannabis Sativa: Implications for a Budding Industry - Journal of Cannabis Research.” BioMed Central. BioMed Central, June 7, 2019. https://jcannabisresearch.biomedcentral.com/articles/10.1186/s42238-019-0001-1.

402. Sawler, Jason, Jake M. Stout, Kyle M. Gardner, Darryl Hudson, John Vidmar, Laura Butler, Jonathan E. Page, and Sean Myles. “The Genetic Structure of Marijuana and Hemp.” PLOS ONE. Public Library of Science, August 26, 2015. https://journals.plos.org/plosone/article?id=10.1371%2Fjournal.pone.0133292.

403. Pearson, Jordan. “Are Weed Strains Really That Different or Mostly Bullshit?” VICE, April 20, 2017. https://www.vice.com/en/article/kbvz9m/weed-strains-are-mostly-bullshit-weedweek2017.

404. Bacca, Angela. “Who Really Owns Cannabis Genetics?” Big Buds Magazine, August 30, 2018. https://bigbudsmag.com/what-happens-if-corporations-patent-cannabis-genetics/.

405. Borchardt, Debra. “Cannabis Lab Testing Is the Industry’s Dirty Little Secret.” Forbes. Forbes Magazine, April 5, 2017. https://www.forbes.com/sites/debraborchardt/2017/04/05/cannabis-lab-testing-is-the-industrys-dirty-little-secret/?sh=7f4696e11220.

406. “What Is Dabbing?” Leafly, August 3, 2022. https://www.leafly.com/learn/consume/dabs.

407. Chemat, Farid, Maryline Abert Vian, Harish Karthikeyan Ravi, Boutheina Khadhraoui, Soukaina Hilali, Sandrine Perino, and Anne-Sylvie Fabiano Tixier. "Review of Alternative Solvents for Green Extraction of Food and Natural Products: Panorama, Principles, Applications and Prospects." Molecules (Basel, Switzerland). U.S. National Library of Medicine, August 19, 2019. https://www.ncbi.nlm.nih.gov/pmc/articles/PMC6721174/.

408. https://newfrontierdata.com/cannabis-consumers-in-america-2022/

409. Joshi, Manish, Anita Joshi, and Thaddeus Bartter. "Marijuana and Lung Diseases." Current opinion in pulmonary medicine. U.S. National Library of Medicine, March 2014. https://pubmed.ncbi.nlm.nih.gov/24384575/.

410. Armentano, Paul. "All Smoke Is Not Created Equal." NORML, June 24, 2022. https://norml.org/blog/2016/01/07/all-smoke-is-not-created-equal/.

411. Abrams, DI, HP Vizoso, SB Shade, C Jay, ME Kelly, and NL Benowitz. "Vaporization as a Smokeless Cannabis Delivery System: A Pilot Study." Clinical pharmacology and therapeutics. U.S. National Library of Medicine, April 11, 2007. https://pubmed.ncbi.nlm.nih.gov/17429350/.

412. Spindle, Tory R, Edward J Cone, Nicolas J Schlienz, John M Mitchell, George E Bigelow, Ronald Flegel, Eugene Hayes, and Ryan Vandrey. "Acute Pharmacokinetic Profile of Smoked and Vaporized Cannabis in Human Blood and Oral Fluid." Journal of analytical toxicology. U.S. National Library of Medicine, May 1, 2019. https://pubmed.ncbi.nlm.nih.gov/30615181/.

413. Colbert, Mitchell. "Cannabis Cartridges Have a Heavy Metal Problem & It Is Worse than Reported." Cannabis Now, February 19, 2021. https://cannabisnow.com/cannabis-cartridges-have-a-heavy-metal-problem-it-is-worse-than-reported/.

414. Gieringer, Dale H. "Cannabis 'Vaporization': A Promising Strategy for Smoke Harm Reducation." Cannabis-Med.org. Haworth Press, 2001. https://www.cannabis-med.org/data/pdf/2001-03-04-7.pdf.

415. "Vaping Cannabis Produces Stronger Effects than Smoking Cannabis for Infrequent Users." ScienceDaily. Johns Hopkins Medicine, December 4, 2018. https://www.sciencedaily.com/releases/2018/12/181204131115.htm.

416. Azorlosa, JL, MK Greenwald, and ML Stitzer. "Marijuana Smoking: Effects of Varying Puff Volume and Breathhold Duration." The Journal of pharmacology and experimental therapeutics. U.S. National Library of Medicine, February 1995. https://pubmed.ncbi.nlm.nih.gov/7853169/.

417. Zacny, JP, and LD Chait. "Breathhold Duration and Response to Marijuana Smoke." Pharmacology, biochemistry, and behavior. U.S. National Library of Medicine, June 1989. https://pubmed.ncbi.nlm.nih.gov/2554344/.

418. Azorlosa, JL, SJ Heishman, ML Stitzer, and JM Mahaffey. "Marijuana Smoking: Effect of Varying Delta 9-Tetrahydrocannabinol Content and Number of Puffs." The Journal of pharmacology and experimental therapeutics. U.S. National Library of Medicine, April 1992. https://pubmed.ncbi.nlm.nih.gov/1313866/.

419. Huestis, Marilyn A. "Human Cannabinoid Pharmacokinetics." Chemistry & biodiversity. U.S. National Library of Medicine, August 2007. https://www.ncbi.nlm.nih.gov/pmc/articles/PMC2689518/.

420. Benson, Heather A E, Jeffrey E Grice, Yousuf Mohammed, Sarika Namjoshi, and Michael S Roberts. "Topical and Transdermal Drug Delivery: From Simple Potions to Smart Technologies." Current drug delivery. U.S. National Library of Medicine, June 2019. https://www.ncbi.nlm.nih.gov/pmc/articles/PMC6637104/.

421. Colbert, Mitchell. "Using Cannabis for Sexual Health." Cannabis Now, May 2, 2018. https://cannabisnow.com/using-cannabis-for-sexual-health/.

422. Lawson, Kimberly. "Marijuana Use before Sex Leads to More Satisfying Orgasms, Study Finds." Marijuana Moment, March 7, 2019. https://www.marijuanamoment.net/marijuana-use-before-sex-leads-to-more-satisfying-orgasms-study-finds/.

423. Parenthood, Planned. "Why Can't You Use Baby Oil with a Condom?" Planned Parenthood. Accessed January 25, 2023. https://www.plannedparenthood.org/learn/ask-experts/why-cant-you-use-baby-oil-with-a-condom.

424. Ludlow, Fitz Hugh. "The Hasheesh Eater (1857)." The Public Domain Review. Harper & Bros New York, 1857. https://publicdomainreview.org/collection/the-hasheesh-eater-1857.

425. Geisterfer, Eric. "The Bioavailability of Cannabis." Medium, December 15, 2022. https://ericgeisterfer.medium.com/the-bioavailability-of-medical-marijuana-6d05b712baa0.

426. "Department of Justice/Drug Enforcement Administration Fact Sheet." GetSmartAboutDrugs.com. United States Drug Enforcement Administration, April 2020. https://www.dea.gov/sites/default/files/2020-06/Marijuana-Cannabis-2020_0.pdf.

427. "25 Years Ago: DEA's Own Administrative Law Judge Ruled Cannabis Should Be Reclassified under Federal Law." NORML.org. National Organization for the Reform of Marijuana Laws, September 5, 2013. https://norml.org/news/2013/09/05/25-years-ago-dea-s-own-administrative-law-judge-ruled-cannabis-should-be-reclassified-under-federal-law/.

428. Canada, Health. "Government of Canada." For health care professionals: Cannabis and cannabinoids - Canada.ca. / Gouvernement du Canada, October 12, 2018. https://www.canada.ca/en/health-canada/services/drugs-medication/cannabis/information-medical-practitioners/information-health-care-professionals-cannabis-cannabinoids.html#a3.0.

429. Aggarwal, Sunil K, Muraco Kyashna-Tocha, and Gregory T Carter. "Dosing Medical Marijuana: Rational Guidelines on Trial in Washington State." MedGenMed : Medscape general medicine. U.S. National Library of Medicine, September 11, 2007. https://www.ncbi.nlm.nih.gov/pmc/articles/PMC2100129/.

430. Roubein, Rachel. "The Budtender Will See You Now." POLITICO, December 7, 2019. https://www.politico.com/news/2019/12/07/the-budtender-will-see-you-now-077314.

431. Moeller, Karen E, and Barbara Woods. "Pharmacy Students' Knowledge and Attitudes Regarding Medical Marijuana." American journal of pharmaceutical education. U.S. National Library of Medicine, August 25, 2015. https://www.ncbi.nlm.nih.gov/pmc/articles/PMC4584377/.

432. Benavides, Abraham, Nicholas Gregorio, Puneet Guptaa, and Mikhail Kogan. "Medical Students Are Unprepared to Counsel Patients about Medical Cannabis and Want to Learn More." Complementary Therapies in Medicine. Churchill Livingstone, November 13, 2019. https://www.sciencedirect.com/science/article/abs/pii/S0965229919312956?via%3Dihub.

433. Balneaves, Lynda G., Abeer Alraja, Daniel Ziemianski, Fairleth McCuaig, and Mark Ware. "A National Needs Assessment of Canadian Nurse Practitioners Regarding Cannabis for Therapeutic Purposes." Mary Ann Liebert, Inc. Publishers, March 1, 2018. https://www.liebertpub.com/doi/10.1089/can.2018.0002.

434. St Pierre, Michelle, Liam Matthews, and Zach Walsh. "Cannabis Education Needs Assessment among Canadian Physicians-in-Training." Complementary therapies in medicine. U.S. National Library of Medicine, January 31, 2020. https://pubmed.ncbi.nlm.nih.gov/32147035/.

435. https://www.ncbi.nlm.nih.gov/pubmed/

436. https://www.cannabis-med.org/

437. https://www.cmcr.ucsd.edu/

438. "Dronabinol Dosage Guide + Max Dose, Adjustments." Drugs.com. Accessed January 25, 2023. https://www.drugs.com/dosage/dronabinol.html.

439. "Epidiolex Oral Solution Dosage Guide." Drugs.com. Accessed January 25, 2023. https://www.drugs.com/dosage/epidiolex-oral-solution.html.

440. Hoffman, Adam. "Microdosing with Cannabis: Benefits without the Buzz." Healer. Leafly, May 27, 2022. https://healer.com/blog/microdosing-cannabis-benefits-without-buzz-healer/.

441. https://newfrontierdata.com/cannabis-consumers-in-america-2022/

442. Ibid.

443. Ibid.

444. "Why More THC Does Not Always Get You Higher." Dutch Passion. Accessed January 25, 2023. https://dutch-passion.com/en/blog/why-more-thc-does-not-always-get-you-higher-n990.

445. Greenberg, Gary. "Cannabis Scientists Are Chasing the Perfect High." The New York Times. The New York Times, April 1, 2020. https://www.nytimes.com/2020/04/01/magazine/cannabis-science.html.

446. Roberts, Chris. "Science Reveals the Cannabis Industry's Greatest Lie: You're Buying Weed Wrong (and so Is Everyone Else)." Forbes. Forbes Magazine, October 12, 2022. https://www.forbes.com/sites/chrisroberts/2020/06/16/science-reveals-the-cannabis-industrys-greatest-lie-youre-buying-weed-wrong-and-so-is-everyone-else/?sh=46055c42ee35

447. UCSF Health. "Communicating with People with Hearing Loss." ucsfhealth.org. UCSF Health, June 24, 2022. https://www.ucsfhealth.org/education/communicating-with-people-with-hearing-loss.

448. Garcia, Arianne. "A Neurotypical's Guide to Speaking to Someone with Autism." Healthline. Healthline Media, April 19, 2019. https://www.healthline.com/health/autism/dear-neurotypical-guide-to-autism.

449. "Top Ten Tips: Working with Someone with Autism Spectrum Disorder or Aspergers." Welcome to the Inclusive Communication Hub, February 27, 2021. https://inclusivecommunication.scot/top-ten-tips-working-with-someone-with-autism-spectrum-disorder-or-aspergers.

450. https://www.merriam-webster.com/dictionary/consultant

451. "What Is an Executive Order?" Americanbar.org. American Bar Association, January 25, 2021. https://www.americanbar.org/groups/public_education/publications/teaching-legal-docs/what-is-an-executive-order-/.

452. https://norml.org/act/

453. https://www.mpp.org/policy/federal/

454. https://www.safeaccessnow.org/advocacy

455. https://www.safeaccessnow.org/the_abcs_of_citizen_advocacy

456. "George Lakoff's 'Framing 101.'" Medium, May 27, 2017. https://medium.com/@ennuid/george-lakoffs-framing-101-7b88e9c91dac.

457. https://oaksterdamuniversity.com/oaksterdam-cannabis-terminology-style-guide/

458. https://oaksterdamuniversity.com/product/advocacy/

459. Sauls, John Gales. "Obtaining Consent to Enter by Deception." The Free Library. The FBI Law Enforcement Bulletin, January 1, 1994. https://www.thefreelibrary.com/Obtaining+consent+to+enter+by+deception.-a015155550.

460. Sauls, John Gales. "Obtaining Consent to Enter by Deception." The Free Library. The FBI Law Enforcement Bulletin, January 1, 1994. https://www.thefreelibrary.com/Obtaining+consent+to+enter+by+deception.-a015155550.

461. https://420laws.com/pdf/MargolinBook2019_Final_Web.pdf

462. https://indicators.ohchr.org/

463. https://indicators.ohchr.org/

464. Small, Ernest. "The Species Problem in Cannabis: Science." Google Books. Corpus, 1979. https://books.google.com/books/about/The_Species_Problem_in_Cannabis_Science.html?id=Ei8xvgAACAAJ.

465. Gertsch, Jürg, Roger G Pertwee, and Vincenzo Di Marzo. "Phytocannabinoids beyond the Cannabis Plant - Do They Exist?" British journal of pharmacology. U.S. National Library of Medicine, June 2010. https://www.ncbi.nlm.nih.gov/pmc/articles/PMC2931553/.

466. Russo, Sarah. "SCC Consensus on Delta-8-THC." Society of Cannabis Clinicians. Sarah Russo https://www.cannabisclinicians.org/wp-content/uploads/2020/06/scc_logo-long-R-2-1.png, December 27, 2021. https://www.cannabisclinicians.org/2021/08/30/scc-consensus-on-delta-8-thc/.

Index

Symbols

A

B

C

D

H

I

J

K

L

M

N

O

P

Q

R

S

T

U

V

W

Made in the USA
Columbia, SC
29 July 2024